FEAST OF LEVIATHAN

BOOKS BY LEO W. SCHWARZ

Collections

THE JEWISH CARAVAN: GREAT STORIES OF THIRTY-FIVE CENTURIES (1935)

A GOLDEN TREASURY OF JEWISH LITERATURE (1937)

MEMOIRS OF MY PEOPLE: THROUGH A THOUSAND YEARS (1943)

THE ROOT AND THE BOUGH: THE EPIC OF AN ENDURING PEOPLE (1949)

FEAST OF LEVIATHAN: TALES OF ADVENTURE, FAITH AND LOVE (1956)

History and Social Criticism

WHERE HOPE LIES (1940)

THE REDEEMERS (1953)

THE GREAT AGES AND IDEAS OF THE JEWISH PEOPLE (IN COLLABORATION WITH OTHERS, TO APPEAR IN 1956)

FEAST OF LEVIATHAN

Tales of Adventure, Faith and Love from Jewish Literature

In the age of the Messiah a blast of Gabriel's trumpet will open a great feast. Leviathan, monarch of the animal kingdom, will be roasted and every man good and true will be served a portion. Then the sages will join God in matching wits, and the guests will listen to tales of men of renown and of deeds of valor.
Legend of the Talmud

Compiled and Edited By

LEO W. SCHWARZ

RINEHART AND COMPANY, INC.   NEW YORK   TORONTO

LIBRARY OF CONGRESS CATALOG CARD NUMBER: 56-7480

ACKNOWLEDGMENTS

Grateful appreciation is herewith expressed to all authors, agents and publishers who granted permission to include copyrighted material:

Charles Angoff for "Zayde Tsalel" from *When I Was a Boy in Boston,* copyright 1947 by Charles Angoff, published by The Beechhurst Press.

Myron Brinig for "Day of Atonement" from *Singermann* by Myron Brinig, copyright 1929 by Myron Brinig, published by Rinehart & Company, Inc.

Doubleday & Company, Inc., for "Shylock, the Original Ancestor" from *There Goes An Actor* by Alexander Granach, translated by Willard Trask, copyright 1945 by Doubleday & Company, Inc.

Louis Falstein for "Tail-Gunner Over Europe" from *Face of a Hero,* copyright 1950 by Louis Falstein, published by Harcourt, Brace and Company, Inc.

Edna Ferber for "Molly Brandeis Takes Hold" from *Fanny Herself,* copyright 1917 by Edna Ferber, published by Frederick A. Stokes Company.

Irving Fineman for "The Prophet Elijah" from *Hear, Ye Sons,* copyright 1933, published by Longmans, Green and Company.

Edmond Fleg and the World Jewish Congress for "The Boy Prophet" from *La Terre Que Dieu Habite,* copyright 1953 by Edmond Fleg, published by Bibliotheque Juive, Paris, France.

Lee Furman, Inc., for "The Slaying of the Wolf" from *Noah Pandre* by Zalman Schneour, translated by Joseph Leftwich, copyright 1936 by Zalman Schneour.

Albert Halper for "Warm Matzos" from *The Golden Watch,* copyright 1953 by Albert Halper, published by Henry Holt and Company.

Alfred A. Knopf, Inc., for "A Parable of Peace and War" from *Tapiola's Brave Regiment,* copyright 1941 by Robert Nathan.

Israel M. Lask for the stories of Israelian writers, translations internationally copyright by I. M. Lask, Tel Aviv, Israel.

Meyer Levin for "The Dance" from *The Old Bunch,* copyright 1937 by Meyer Levin, published by The Viking Press, Inc.

Harold Matson Company for "Herbie Solves a Problem" from *The City Boy* by Herman Wouk, copyright 1948 by Herman Wouk, published 1948 by Simon & Schuster and 1952 by Doubleday & Company, Inc.

Menorah Journal, Inc., for "Holy Writ" by Louis Berg and "Plow Deep" by Jessie E. Sampter.

G. P. Putnam's Sons for "The Duty to Live" from *Tales of My People,* translated by Meyer Levin, copyright 1948 by Sholem Asch.

Cecil Roth for "The Tree of Liberty" from *Personalities and Events in Jewish History,* copyright 1933 by Cecil Roth, published by The Jewish Publication Society.

Simon & Schuster, Inc., for "Music in the Air" from *Thunder Over the Bronx* by Arthur Kober, copyright 1935 by Arthur Kober.

FOR *Barbara* AND *Barry*

THAT THEY AND THEIR GENERATION MAY
BE IMBUED WITH THE ADVENTURE, FAITH
AND LOVE WHICH ARE THE COMMON
THEME OF THIS FESTIVAL OF STORY.

A WORD TO THE READER

"TELL ME A STORY!" HAS BEEN A PLEA IN ALL EPOCHS AND COUNTRIES since man awakened to the wonder of life and nature. Even before man learned how to write, there were storytellers who entertained young and old with tales of adventure, heroism and wisdom. Many of these storytellers remain unknown by name, but as time went on each people crowned a king of story. The Greeks had their Homer, the Indians their Buddaghosha, Chinese their Chauangste and the Irish their Dall O'Huiginn. Each of these men—and others like them among peoples of ancient and modern times—were followed by men and women who picked up the thread of story and song and spun it into a marvelous cloth of many colors, which we now call world literature.

Among the oldest of these members of the human family are the Jewish people. They are best known for the religion to which they gave birth and out of which came both Christianity and Mohammedanism. But they also, over the course of more than 3,500 years, composed a vast, many-tongued literature. It began with the Bible which has been read all over the earth, in more than six hundred translations. Then came other great books —the Apocrypha, the Talmud, the Midrash and others too numerous to mention here—made up of the writings of many hundreds of storytellers. The narrators lived on several continents, in many old empires and modern states, and they wrote in numerous languages. Stories in this book have been translated from Hebrew, Aramaic, Greek, Yiddish, German, French and Spanish.

To give even a glimpse into this immense literature would require many volumes—shelves full of them. In this book I have gathered only a comparatively small number of stories—fifty in all—which are intended to whet the appetite. So it may be well to say a word about why and how I have chosen the contents.

There are stories in this book to fit a variety of interests. If the reader would like to get away from the noises and nuisances around him, he should turn to those under "Spices of Yesteryear." Living in other times and countries, the storytellers whisk one to strange worlds and stranger people. The tales are filled with characters from legend, fable and myth-heroes, demons, animals, all out of a world of make-believe. They are different from your favorites out of Greek or Indian mythology, but quite as exciting and adventurous. There are, for example, Leviathan, king of the creatures of all the seas, who when he must, can even quote from the Bible; the man in the bottle, smaller than Tom Thumb, whose little finger makes even the great Maimonides tremble; and the great man made of clay, the Golem of Prague, who was more powerful than Samson against the Philistines of his time.

If on the other hand the reader is in the mood to pass some time with interesting people and experiences in all parts of the United States, he can read any or all of the stories in the first section. America is so big and so full of curious and lovable persons that the writers find it easy and natural to have them overflow in their stories. One can find himself at home for all of the writers in this section are still alive and their characters and plots are as real and American as three-decker sandwiches. And while the main characters are chiefly Jewish, they share the freedom and the abundance and the dreams of all Americans.

If the reader is a Jewish boy or girl, he must have heard a great deal about an ancient dream that has come true in our days. I mean the birth of the new republic of Israel. There is much that is entirely different in the life of Jews who are building that new country, yet there is a good deal that is akin to our own history and life. Life in the kvuzoth, the agricultural colonies and especially in the great plains and desert of the Negeb, is remindful of the adventures of the pioneers in the old Wild West. And the huge numbers of immigrants and settlers from all parts of the globe, struggling to bring civilization to rough country and fighting in their War of Independence, read like pages from our own history. As in Bible days, the writers of Israel are telling their stories once more in the Hebrew language, and apart from the excitement of their tales you will discover in them engrossing people.

In his own home and with his family, the reader must have heard many stories of his parents and grandparents about the old days in countries across the seas before they came to America. Life in those days and lands was entirely different from today, as one may know from the study of history. Out of them came many famous storytellers who wrote in other tongues. You will find some of the very best of them in the section called "Old World Pomegranates." They are full of mystery, courage and faith and, in their quaintness and color, are of great fascination. But life then also had its joy and humor as you will discover in the stories of Sholem Aleichem, who had a genius for tickling his readers' funny-bones.

Every story bears the imprint of its teller. He is born with a gift, but the material he puts into his story comes from his family, his home, his community, his friends, his travels, his reading; in short, from the world he lives in, the people he knows and the ideas and fancies of his mind. An ancient Jewish sage, a great teller of tales himself, once said of writers: a new flask can be full of old wine and an old flask can be without new wine. We can enlarge this saying and suggest that there are three kinds of storytellers: Those who pour old wine into old flasks, those who pour new wine into old flasks, and those who fill new flasks with new wine.

All three kinds of writers are represented in this book. Taking them in order, the anonymous author of *The Romance of Esther*, who was following the custom of the Biblical storytellers, related an event in history, well-known and oft-told of his people in Persia, in the same form used by his predecessors. This practice is sometimes followed by writers of today, and you have a good example of it in the dramatic happening in the ghetto of Venice told in Cecil Roth's *The Tree of Liberty*. The old-wine-in-new-flask writers are numerous in all literatures. You will find a fine example in the eminent Yiddish poet and raconteur Isaac L. Peretz, some of whose stories rank with the best written in our times. His *Seven Good Years* will remind you of the awesome Faust tale, famous in story art and music. But Peretz has simply taken an ancient myth of Talmudic times, told and read generation after generation by readers of Hebrew, and changed the setting to a poor Jewish family in a village of Old Russia. It is Elijah who was the ancestor of Faust, and he will be found coming to life again in another form in the story of Irving Fineman, an American writer in the second section of this book. The new-wine-in-new-flask writers, although they too have been influenced by earlier modern storytellers, are the experimenters, or you may say, pioneers. They describe events and persons in the world about them and choose the form of the short story—as the poet chooses verse—to distill the wine of their experience and imagination. You will find many examples in the stories included here from the writers of America and Israel.

I have often wondered whether an invented story is more exciting than a real story. Much can be said on both sides of this question. But I am convinced that a real experience, if well told, can match the best tale of a writer's imagination. So I have taken an unusual step and I have included a number of autobiographical selections. Of course, some of our experiences in life are so extraordinary that they seem unreal. I do not mean a story like Louis Berg's curious friendship with an old Negro snowball vendor. This could—and did—happen. But when one reads Marek Edelman's narration of the battle in the Warsaw Ghetto, one can believe that life is really stranger than fiction. However, it may be best to let the reader try to discover for himself which of the storytellers has chosen to describe an actual happening in his life, and come to his own decision about the question in the first sentence of this paragraph.

Editors do not live or work in a vacuum. They spend a great deal of their time with books and the people who make them. That is how it is possible to make a book of this kind. I have chosen the stories assembled here from a library of writings, but I have also discussed the selections with many of the writers and many friends whose literary taste I admire and respect. As a consequence, I should like to end this preface with an expression of my appreciation to them.

I wish to record my deep gratitude to all the authors, dead and living, and to my fellow-translators who made this book possible. For cooperation and permission to publish their stories, I wish to thank Charles Angoff, Louis Berg, Louis Falstein, Edna Ferber, Irving Fineman, Albert Halper, Meyer Levin, Cecil Roth, Herman Wouk, and Yehuda Yaari. To Miss Kathryn Mansell of Sarah Lawrence College, Mr. Robert D. Loomis, associate editor of Rinehart and Company, and Mr. Herbert Poster, associate editor of *Congress Weekly*, who undertook the task of reading critically the whole manuscript, I owe a great debt for many suggestions which improved the quality of the book.

Finally, I must thank Dr. Joshua Bloch, Chief of the Jewish Division of the New York Public Library, and Mrs. Sylvia Landress, Librarian of the Zionist Archives and Library of New York, as well as the members of their staffs for their consistent kindness and helpfulness.

LEO W. SCHWARZ

CONTENTS

PART 1 *American Cornucopia*

PART 2 *Old World Pomegranates*

PART 3 *Israelian Fruit*

PART 4 *Spices of Yesteryear*

PART ONE

American Cornucopia

HERBIE SOLVES A MYSTERY

by HERMAN WOUK

HERBIE BOOKBINDER REGARDED GIRLS AS LOW IN THE SCALE, A botched job. They played silly games; they had unpleasant shrill voices, they giggled; they pretended to be holy; they were in an everlasting conspiracy against normal human beings (boys of eleven) ; they wore queer clothes; and they were sly. He regarded most of these squeaky beings with plain scorn.

It was nevertheless part of the mystery of life that from time to time there came to Herbie's view a sublime creation which could only be classified as a girl, since she would have the outside features such as long hair, a dress, and a high voice. But she would be as different from girls as the sun is from a penny candle. One of these angels appeared every year or so. There had been Rosalind Sarnoff, of the black hair and bright smile, in the second grade. Sadie Benz, always dressed in billowy white, in the fourth. Blond Madeline Costigan, who could throw a ball like a boy, in the fifth. And two girls who had lived in his neighborhood, known only as Mildred and Frances respectively, who had reduced his life to ashes twice by moving to other parts of the Bronx.

The radiance of such a divinity could come to surround an ordinary girl. Madeline Costigan had sat beside him in Miss O'Grady's class for two months, undistinguished from the rest of the chirruping females. Then one afternoon they had both been kept after school for tardiness. And while they were beating out erasers together, a grand chord had sounded in Herbert's breast, he had seen the glory envelop Madeline like the dawn, and lo, he was her slave. Equally strangely the spell could die away, as it had in the case of Sadie Benz, leaving a commonplace

3

girl whom Herbie despised. But this was not the rule. Most of these super-beings had been removed from Herbie by the forces of time and change. Diana Vernon had succeeded Madeline Costigan, the first adult in the golden procession.

The little stranger on the other side of the auditorium door who sat on the stairs facing away from him, placidly munching a sandwich, had hair of the same hue as Mrs. Gorkin's, and this may have been the reason Herbert's heart bounded when he first saw her. But a prolonged look persuaded him that, on her own merits, she was a candidate for the vacant office. Her starched, ruffled blue frock, her new, shiny, patent-leather shoes, her red cloth coat with its gray furry collar, her very clean knees and hands, and the carefully arranged ringlets of her hair all suggested non-squeaky loveliness. At the moment of his so deciding, it chanced that she turned her head and met his look. Her large hazel eyes widened in surprise, and at once there was no further question of candidacy. She was elected.

It now became obligatory upon Herbert to pretend that she did not exist. He looked out of the window and began to make believe that an extremely exciting and unusual event was taking place in the girls' playground below—just what, he was not sure, but it called for him to clap his palm to the side of his face, shake his head from side to side, and exclaim very loudly, "Gee whiz! Gosh! Never saw anything like *that!*" (By this time the imaginary sight had started to take shape as a teacher lying in a pool of blood, her head split open, after a jump from the roof.) He was compelled to run, first down the side aisle of the auditorium to look out of the other windows, and then up the aisle again and through the leather door at the rear, feigning amazement at the discovery of the girl on the stairs. She was seated busily reading a geography book upside down, having snatched it after watching all his pantomime up to the point when she saw he intended to come through the door.

After enacting an intensity of surprise at the sight of the girl that would have sufficed had he come upon a unicorn, Herbert recovered himself and said sternly, "What are you doing here?"

"Who wants to know?" said the girl, putting aside the book.

"Me, that's who."

"Who's me?"

"Me is me," said Herbert, pointing to his three-starred yellow armband.

"Huh! Garbage gang," said the girl. Turning her back on him, she drew an apple out of a gleaming new tin lunch box and began to eat it with exaggerated nonchalance, her eyebrows raised and her gaze directed out at the smiling day.

"Maybe you'd like to come down to Mr. Gauss's office with me," said Herbie fiercely.

Mr. Julius Gauss was the principal, a heavy, round-headed gentlemen seen by the children only at special assemblies, where he read psalms in a gloomy singsong and gave endless speeches which nobody understood, but which seemed in favor of George Washington, America, and certain disgusting behavior found only in mollycoddles. He was regarded by the children as the most frightful thing outside the storybooks, a view which the teachers encouraged and which several of them seemed to share.

"And stop eating," added Herbie, "when you're talking to a head monitor."

Red Locks quailed and put down the apple, but she tried to brave it out. "You can't make me go down there," she said. (It was always "down" to Mr. Gauss's office, possibly because of the general analogy to infernal regions.)

"Can't I?" said Herbert. "Can't I? It so happens that as captain of the Social Service Squad I have to see Mr. Gauss every Thursday, which is today, and make my report to him. And anyone who I tell to come with me has to come. But you can *try* not coming—oh, sure, you can *try*. I don't think you would try it more than *once*, but you can *try*."

The contents of this speech, excepting Herbert's rank, were a lie. But Herbert had not learned yet to draw the line between the facts devised by his powerful imagination and the less vivid facts existing in nature, and while he spoke he fully believed what he was saying.

"Anyway," said the girl, "he wouldn't do anything to me even if you did bring me down there, because I'm going to his camp this summer."

"His camp?" Herbie made the mistake of lapsing from his positive tone.

"Yes, his camp, smartie," sneered the girl. "I thought you knew everything. Camp Manitou, in the Berkshires. You just try bringing one of his campers down to him. He'll just demote you off your old garbage gang."

"He will not."

"He will so."

"He will not," said Herbie, "because I'm going to his old camp myself."

This was somewhat too newly minted a fact, even for the credulity of a small girl. "You're a liar," said she promptly.

"You mean you are," said Herbert, with no great logic, but with a natural grasp of the art of controversy.

"I'll bet you a dime I'm going to his camp," said the girl, falling into the trap and taking the defensive.

"I'll bet you a dollar I am," said Herbert.

"I'll bet you ten dollars you're not."

"I'll bet you a thousand dollars *you're* not."

"I'll bet you a million dollars."

"I'll bet you a *billion* dollars."

The girl, unable to think quickly of the next order of magnitude, said with scorn, "Where are you gonna get a billion dollars?"

"Same place you'll get a million," retorted Herbie.

"I can get a million dollars from my father if I want to," said Red Locks, vexed at being continually on the defensive, though sensing she was in the right. "He's the biggest lawyer in Bronx County."

"That's nothing," said Herbert. "My father owns the biggest ice plant in America." (He was manager of a small ice plant in the Bronx.)

"My father is richer than your father."

"My father could buy your father like an ice-cream cone."

"He could not," said the girl hotly.

"My father even has a way bigger lawyer for his ice plant than your father." Herbie speedily searched his memory, reviewing conversations of his parents. "My father's lawyer is Louis Glass."

The girl uttered a triumphant little shriek. "Ha, ha, smartie!" she cried, jumping up and dancing a step or two. "My father *is* Louis Glass."

This astounding stroke left Herbie with no available fact, real or improvised, for a counterblow. He was reduced to a weak, "He is not, either."

"Is too!" shouted the girl, her eyes sparkling. "Here, if you're so clever, here's my name on my books—Lucille Glass."

Herbert deigned to inspect the notebook offered for his view, with the large childish inscription, "Lucille Marjorie Glass, 6B-3."

"You should of told me so right away," he said magnanimously. "You can stay here, as long as your father is Louis Glass. 6B-3, huh? I'm in 7B-1. First on the honor roll."

"I'm third on the honor roll," said Lucille, yielding at last the deference due an upperclassman, a head monitor, and a mental giant.

With this advance in their relationship they fell silent, and became aware of being alone together on the small landing. The gay voices of the girls playing in the yard came faintly to them through the closed window. Herbie and Lucille self-consciously turned and watched the darting, frisking little figures for a while.

"What were you doing up here anyway?" said the boy at last, feeling that ease of speech was deserting him.

"I'm on the girls' Police Squad," said Lucille Glass, "and I'm supposed to watch this staircase during lunch."

She pulled a red band from her pocket and commenced pinning it around her arm. Encountering difficulty, she was gallantly aided by Herbie, who received the reward of a bashful smile. All this while Herbie was struggling with the question, whether it was not inconsistent for a Radiant One to be practically a member of his family, as Lucille's tie to his father's lawyer made her. His sister and his cousins were so empty of grace that he classed all family females in the low rank of girlhood. The aura of Red Locks seemed to waver and dim. However, as they grew silent once more, gazing out at the yard, Herbie felt himself quite tongue-tied, and the glory brightened and shone as strongly as at first, and he realized that charms sufficiently powerful could overcome even the handicap of belonging to the family.

"Well, gotta make my rounds," he said abruptly. "So long."

"Good-by," said the little girl, wrinkling her snub nose and red, firm cheeks at him in a friendly grin. As Herbie walked off the landing into the corridor, she called after him, "Are you really going to Camp Manitou this summer?"

The boy turned and looked down his nose at her in the crushing way teachers reacted to silly questions. He was no taller than the girl, so the effect was rather hard to get, but he managed a good approximation by tilting his head far back, and sighting along the edge of his nose.

"You'll find out," he enunciated after a dignified pause, and stalked off down the hall.

Mrs. Mortimer Gorkin had a weary afternoon of it with Herbie. Shortly after the children came back to class, she was summoned out of the room for a few minutes and returned to find her trusted monitor standing on top of her desk, reciting a parody of "The Village Blacksmith" with an idiotic preciseness that she recognized as a burlesque of herself. "The muss-uls on his ba-rawny arrms," he was saying, "are sta-rrong as rrrrubba bands-sah." She punished this malfeasance of office by ordering Herbie to sit in the last seat of the last girls' row and forbidding him to speak for the rest of the day. He broke the injunction twice by shouting spectacularly accurate answers to questions that had reduced the rest of the class to silence. This put the teacher in the bad predicament of having to reproach brilliance. The second time she tried sarcasm, saying heavily, "And pray, what makes you so very, very clever this afternoon, Master Bookbinder?"

It was a mistake. Herbert was inspired to jump to his feet and rejoin, "Just celebrating your wedding, Mrs. Gorkin," touching off a demonstration of screaming hilarity which the reddened, angry teacher could not control until she stood, pounded her desk and shrieked, "Silence! Silence!" She effectively snuffed out

Herbert by offering to conduct him down to Mr. Gauss's office the next time he uttered a word. But this came too late. By his repartee, and by forcing her to a display of temper, he had clearly won the day.

When the class marched into the school yard at the end of the afternoon and broke ranks, he was at once surrounded, the girls giggling and shouting at him, the boys pounding his back, shaking his hand, and assuring him with various curses that "he was a regular guy, after all." It was admitted by everyone that he had been under the spell of a "crush," an ailment which all the children understood. The great Lennie Krieger himself condescended to lounge up to Herbert and say "Nice work, Fatso," which set the seal on his acclaim. He was received back into society. He was even permitted to pitch the first inning of the softball game as a mark of his redemption, and no criticism was heard of his mediocre efforts.

An ugly little girl with a fat face and straight whitish hair, Shirley Schwartz, who secretly adored Herbie but had learned in lower grades, from other boys, the bitter necessity of hiding her hopeless loves, watched this triumph of her hero with joy. When he left the game after several innings, she decided to follow him home on the forlorn chance that he might speak to her. She hovered while he gathered up his books, and dogged him discreetly as he left the yard. But to her astonishment he did not take the direction to his house which she knew well, but turned and went into the teachers' entrance to the school. Love made her bold—she knew, anyway, that the entrance was not monitored after school hours—so she followed him in.

Five minutes later she returned to the yard, pallid and shaken, with a tale that set heads shaking and tongues clacking among the pupils of 7B-1. Shirley had seen Herbie's amazing new deed with her own eyes. Without being ordered to do so, and with no word to any pupil about his reasons for such suicidal folly, Herbie had walked up to the private door of the principal, Mr. Gauss, which even teachers never used, approaching the Presence only through the outer office; had knocked boldly; and, in response to a muffled, surprised call from inside in the dreaded voice, had vanished within.

The evening was purple, and the naked electric street lights
cast a brightening glow from under their wrinkled reflectors
along Homer Avenue in the Bronx, when Herbie Bookbinder
wrested himself away from a discussion of religion around a fire
in a vacant lot and wended homeward. The argument over the
nature and powers of God had been raging for hours like the fire,
and had been kindled, like the fire, by a piece of newspaper
printed in Hebrew lettering.

It was known to Bronx boys of all faiths that to burn a Jewish newspaper on Friday was a piece of rashness that must bring
disaster, and there was no youngster in Herbie's neighborhood
who would have done it. A fine point of theology had arisen,
however, when Herbie had recalled from a lecture at Sunday
school that this day, Thursday, was a minor festival, the Thirty-
third of the Omer. He suggested that it was perilous to light a
fire with the sheets on this day, too, for, although it was not as
dangerous a time as Friday, there seemed to remain an element
of risk. The Christian boys had at once seen the point and
agreed, but trouble ensued when Leonard Krieger saw a chance
to cry Herbert down with jeers.

Lennie was a big, good-looking, black-haired lad, twelve
and a half years old, a master of the education of the streets, a
hater of school education, a lively athlete, and a natural leader
of boys. His father and Herbie's were partners in the ice business,
and the two boys had always known and disliked each other. The
antipathy had deepened with the years as Herbie overtook the
older boy in school, and it now flourished poisonously, with both
of them in Mrs. Gorkin's class, Herbie as a sparkler and Lennie
as one of the indifferent boys.

The athlete was verging on the age when the grosser super-
stitions break down. Expressing much fine sarcasm at the expense
of "little fat 'fraidy-cats" and "superstitious yellow-bellies," he
proceeded to crumple up the Jewish paper and light it. His
bravado caused mutters of fear among the smaller boys. None of
them would heap wood on the fire, and he was forced to tend it
himself. Herbie darkly observed that he only hoped Leonard
would not come home to find that his father and mother had
dropped dead. Leonard at once offered to "show him whose

mother and father would drop dead," advancing on him with raised fists, but the voice of the group, crying "Pick on someone your own size," stopped the settlement of the problem by force.

A long general debate followed as to the chances of bad luck befalling Leonard Krieger, and the argument finally narrowed to these questions: whether God was watching Jewish newspapers all the time, or only on Fridays; whether He had eyes to watch and, if not, how He accomplished watching; and where God was and what He was like, anyway.

At last Lennie blew the discussion apart by exclaiming, "Aw, all this is a lotta bushwa. I don't believe in God."

None of the boys dared speak for a moment after this. Herbie glanced anxiously at the huge setting sun, as though afraid it would turn green or fall to bits. Frankie Callaghan, a red-headed little Catholic boy, cried, "I ain't gonna stay around here. Lightnin's gonna strike that guy," and galloped out of the lot. The others remained, but moved out of range. If such a spectacular end were to befall Lennie, they wanted to see it.

The Almighty, however, remained unperturbed, and no blue bolt fell on Lennie.

"What are you guys lookin' so scared about?" he sneered. "I said it an' I'll say it again. I don't believe in God."

"O.K., if you're so smart," said Herbie, cautiously moving closer to the atheist, "I suppose you're gonna say *you* made the world yourself."

"I didn't say I did. Who do you say made it?"

"Why, God, of course."

"All right, Fatso, Who made God?"

Two more boys, rendered uncomfortable by the discussion, departed.

"That's a dumb question," Herbie replied impatiently.

"Why is it dumb?"

"Well, *because*. If I could tell you who made God, then God wouldn't be God. The other guy who made him would be God."

"O.K., so nobody made God, is that right?"

"That's right."

"Then there ain't no God," said Lennie with a chortle of triumph.

A couple of boys snickered reluctantly. Herbie was not felled by the stroke.

"You mean to say God couldn't just *be,* without someone makin' him?"

" 'Course not."

"Why not?"

"Because nothin' just is. Somebody's gotta make it."

"O.K.," retorted Herbie, *"then who made the world?"*

There was a general laugh at Lennie's expense this time. Herbie had managed to twist the age-old circular argument so that he was now chasing his opponent. The athlete said angrily, "Well, if there's a God, let Him make a can of ice cream appear right here in front o' you 'n' me."

All the boys stared at the patch of grass between the debaters, half expecting a cylinder of Breyer's Special Chocolate to materialize. The Creator, however, seemed to be in no mood for showing off. He would produce neither lightning nor ice cream on Lennie's behalf.

"Well, what does that prove?" said Herbie after a pause.

"It proves," declared Lennie, with more passion than conviction, "that you're a dumb little fat slob, even though you're teacher's pet."

"Jer-*reee!*" A squawk from a little girl on the distant sidewalk. "Mom's hollerin' for you for supper."

"Holy cats, it's a quarter to seven," exclaimed the boy thus summoned, and ran.

The young theologians awoke to the workaday world again. One by one they left the circle around the fire, tramped away through the high green weeds of the lot, scrambled down a slope of rock to the sidewalk, and went away among the canyons of apartment houses. Herbie who loved fires, arguments, and vacant lots more than anything in the world, except possibly movies, was among the last lingerers around the flames in the gloom. He bade a silent good-by to the cold roughness of rock on which he sat and the fresh smell of the weeds all around him, and dragged himself off to his home, his clothes reeking delightfully of wood smoke.

Not every neighborhood in the Bronx boasted vacant lots.

Even those on Homer Avenue were being systematically blasted with dynamite, gutted by steam shovels, and plugged up with apartment houses. It was lucky for Herbert and his friends that the nearness of the avenue to the Bronx River (known to the boys as "the creek") and its situation along a ridge of tough rock had made building less profitable here than elsewhere, so that the tide of bricks had not yet swamped green earth along Homer Avenue. Of these matters the boys were ignorant. The parents settled on Homer Avenue because rents were cheap, and the children were happy in the choice because of the vacant lots. In Public School 50, teachers were always trying in vain to wake the love of nature in the boys by reading poetry to them. The compositions on the subject of nature were the dreariest and most banal of all the writing efforts wrung from the urchins, and the word "lots" never appeared in them. But the moment the lads were free of the prison of school they scampered to the lots, chased butterflies, dissected weeds and flowers, built fires, and watched the melting colors of the sunset. It goes without saying that parents and teachers were strongly opposed to the practice of playing in the lots, and were always issuing orders against it. This added the final sauce to the deed so grateful to the palate of boyhood.

Herbie went into 1075 Homer Avenue, a brick cliff very much like the other brick cliffs that stood wall to wall for many blocks along the less rocky side of the street. It was gray, square, five stories high, punctured with windows, and saved from bleakness only by the entrance, which tried on a little matter of plaster gargoyles overhead and dead shrubs in cracked plaster urns on either side of the iron-grilled glass doors. The stucco hallway had once been frescoed with highly colored fruits, but these, under the grime which gathers equally on walls and boys' necks in the city, had soon looked sickly. The wise landlord had repainted the hallway with a sad green tint that grew grayer and grayer each year without exciting protest. The boy skipped up two flights of the staircase, his little shoes wearing the grooves in the stone slab steps infinitesimally deeper, and paused outside the door labeled "3A," which led into the brick pigeonhole sacred, while the lease ran, to the Bookbinder family and known to them as home.

He could hear his mother stirring about in the kitchen, just inside and to the left of the door. Chances seemed favorable for a tiptoe entrance and swift concealment of his wool sweater, which for some reason retained more smell of fire than all the rest of his clothing together. He tried the doorknob. It was unlatched. Softly he pushed open the door, counting on the clatter of dishes to cover the squeak of the hinges, and darted inside, past the steamy kitchen, down the hall to the bedrooms.

"Look, Ma. Here's Herbie." It was the voice of his sister, Felicia, full of the tones of righteousness.

"Herbie, you come here!" called his mother.

The boy arrested his flight and turned heavily back. The treachery of his sister caused no bitterness in his heart. It was one of the evil things of life, like school and bedtime, against which he had long ago worn out his indignation. He now bore it stoically, convinced that release would only come in the latter days of eternity when he reached the age of twenty-one.

Felicia's long, curly black hair hung about her face as she bent over a loaf of bread she was slicing when Herbie came into the kitchen. She was almost thirteen, short and slight for her age, and by some older lads she was judged very good-looking. Herbie regarded this judgment as lunacy, but he knew that as boys passed into the fourteenth year and beyond they underwent severe changes that seemed to lessen their common sense.

Felicia looked up from her work, shook the hair out of her eyes, inhaled with a loud sniff, said, "Ugh! Smoke!" and fell to cutting bread industriously again.

"I guess I'd smell better," replied her brother, "if I went up to Emily's house and tried on her mother's lipstick."

"Oh, that old thing again," said Felicia scornfully.

Herbie knew that he had worked dry his discovery of his sister's dabbling in cosmetics a month ago, but any attack on another theme, however feeble, seemed better than staying on the topic of smoke. His mother put down her soup ladle, wiped her hands on her apron, turned away from the stove, and unexpectedly gave Herbie a hug and a kiss. "You do smell of smoke, but I forgive you this once," she said in a tired, good-natured tone. "Go, take off that sweater. Papa'll be home for supper in a minute." She held him at arm's length, surveying him fondly as though seeing him after a long absence, then let him go. Herbert fled, rejoicing in the unlooked-for mercy.

A half hour later, when the family was seated around the table in the dining room Mrs. Bookbinder filled Herbert's plate almost to the brim with lamb stew, carefully fishing the choice morsels of meat out of the tureen for him. Felicia's outraged protests at this strange favoritism were cut short by her father, whose conversation she had interrupted.

The father was a thin, stern-looking man with scanty, graying hair, a long, fleshy nose, many deep, downward lines in his narrow face, and the abstracted look of one whose life passes in urgent business calculations. His talk at table always consisted of narrations to his wife of the day's problems at the ice plant. He greeted the children pleasantly when he arrived home and forgot about them for the rest of the evening. Herbie and his sister were used to playing little games at table while their father talked about "the Place," about his perpetual difficulties with his partner, Mr. Krieger, about something called a mortgage, and about someone called a mortgagee. It would have required an impossibly long lecture on the law of mortgages to make clear to the children some thousands of hours of conversation dinned into their small ears. Yet Herbie and Felicia had made many such transactions. Indeed, even now the boy's cousin, Cliff, held his roller skates pending Herbie's repayment of fifteen cents, which he had borrowed in order to see a crucial episode of a serial movie. Herbie would have been amazed to know that he had thereby been granted a "mortgage" and that Cliff was a "mortgagee."

"Papa," said the mother at last as her husband fell silent long enough to eat some stew, "I had an interesting phone call today."

"You had a phone call?" Mr. Bookbinder's surprise was genuine. He was not aware that anything resembling an event had taken place in his wife's life for fifteen years.

"Yes, from a very important gentleman. A gentleman who happens to think highly of your son."

The mystery of his mother's unusual kindness was suddenly explained for Herbie. His heart thudding, he began to plan speedily how to handle the coming crisis.

"In fact," went on the mother, her weary face lit with liveliness, momentarily suggesting beauty that had faded many years ago, "this very important gentleman thinks so highly of your son that he's coming here after supper to pay us a visit."

"Who is it?" asked the father, in whom the spirit of banter was not strong.

The mother uncovered the glowing gem of news with reluctance. "Mr. Gauss, the principal—the *principal*—of Herbie's school."

"That's very nice of him," said Jacob Bookbinder awkwardly, after a pause.

"Aw, I bet I know what that old Mr. Gauss wants," said Herbie.

"Ah, he wants something," said Mr. Bookbinder. This brought the situation nearer reality.

"Sure, I bet he wants me and Fleece to go to that old camp of his," said Herbie, adding quickly as he saw disapproval on the faces of both parents, "that camp that Lucille Glass and Lennie Krieger are going to."

"Krieger's boy going to camp? Since when?" said the father.

"How do you know Lucille Glass?" said the mother.

"I met her in school," answered Herbie, shrewdly ignoring his father's question. He went on, "I don't feel like going to no camp, an' I bet Fleece don't either."

"I hate camps," said Felicia, whose knowledge of the ways of a parental mind was not inferior to Herbie's.

"How do you know you hate camps when you've never been to one?" said Mrs. Bookbinder.

"What I'd like to know is, where does Krieger suddenly get money to send a boy to camp?" said the father irritably.

Herbie detected a drift toward a collision between the facts of his imagination and those of brute nature. "Well, Lennie *says* he's going anyway," he observed, "but he's an awful liar, you know."

"That's Krieger, isn't it?" said Mr. Bookbinder to his wife.

"A man with a bank loan on his furniture and a Chevrolet car he has to borrow money from the business to pay the installments on, and the boy goes to camp. Glass, of course, can send a girl to camp."

"She's a sweet little thing," said Mrs. Bookbinder. "Help me clear, Felice."

"She has red hair," said Herbie, tingling all over at the mention of the girl. "I hate girls with red hair."

"I see her in gym. She's a baby," said Felicia as she scraped and stacked the dirty dishes.

The doorbell rang. Herbie jumped in his chair.

"That must be Mr. Gauss, but he's so early!" cried Mrs. Bookbinder, untying her apron with swift hands. "Pa, put on your jacket and go in the parlor. Herbie, answer the bell. Felice, shut the dining-room doors and finish cleaning up quietly."

These directives issued, she hurried to her bedroom, while the family moved to obey. The lines of authority were laid down in the Bookbinder household, and Mrs. Bookbinder was as clearly in command in matters of diet, furniture, clothing and etiquette as she was subordinate in everything else.

Herbie's first feeling upon opening the door to the terrible visitor was disappointment at his size. In the assemblies, and behind his desk, Mr. Gauss gave the impression of skyscraping grandeur, but he managed to pass through the doorway without crouching. He was corpulent, and rather shiny of visage. His mouth, Herbie observed, was fixed in a peculiar smile, consisting of a straight, thin line of lips pushed upward at both ends and apparently held so by a pair of firm invisible fingers.

"Good evening, Master Bookbinder," said the principal loudly, his mouth retaining the shape of the smile as it opened. "I trust your good dad and mother are expecting me?"

"Yes, sir," the boy mumbled, and led the way to the parlor. His good dad was standing by the upright piano (Felicia's chief sorrow in life) looking fully as wooden, upright and hard to play upon as the instrument. Mr. Gauss, by way of compensating, unbent to the verge of slumping out of human shape as he exchange greetings with the parent. The two men sat down on the red velours-covered sofa, driving a couple of feathers into the air through a seam Mrs. Bookbinder had planned to mend that very evening.

"Allow me to say, Mr. Bookbinder," began the principal, "that you have a wonderful daughter and a very wonderful son. Absolutely outstanding children, both of them."

"Their mother signs the report cards, so I wouldn't know," said Jacob Bookbinder, putting one hand in a jacket pocket and leaning back on the other in an awkward, self-conscious way.

"Absolutely outstanding. I keep my eye out for these outstanding children, you know. I want to remember in later years when they're grown up and famous that a very little bit of their success—just a very little bit—is due to the molding they received at my hands when they were still in the childhood state of impressionable clay."

"Education is a fine thing," answered the father, not being able to think of a more noncommittal remark.

"You have stated it in a nutshell," said Mr. Gauss. "My one sorrow is—"

Mrs. Bookbinder appeared, splendid in a red silk gown. Her face was newly powdered, her hair carefully arranged, and a long double string of amber beads clicked on her bosom. The men stood.

"And this is Mrs. Bookbinder, I'm sure," cried the principal, with an immensely happy smile. "No mistaking the resemblance to little Herbie."

"It is an honor and a privilege to welcome you to our home, Mr. Gauss," said the mother with a formal little bow.

"An honor and a privilege to be here, I assure you," said the principal, returning the bow with a nice mixture of grandeur and humbleness. As they all sat Mr. Gauss proceeded, "I have just been telling Mr. Bookbinder that you have a wonderful daughter and a very wonderful son. Absolutely outstanding children, both of them."

Herbie noticed the repetition of the extra adjective "very" applied to himself, and while it pleased him, he calculated that it might be due to the fact that he, not Felicia, had invited the principal to visit. He was already in an agony of fear that Mr. Gauss might reveal his rash deed, so the extra praise made him more uneasy than otherwise. But Mr. Gauss's motive was really much simpler. He knew that parents usually set more store by sons than daughters, and distributed his adjectives on that basis.

"And I was telling Mr. Bookbinder," he went on, "that I like to keep my eye on these outstanding children so that in after years when they are famous—as I'm quite sure Herbie will be—"

Mrs. Bookbinder turned to beam at her boy. Herbie was making a careful study of the wan roses and foliage in the carpet.

"—I will be able to remember that I contributed a tiny, just a tiny bit to their success by molding them while they were still in the childhood state of impressionable clay."

Herbie wondered vaguely what constituted molding at Mr. Gauss's hands, inasmuch as he had never spoken to the principal or even seen him at a distance of less than a hundred feet until today. But Mrs. Bookbinder had no such reservations.

"I'm sure the boy owes a great deal to you, Mr. Gauss," she said, "and I only hope when he grows up he'll appreciate it."

"Why, that's extremely gracious of you. I was just telling Mr. Bookbinder that my one sorrow in the case of these outstanding children is that I lose touch with them for two months each summer. Oh, for the common run of children it doesn't make much difference. But you know from your industrial experience, Mr. Bookbinder, that a fine, delicate piece of machinery, neglected for two months, can really be injured."

The father, who saw where the talk was leading, did not wish to assent to anything the principal proposed, but he was cornered. "That much is true," he said unwillingly.

"I'm glad we agree. And that is how I happened to hit on the idea of Camp Manitou."

The hour had struck. Herbie began to sidle from the scene.

"Must you go, Herbie?" said the principal at once, training his smile at the boy. "I should think you would be interested."

"Stay where you are," commanded the father.

Herbie stopped and leaned against the piano, looking unhappy.

But his fears were needless. Mr. Gauss launched into his "sales talk" without ever mentioning the boy's call at his office. Once or twice he nodded at Herbie with the cunning geniality

of a fellow-plotter; that was all. He expanded on a double-bar-
reled theme: the delights of Camp Manitou and the peculiar
worthiness of the Bookbinder children. The boy was grateful to
the schoolmaster for keeping mum, but he was also struck by
his readiness to bypass the truth—a horrid sin, according to Mr.
Gauss's own speeches in assembly. As the camp owner went on
with his plea, passing booklets of photographs to the parents and
to the boy, he fell into a manner of speech and conduct that
seemed more and more familiar to Herbert. The boy had uncles
and aunts who came periodically to wheedle favors from his
father. So poor Mr. Gauss talked on and on, unaware that his
shiny face and roly-poly form were sinking, in the lad's view,
from his height of office to the depressed level inhabited by
needy relatives.

"Herbie tells me," the mother put in after a while, "that
Lucille Glass is enrolled in your camp."

"Ah, yes, Lucille. Lovely little child. Perfect example of a
Manitou camper."

"And Lennie Krieger, too—is that right?" asked Jacob
Bookbinder.

"Krieger?" said Mr. Gauss doubtfully. He reached for a
notebook.

"Lives here on Homer Avenue, two blocks down. A tall boy,
twelve or so. He's the son of my business partner."

"Of course. Lennie. I'm glad you mentioned that," said the
principal, dropping his voice to a confidential tone. "I have a
question to ask you. Do you feel—I must ask your honest opinion
—that Lennie Krieger is the type I have described to you as a
Manitou camper? The kind of boy you'd like to see side by side
with a lad of Herbie's caliber?"

Mr. Bookbinder grumbled, "Nothing wrong with him that
I know of."

The principal unscrewed his fountain pen and made a careful note in his book, saying, "Thank you. In that case perhaps—
I say, perhaps—Lennie may be coming to Manitou after all." And
he privately decided to call next evening upon the parents of the
boy, of whose existence he had not been aware until a few
minutes ago.

There were seven other children in the neighborhood deserving the honor of a summer at Camp Manitou, at the price of three hundred dollars per child, so Mr. Gauss did not tarry. His visit had clearly had some effect. Mr. and Mrs. Bookbinder were taken with the flattery of the principal's presence, the charm of the pictures of cabins by a mountain lake, and the descriptions in the booklet of the amazing mental, physical, and religious improvement of children in a summer at Manitou. When the principal left, he received their humble thanks for the honor he had offered them, and a promise that they would earnestly examine their resources to see whether they could afford to accept it.

Herbie went to bed that night in a fever, and dreamed, until Felicia shook him at seven the next morning, of lakes, cabins, shrubbery, Indians, campfires, roasting frankfurters, a lovely little red-headed girl darting among green trees, and religious improvement.

TAIL-GUNNER OVER EUROPE

by LOUIS FALSTEIN

THE JEWISH CREW CHIEF, WHOSE SHIP *Violent Virgin* WE WERE FLYing on the mission to Munich, whispered to me as I was taking the last nervous puffs on a cigarette before takeoff, "If I was you, Isaacs," he said, "I wouldn't take along your dog-tags to Germany. If the Nazis bring you down and see that H for Hebrew on them tags, it'll be tough on you."

"That's nonsense," I said, taking offense quickly, although momentarily I was grateful for his solicitude. "There's the Geneva Convention setting down behavior towards prisoners of war." Then I proceeded to explain to him that according to this convention, signed in Geneva by the present belligerents, a prisoner of war was required to give only his name, rank, and serial number. And no more. The Germans, we understood, had ways of coaxing information by intimidation, ruse, threats, and physical violence. They threatened to inject recalcitrants with syphilis and other diseases; they put men in solitary confinement, and on occasion they killed "while the prisoner was trying to escape." I never dwelled on these matters or I could not go on flying. Like a young person who rejects thoughts of death, I tried not to speculate on what would happen to me if I were shot down over Germany.

"But you're a Jew," the crew chief said significantly.

"That hasn't a thing to do with it," I said, resenting his reminder. "I'm an American." I suddenly disliked this chubby, inoffensive man for adding fuel to my already considerable fears, for spreading rumors for which he had no proof, and for displaying a persecution complex which always surprised me when I found it among American-born Jews.

I dismissed his warning and thought no more about it until we started crossing the Alps into Germany proper. Suddenly I took off my identification tags, without any thought or reason, and dropped them in one of the dark crevices on the turret floor where nobody would find them. My action was completely irrational, influenced no little by the terrifying mountain peaks that rose to a height of sixteen thousand feet. The Alps looked like a monstrous forest of jagged rocks jabbing up at us, as if they were the first harbinger of what was to follow once we entered the enemy land.

Aside from the dog-tags I had no other identification with me, and according to the same Geneva Convention which I had quoted to the ground man earlier that morning, my captors were entitled to execute me as a spy. But for some reason which I could not explain to myself being executed as a spy did not hold as much terror for me as being put to death as a Jew. I hadn't the slightest idea what they did to captured American soldiers of Jewish extraction. I started cursing the crew chief who was safe, back in Italy. I ground the metal dog-tags with my fleece-lined boot, mumbling crazily to myself: So the Nazis will inject syphilis in my veins. They'll kill me. They've killed six million Jews already; this will make it six million and one. The point is: one must act with dignity. Remember: in the face of threats or intimidations you tell them only name, rank, serial number; name, rank, serial number; name, rank, serial number. . . .

"We've just entered Germany," Andy Kyle said over the interphone as if he were conducting a tour. "Right underneath you, men. This is it!"

I looked down past the armor-plated glass at the land twenty thousand feet below us. And though the land was clean and furrowed and neat, it seemed to me as if it were in the throes of some terrible plague. The land appeared diseased. I tried to spit down but the slashing wind only pasted my sputum against the Plexiglas. Angry at this failure, I unplugged my heated suit cord and made my way to the relief tube in the waist section, where I urinated defiantly on Hitler's Reich.

Some flak batteries picked us up before we got to Munich. Over the target the sky was full of black puffs. By some strange impulse I pointed my twin-fifties downward and opened fire. I fired the guns with my eyes shut, my face buried in my knees. I did not see where I was firing. I surmised my fire was directed in the general direction of Hitler's beer-cellar below, in whose damp confines were hatched the first foul eggs of National Socialism. My eyes were shut. I heard the flak bursts around the ship like claps of thunder, like trains passing each other at high speeds, like pebbles striking a moving automobile. I heard a scream over the interphone, it sounded like Cosmo Fidanza who was hanging below the ship's belly, his child's eyes probably wide with terror at the black puffs bursting all about him. I heard his scream, and suddenly I was sitting up, my eyes wide open, shouting: "--------!" You dirty --------!" I pumped bullets at the smoke-quilted city below. The recoil of my guns shook the turret. My oxygen mask came loose, my flak helmet fell off my head, and my heated suit caught fire. But I continued firing in a mad frenzy as if in this one act I was getting even with Hitler and his fat burghers for all the lives they'd snuffed out, for the tears they'd caused, for the dreams they'd shattered, for the lives postponed, for my wife who was at this very moment exiled to the choking atmosphere of a small town to sit and watch the waste of precious days. And I was getting even for myself, because they threatened to brand upon my flesh the yellow Star of David after I'd discarded it with all the rest of the nightmarish memories of a ghetto childhood.

"Bommmmbs Awwwway!" Dick's words snapped me out of the reverie. I made a motion as if to wipe the perspiration off the exposed, upper part of my face. My breath felt hot and moist inside the oxygen mask. I stood up in my turret and bent forward and watched the bombs go away and a feeling of exultation gripped and held me. I was completely oblivious of the flak bursts as if they no longer had the power of harming me. I watched the clusters streak earthward like savage bouquets. "Hit!" I screamed "Hit—" I was anxious for the many clusters of bombs to explode in crowded areas of the city among the men and women who had grown fat on the loot of Europe and on the bones of the world. I wanted to see Munich blown up, Munich the infamous, Munich of Chamberlain's umbrella and peace for our time and appeasement. . . . I was eager for our bombs to blanket the city, erase it, kill its inhabitants and let the tongues of flame from its slow pyre reach toward the heavens to ask for forgiveness. There were no innocents below, as there were in Yugoslavia or Rumania or even in Austria, where you felt sorry when bombs went astray and often killed civilians. Below me was the battlefield, all of it was the enemy. . . .

I didn't realize we were out of the flak until I heard the waist-gunners shouting to each other while they were pumping up Cosmo's turret to examine his wound. I stowed my guns, and ignoring the pilot's query as to why I had fired my guns when there had been no enemy fighter interception. I started rubbing out the fire which was eating away at my suit. The electric wires had shorted along the shoulder blades and a fire had chewed away at the cloth, singeing my flesh.

Billy and Leo pumped up Cosmo's turret and opened the tiny door. They pulled him out slowly and stretched him out in the waist section. Cosmo was bleeding in the right thigh, where a piece of flak the size of a fifty-caliber bullet was lodged. They reported to the pilot.

"We'll peel off and go home by ourselves," Pennington said without any hesitation. The pilot's bold suggestion caught the rest of us unaware. In view of Cosmo's wound, not one of us raised the obvious objection against leaving the well-protected formation to go home alone. What disturbed me, and the others, no doubt, was the alacrity with which Big Wheel seized upon this challenge of returning alone by a route where one hundred and fifty enemy fighters were known to roam among the crevices and gorges of the Alps, preying on stray American bombers and decimated formations.

We banked sharply and peeled off, after Big Wheel had called the flight leader and told him he had a wounded man on board. We left the security of the formations behind us. We were alone in the sky over Germany, flying at sixteen thousand feet. Pennington flew the ship just above the peaks, maneuvering it as if the clumsy 110-foot wingspread of the Liberator was suddenly shrunk to the diminutive size of a swift Mustang. And *Violent Virgin,* though old and battle-scarred, responded to the pilot's masterful touch, as if she were eager for him to forget that she was not a graceful Mustang at all, but a lumbering B-24 that has no business flying so low among the peaks of the Alps.

In the morning I wondered whether the laundresses had lit a candle for me. We had been briefed to strike the Rumania-Americana oil wells in Ploesti. I had taken along a few additional flack vests and draped them around my genitals, thighs and feet. But a man flying over Big P needed more than that. And I thought of the candle, absurd though it was. The image of a burning candle clung to my brain as we came off the target. Suddenly I heard Pennington's congealed voice: "Enemy fighters at twelve o'clock—high!"

As if in response to the pilot's scream, Mel's nose guns started chattering wildly and Dooley swore briefly and opened fire.

"Watch them, Leo!" Pennington cried, "they're sliding over to three o'clock. Coming in on a pursuit curve." Leo's gun started palpitating and the battered plane shook from the recoil.

"Ben, watch them!" This was Leo's voice.

Suddenly they came on. It's happened, the thought flashed in my mind. No drunken leer, no hobnailed boots, no swastika on a sleeve. No storm trooper pointing a bayonet at you and screaming *Sieg Heil;* instead, swift planes that looked like our own P-51's, like toy-machines suspended from heaven by some puppeteer. What harm could come from them? I wondered. Then a swastika streaked across my vision, and though my mind was in the slow process of registering incredulity and disbelief that I was not seeing the coiled serpent in a motion picture newsreel but facing it, my fingers were pressing the triggers. Forgetting the sight, I rose in my seat and, throwing off the flak helmet which kept sliding down on my nose, I started tracking the enemy pursuit planes. It dawned on me that the battle had been joined and I was not afraid. In fact, I was calm.

The plane shook from the recoil and I shook inside the turret as if electric shocks were passing through me. Pennington was screaming with the helpless cries of a man who does not have a gun but points out the dangers to those who are armed: "Watch him coming towards three o'clock, Leo!"

"I see him! Oh, you s-o-b—watch him, Ben!"

"See him!"

They came singly, sliding down with deadly grace in their pursuit curve. Then they came like a pack of wolves, starting their fire at the front end of the ship and raking us in a complete semicircle with the fixed machine-guns mounted in their wings. Then they came from the top, and some came from underneath to probe our belly-gunner's effectiveness. The world was a churning dog-fight. The firing and the short, crisp oaths mingled in my ears, and the directions; watch him at three; Roger, he's sliding down to six, watch him, tail; okay. . . .

I felt no emotion. My calmness surprised me. I felt no cold or heat. I did not hear the enemy's fire. I saw only the wings of their ships, the wings lighting up with bullet-bursts like fireflies at night. The whole thing appeared so improbable and fantastic that even while I was firing, there was this insane thought: pinch yourself and see whether you are awake; this must be a dream, this cannot be you . . . Briefly I toyed with the dreadful idea that the enemy might recognize it was I, Ben Isaacs, whose eyeglasses were tucked away in the upper breast pocket, firing at them, and they would lose what little respect they had for my guns and slide in closer to our formation. I began to pucker my face, to grimace savagely, trying to impress Goering's yellow spinners with the grimness of my purpose. I pressed hard on the triggers.

I watched an enemy fighter saw one of our ships in half with his bullets. The Liberator fell apart in two pieces like a watermelon sliced through the middle. Perhaps as a reflex action I pressed the triggers too eagerly and both my guns jammed and I sat helplessly for a moment. Somebody screamed: "What's the matter, tail?"

"My guns are jammed!" I cried. With one hand I rode the turret in azimuth and elevation, pointing my guns at the enemy fighters, while with the other hand I tried fixing my guns, one at a time. The ME's were firing at us, and I sat there pointing my guns at them. But my guns were dead. I tore off one glove and felt the burning cold extractor. I charged the gun, and luckily it started its song again. The other gun remained dead.

"I'm okay," I said.

"Keep it up, men!" Pennington cried with a choked voice. He was at the stick, both he and Chet, and neither of them had any guns to fire. All four officers were crouching, feeling helpless, superfluous, and afraid. Only the gunners were busy. In the upper turret Dooley's oxygen mask slipped off and fell down to the flight deck. Dooley forgot all about the mask. He flew without oxygen for twenty minutes. He shot down one enemy plane. When our escort finally showed up, late, and the enemy broke off the engagement and fled, Dooley collapsed in a dead faint.

The enemy suddenly vanished from the skies as suddenly as they had come. And my mind was slowly adjusting itself to emotions and thoughts I had never before experienced. The meaning of triumph. I had never known the meaning of triumph. I had feared I might lose my head, become paralyzed by terror, but none of these things had happened. There wasn't the hysteria I had experienced over Munich, firing at remote objects on the earth. Here we had matched guns with professional soldiers. We had adopted their language, their tactics, their weapons.

In the one act of firing, I felt as if an end had come to all the years of temporizing. By pulling two triggers, just squeezing them gently, I had felt a completeness.

It was amazing, I thought, how again the simple proved to be the most direct. The most eloquent rebuttal to brutality was brutality in return. Such was the logic of our life, our civilization, and of the moment. A man could express himself most fully only through killing. Any other way was compromising. The world was not for passive people. They perished. Only they who fought back would remain alive, even if only in the consciousness of those who came after them.

The dog-fight had lasted twenty minutes, Andy Kyle later told us. To me it had seemed like a second. But into this second a lifetime of grievances had been crowded. My guns had spoken for the pogroms I had lived through, for the pregnant mothers whose bellies I had seen torn open, for the cellar days of my childhood, for the yellow Star of David, for the anguished screams of people, my people, who were at this very moment burning in Hitler's extermination ovens, for Guernica, Coventry and Pearl Harbor. . . .

Pennington came back to the waist section and slapped the gunners on the back and said: "You men were wonderful. You really gave them hell and I'm proud of you."

WARM MATZOS

by ALBERT HALPER

I WAS WALKING DOWN THE STREET ONE AFTERNOON—SPRING WAS in the air—when I passed Father Aiken coming out of St. Stephen's. Through the briefly opened door I could hear the boys' choir rehearsing, and their blended voices sounded pleasant to my ears.

"Hello, Dave," the priest smiled as he passed me.

"Lo' " I answered, ducking my head briefly.

I knew the kids inside the church were practicing for Easter services, and I was a little jealous because they were enjoying singing in the ornate gallery above the pulpit, where they could see the glittering architecture and trappings of the holy place. But I wasn't envious, really. I knew that at about this time of year our people had a big holiday, too—a whole week during which we celebrated and gorged ourselves on the best food in the world.

I trudged up Kedzie Avenue, where my father had bought a new grocery, warming over memories of past holidays in my mind. Up ahead, near Franklin, was the big, dull block of apartments in which my family lived.

I climbed the back stairs, whistling a song, and, coming into the flat, said, "Ma? Anybody home?"—which really meant *how about a sandwich before supper, Ma?*

I found my mother in the kitchen where, bent over, she was engaged in her weekly battle with some intruders. She was spraying the cracks under the sink with some green powder, muttering, "Bandits, holdups!"—directing her phrases at some fleeing cockroaches. "Wait, wait," she told them. "I'll get you, where are you going so fast?"

I waited until the battle was over, then my mother washed her hands and made me a big jelly sandwich. I had planned to ask her a question about our big holiday which I knew was due soon, but the sandwich tasted so good I forgot all about it.

That night my father came home from his grocery a block away, stepped into the flat, and, with an important look on his face, announced to my mother: "Etta, I looked at the calendar today. Passover is only a week off. I'll have to go for the matzos soon."

Then I remembered!

"Is that so?" asked my mother, who had been as cognizant of the date as her husband. "So soon—next week?"

And the following day my mother started cleaning the flat for the coming Passover holidays. It wasn't an ordinary cleaning.

It was like tearing the house apart and putting it together again. She stood on a chair in the pantry and took down special sets of dishes, glasses, and silverwear, which she used only once a year, during Passover week. She boiled and scalded them and shined them. She went to a special drawer in a bureau and drew out tablecloths and napkins which had reposed there for fifty-one weeks; these she tubbed and scrubbed and ironed. She gave my brother Irving and me twenty cents each for washing all the windows of the flat—nine windows. Afterward she hung fresh curtains. Of course she scrubbed the floors, twice.

It was a week of almost terrifying activity that wore her out, but I believe she loved it. It was something she did every year, and was something her mother and her mother's mother had done before her, annually, in Europe.

As the days of preparations continued, the flat grew shinier and shinier. My brothers, my sister, and I walked on tiptoe through the rooms; we didn't want to displace or soil anything. We were careful how we spoke, too.

"No rough talk in the house this week," our mother had warned us, which meant Irving, Louis, and I couldn't face each other and say, "Give me that ball or I'll pin your ears back," or, "I'll spit in your eye and drown you!"

During that week of hectic preparations we often heard our parents talking at the super table, after my father returned from his grocery. They spoke of Milt, who, at twenty, was making his first trip on the road as a traveling shirt-salesman.

"Here's another letter from Milt today," my mother said, showing the latest letter. "Tomorrow he's going to Cedar Rapids, Iowa. I hope he'll be able to come to the seder, on Tuesday."

My father took the letter from my mother, putting on his gold-rimmed glasses, and read Milt's note.

"Hm, he writes business is good . . . opened up two new accounts in Muscatine." He cleared his throat. "Of course he'll come home for the seder!" He stood there, short and stocky, his words booming powerfully in the flat. "Of course! He's still one of the family, the oldest son, isn't he? Of course!"

None of us dared to speak; we knew better than to challenge that stern note of authority.

"Sit down and write a letter," he commanded Ben. "Write Milt he has to come home for the holiday, even if he's out in California."

And Ben, who had come home tired from his order-picker's job in a wholesale hardware concern, sat down and wrote while we crowded around him.

"How far is Cedar Rapids, Iowa?" my mother asked timidly, while Ben was scribbling away.

"One hundred miles, one thousand miles," my father answered clearly. "What difference does it make? Huh?" He pointed a finger at Ben. "Tell Milt we're expecting him!"

The violent house cleaning, the talk about Milt, and all the other preparations keyed us up. Two days before the holiday we watched our mother buying chickens, special flour, special salt, holiday candles, and new spices; and we saw her readying her biggest cooking pots and pans for action.

On the day of the seder, the feast that celebrates the liberation of the people from Egyptian bondage, I was startled when my father addressed me.

"This year I want you to go with me to get the matzos. We're going this afternoon, in a little while. Irving will mind the store with your mother. Louis is too young to carry anything, and your sister Ruth is only a girl. So I'm taking you along. Go wash up now."

I tried to hide my excitement. I had never gone with my father for the matzos before.

In a little while, my face and hands scrubbed, I was ready to accompany my father. Mother was standing behind the counter with Irving. My sister Ruth was at the flat, watching the pots of food cooking on the stove and in the oven.

"Don't give him any heavy packages," my mother warned my father. "He's still a small boy."

"I know, I know," my father answered. "I always carry the large ones, don't I?"

"Twenty pounds of matzos, that's enough this year. We had too much last year again, remember? Twenty pounds, just buy twenty pounds."

"Yes, yes," My father was putting on his coat and hat,

"Twenty, twenty." He scowled. "All right, we're going." He walked out of the grocery, still frowning, and I followed obediently.

We rode a trolley east and transferred on Halsted Street. My father paid half fare for me. We transferred on south Halsted, riding past desolate junk-yards, factories, and rooming houses, and soon we approached Taylor Street, where the big Jewish settlement began.

Having lived in Gentile neighborhoods all my life, I found this section fascinating. Retail stores crowded one another here, displaying all types of merchandise, while at the curbs stood push-carts manned by aggressive men and women who advertised the good points of their wares, shouting in English and in Yiddish.

"Bargains today, big bargains! Look, mister, see, missus, feel the cloth! Half price, half price!"

We got off near Twelfth Street, where the hucksters stood thicker than ever, and made our way up the jammed sidewalk. My father pushed forward steadily and sometimes I had to run to keep up with him. In the middle of the block, he stopped before a building that resembled a garage, or a small warehouse. A six-pointed star was painted on a wooden sign overhead. "Pearlstein's Matzos. The World's Best."

"In here," my father commanded, and I stood behind him as he swung open a big, iron, fireproof door.

As we entered a long, low building, I felt warm waves of heat brushing my face. Suddenly, under strong overhead lights, I saw what looked like a hundred men working before big ovens. Actually, when I counted them later on, there were only thirteen men in the place. Most of them wore long white aprons and small white cotton caps; their sleeves were rolled to their elbows, and their faces looked healthy and red from the heat. Near us, against the wall, was a sign: "No admittance. Wholesale only."

My father did not advance further, but stood hesitantly near the sign. The men at the ovens did not notice him. Looking around, I saw white matzos stacked on tables and on racks in tall, neat piles. The pleasant smell of the fresh matzos, different from the odor of new bread, filled every inch of the place.

Suddenly my father made a motion with his head toward a

tall, strongly built baker in a white apron. The workman didn't see the gesture as he bent near an oven to examine the gauges, after which he opened one of the iron doors, revealing the gas flames. When he shut the oven, he turned and saw my father.

"Hello, hello!" he called above the hubbub of the place, grinning. "Guten yuntif, bruder!" He came over briskly and shook hands vigorously with my father, then glanced smilingly at me. "Who is this one? Number three or four?"

"No, he's number five," my father said with a laugh. "He's the next-to-the-youngest. Shake hands with Mr. Kleinholtz. Go on, shake hands."

Shyly, I stuck my hand out and in a moment felt it shallowed in the large, warm, friendly paw of the broad-shouldered baker; he pumped it a few times, then released it, grinning at me.

"You came to help your Pa carry the matzos, right?"

"Yes."

"Good, good. This year it turned out better than ever. The flour is better."

"You said the same thing last year," my father remarked with a smile. "And the year before that."

"No, no. Did I? The matzos is really good this year." His broad smile reflected my father's. I could see they were fond of each other. They looked like brothers, only Mr. Kleinholtz was much taller. "How's the missus, how're the other children?"

"Everybody is fine. Now I want some good matzos, not too well done but not underdone, either. Listen, I want it from the last batch, like I get it every year."

A side door opened and a little middle-aged man approached us excitedly. "What do you want here? Can't you see the men are working?" He continued shouting and waving his hands nervously. "It's against the rules of the union—it's against the rules!"

"Listen, Mr. Epstein," Mr. Kleinholtz lied calmly, "This man is my brother, my blood brother. He wants to buy some matzos. He buys here every year. He pays for it. So what's against the union? I'm the shop chairman, right? What's criminal about it?"

A phone began ringing somewhere and a young woman stuck her head out of the little office.

"Telephone—Mr. Epstein!"

"They're always pestering me, the union!" Mr. Epstein shouted. "Better working conditions, a new toilet! Yes, yes! Tomorrow you'll want showers!" He waved his small hands wildly, then disappeared into his office and slammed the door.

"So how much do you want this year?" Mr. Kleinholtz asked my father pleasantly, as though the owner had never made his appearance. "One hundred pounds? Three hundred pounds?"

My father chuckled. "That all? That all? The missus says not to bring home more than twenty pounds, but I think I ought to buy thirty. The boys are big eaters."

We began following Mr. Kleinholtz, who was heading for one of the big tables directly in front of the first oven. A minute later we stood before ten big piles of freshly baked matzos which had just been drawn from under the flames by one of the bakers; they were snow white, with here and there a faint, faint tint of tan at the edges. A wonderful smell rose from them. Mr. Kleinholtz smiled proudly at the piles but said nothing.

"I'll take thirty—" my father weakened—"no, make it thirty-five pounds from this batch," my father concluded simply.

"Good, good. They're the best. You won't be sorry."

Instead of calling over one of the young apprentices, Mr. Kleinholtz himself wrapped them in double thicknesses of smooth, shiny, white paper sheets. He tied the four bundles with strong, thick, hairy, yellow cord, two big bundles and two small bundles.

Afterward, my father and Mr. Kleinholtz stood talking together near the ovens. Their friendship was of a curious nature. They had met, accidentally, at the wedding of one of our distant cousins fifteen years ago, long before I was born, and for a time our families had been on friendly terms. My mother and Mrs. Kleinholtz, however, did not get on well together, so the family social calls had terminated. These annual pilgrimages to the Matzoth factory formed the sole contact between my father and the baker, who bowed their heads philosophically before the quarrels of the women.

At last my father picked up the two bigger bundles. Turning to Mr. Kleinholtz, he said, "Well, a good holiday, a good Passover. And may the next year be a healthy and prosperous one for you and your family."

"Thank you," the big, smiling baker boomed. "Same to you. And if that's not the best matzos you ever ate, bring it back and I'll eat it all up, together with the paper and the string!" He laughed and stroked my head. "I mean it. Swear to God!" He accompanied us to the door where he and my father shook hands again.

"Good-by," my father said. "We'll see each other soon. Why do we have to wait till next year? Soon, soon."

Nodding in agreement, the baker waved at us and then we were out on the chilly street. Darkness was coming and we hurried toward the corner. We got aboard a trolley, and as we rode home my father was silent, his wide face moody. Sitting on the cane seat, I began to feel the heat from the freshly baked matzos slowly working itself through the thick wrappings of paper. In the cold trolley the warmth was comforting.

When we reached the store, my mother threw up her hands when she saw the four bundles. "Every year," she cried, "every year it's the same! No, you bought too much!"

"Passover is a whole week," my father argued. "Listen, we'll eat it, we'll eat it."

Irving, Louis, and I carried the bundles of still-hot matzos to our flat a block away, while our father took over the duties of the store. When we reached our apartment, we smelled the wonderful odors of the holiday food coming from the stove; the rooms were filled with aromas.

"All right, children, change into your best clothes," our mother commanded. "But first wash yourselves good. Remember, you have to be real clean for the seder."

We went to our bedroom where we found our best clothes had been placed on the bed for us. After washing and dressing, we came into the dining room.

A familiar but dazzling sight met our eyes. The big, square, mission-oak table, expanded to its utmost and covered with a snowy-white tablecloth, was already set. The water tumblers and cut-glass wine glasses sparkled like crystal. The Passover silverware gleamed. Newly folded linen napkins—we never used even paper napkins during the rest of the year—were placed next to each large dinner plate. The decanter filled with home-made red wine stood on a glass tray in the center of the table, shining under the twin gas-mantles overhead. As we stared, my sister Ruth came from the kitchen and set down tiny silver saltcellers, which we used one week each year.

The door opened and Ben came in, home from work. He went into the bathroom to clean up and to change into his best suit.

Then, at six, our father came home, closing the store a whole hour earlier tonight. He, too, washed up and began changing into his dark blue Sunday suit. As he struggled into a starched white shirt, he shouted toward the kitchen, "Isn't Milt home yet?"

He knew, of course, that Milt's train did not arrive until six-nine, that it was at least a forty-minute trolley ride from the railroad station, but he inquired about Milt just the same. "Isn't he home?"

"I'm so worried," my mother called in a high, nervous voice from the kitchen. "We can't start the seder without him. Do you think something's wrong with his train?"

"Maybe an accident?" my father said, worried also.

"Look, what's all this talk?" Ben cut in, smiling but a little exasperated. "His train doesn't get in until after six, does it? Is this a night to talk of wrecks and accidents?" He turned to Irving. "How about putting on a dance record to liven up things?"

Irving cranked the phonograph and put on "Alexander's Ragtime Band," opening the little doors of the machine so that the strains emerged with strident force.

"No!" my father shouted. "Stop it! Tonight's a holiday—no ragtime!" He walked over and stopped the record. "Quiet!" he roared. "Let it be quiet!"

No one said anything. In the silence, the pungent smells of cooking drifted tantalizingly from the kitchen. Our appetites were increasing with the passing of each second. The doorbell rang.

"Milt!" my sister screamed happily.

We heard our oldest brother pounding up the stairs, his heavy Gladstone bag bumping against the banister in his triumphant ascent. My mother rushed from the kitchen, shouted his name, and, when he reached our door, gathered him into her arms with a sob.

"So late?" she exclaimed worriedly. But a moment later, ashamed of her show of emotion, she wiped her eyes and smiled. "We were waiting so long, we thought maybe something happened—"

"What could happen?" Milt grinned. Though still a boy, he stood before us, tall, handsome, mature, and magnetic. "I couldn't make the train go faster, could I? I even took a cab home."

"A taxi?" cried our father. "All the way from the station?" His face shone proudly, for he knew some of the neighbors must have seen his son arrive like a potentate from the railroad terminal. "Well, well!" He blew his nose loudly into his handkerchief. "So how was the trip? Did you do good business for the firm?"

Irving, Louis, and I fought for the privilege of lugging Milt's heavy bag into his bedroom.

"If I go over my quota by twenty per cent this trip," Milt said, "Mr. Liebman promised me Omaha and Kansas City on the next trip."

"Is that right?" cried our father. "You really mean it?"

"I'm running close to twenty-five per cent above quota right now, Pa."

"You hear that, Etta?" my father shouted. "You hear what Milt said?"

Fifteen minutes later, having changed into a clean white shirt and sporting a brand-new silk necktie he had received from a necktie salesman in Peoria as a gift, Milt joined us in the living room, in his pencil-striped blue suit. As he saw us standing assembled, as if rendering him homage, he suddenly looked confused and warmly pleased. For a moment he wasn't a traveling salesman sleeping in strange hotels, but only a boy. The moment passed, and he smiled with self-confidence. "Well, when do we eat?"

My mother bustled in from the kitchen. "All right, sit down, everybody. Everything is ready. I'll be with you in a minute, so sit down please, everybody."

The male members of the family came to the dining table wearing their hats, according to the orthodox tradition. Irving, Louis, and I were too young to own hats, so we put on our caps; wearing our hats and caps at table lent us an air of solemnity.

Ruth sat primly between Ben and Milt, in a new pink dress, her blonde hair in neat, beribboned braids down her back. At the head of the table our father sat on two big white pillows. His nose was twitching, for the luxurious smells of the food were driving him half mad. All thoughts of his little grocery, with its bills and disappointing business, were forgotten tonight.

"Well?" he said, turning impatiently toward the kitchen. "So?"

"One second, one second." Hastily our mother joined us, in a blue shot-silk shirtwaist and a new skirt, protected by an apron. She sat at my father's left, her happy face flushed, and gave her six children a quick, almost imperceptible nod of approval as, taking her place, she noticed that we were spruced to shining for the occasion.

My father reached for his big, heavy, old-fashioned prayer book, the Haggadah. Turning to Milt, he said, "Open the hall door, so that any stranger can come in and join us at this seder."

Milt opened the hall door, the standard proceeding before the feast, and returned to his chair. My father bit his lip, lowered his eyes and, in a singsong, semi-oriental monotone, began intoning the opening, sanctification prayer, the Kiddush, in Hebrew. On the sideboard, two white Sabbath candles, which my mother had lit at sundown, burned steadily.

I sat patiently, my eyes alert, half-listening to my parent. As my gaze roved about the table my mouth began to water. The prospect of a solid week of eating the tasty, special, Passover dishes was almost more than I could bear. No matter how expensive meat or chicken was, this was one week when our mother went all out in her cookery.

My restless glance strayed to the shankbone of a lamb on a plate—symbol of the paschal sacrifice in biblical times; I saw the dishes of parsley and radishes, the hard-boiled egg, the bitter herbs floating in water—all religious and historical symbols which did not interest me, though I knew the bitter herbs were very important tonight because they were a reminder of the bitter years of bondage the Israelites had suffered under the yoke of the cruel Egyptians. Near the plate of bitter herbs stood a squat jar of red, home-made, powerful horse-radish that, tasted, instantly

drew tears to the eyes as well as a stinging sensation inside one's
nostrils.

Other plates held cut-up slices of cold meats, cold chicken
wings, giblets and chicken hearts and livers. There was no bread
and butter on the table; at my father's elbow was a plate covered
with a snowy linen napkin, which we all knew hid three big un-
broken squares of matzos, in keeping with the ritual. My gaze
strayed to the left. Near the bulging wine decanter which was
ringed by eight empty glasses that seemed to lift up their hollow
cups like the open, beseeching mouths of baby birds, stood a large
plate of home-made macaroons, a dish holding nuts and raisins,
and a large, fluffy, uncut yellow cake made from matzoh flour.
From the kitchen, in waves, flowed the tantalizing, heavy odors of
hot soup, roast chicken, simmering meats bedded in luscious
sauces. Next to me Louis began to fidget and wriggle his knees
under the table. Irving and I began to stir and move restlessly.
Ruth, usually so proper, began to moisten her lips as the aromas
continued to inundate the room. On the other side of the table,
Milt and Ben grinned at each other; as kids, they, too, had
squirmed during the lengthy ceremony.

My father continued his praying, peering over his glasses occasionally at us to see if we were listening. Around his shoulders
was draped his white silk, fringed prayershawl. In a few minutes,
as the spirit of the ceremony fastened its grip upon him, he began to rock up and back in rhythm, as the rich, Hebraic phrases
issued from his lips.

" 'I will bring you out from under the burden of the Egyptians, and I will rid you of their bondage, and I will redeem
you . . .' " He wet his forefinger and turned another yellowed
page of the Haggadah, and young as I was I began to feel the
immediacy of the prayer. " '. . . and I will take you to Me for a
people . . .' "

He looked up, bending his gaze upon little Louis. The table
fell silently attentive. Fingering the heavy book, our father asked
his youngest, in English, "Well? Well?"

Louis reddened as he struggled to recall what he had to say.
He had been coached beforehand, by Ben, but now his memory

deserted him. His lower lip trembled, but finally he remembered. In a high, faltering voice, he said, "Why is this—this night different from all other nights?"

"Because," our father answered, "on all other nights we eat leavened and unleavened alike, but on this night only unleavened bread. On all other nights we eat any kind of herbs, but on this night only bitter herbs. On all other nights we do not dip even once, but on this night twice. On all other nights we sit either upright or leaning, but on this night we all lean!" As we saw our father's face relax, we all smiled.

"Pop," Milt cracked, "how about hurrying the ceremony tonight? We're all starved."

Ignoring the request, my father returned to his singsong incantations, rocking up and back. He halted to dip his wine into the big, cut-glass rimmed base upon which the decanter rested, and we followed suit, dribbling a few drops of the red, red wine in unison as he intoned the command to dip. I stared at the large filled goblet of wine standing in the center of the table which was for the prophet Elijah. As an unseen guest in our house on this auspicious night, we welcomed him as a precursor of the Messiah.

As the lengthy ceremony continued and Ruth, Irving, Louis, and I grew more hungry and fidgety, our father, we noticed, began to skip a few pages surreptitiously, after reading a few words at the top of a page. Our spirits rose, and we nudged each other under the table. Once or twice my mother put her finger to her lips, in an admonition for better behavior; but now we sensed our father was shortening the service for us, and we grinned and grew more restless than ever.

"Hurry up, Pa," Irving had the temerity to whisper. "Us guys are dying at the table."

After glaring at Irving for a moment, my father turned five pages of his Haggadah unobtrusively and continued his singsong. He finished by clearing his throat and raising his voice righteously, as a cover for his guilt at finishing so quickly. The final phrases of the prayer died over our bent heads. The tall candles on the sideboard still gleamed steadily. Our father closed the heavy Haggadah.

"All right," he said in English. "So it's finished. Now we can eat."

"Yippee!" Louis and I cried, clapping our hands. "Food, food!"

My mother rose, smiling, and hurried toward the kitchen. "Ruth, Ruthie," she called. "Come help me."

A few minutes later we were bent over steaming plates of tasty chicken soup in which two giant matzoth dumplings stood up like islands in each dish. Irving, Louis, and I were the first to finish; we scraped the bottoms of the plates clean. My mother went into the kitchen and returned with a great platter of roast chicken; she made another trip and brought back a second platter holding a large, steaming, roasted stuffed veal. Ruth helped her bring bowls of string beans, potatoes, and apple sauce to the table, as well as two plates stacked high with matzos which we began eating.

With his napkin tucked under his chin, and still wearing his hat, our father proceeded to make the greatest inroads in the piles of food. Short and powerfully built, he had never suffered from a loss of appetite. He set us all an example and, except for Ruth who was a skimpy eater, we did not fail him. With every dish of food we continued to eat pieces of matzoth, which the grownups washed down with wine.

Every time our mother came from the kitchen with a fresh supply of matzoth from the first of the opened bundles, she cried out, "Feel! The matzoth is so fresh it's still warm!"

"You can thank Mr. Kleinholtz the baker," my father remarked proudly. "He gave me the best, right from the oven!"

Curious, Louis and Irving rose from their chairs and, walking into the kitchen, investigated the bundles. "Still warm!" they cried. "Gee!" They returned to their chairs and continued eating.

In the middle of the meal, when all of us were on our second helpings of chicken and third helpings of veal and apple sauce, the phone rang in the front room. Milt rose instantly, and as he left the room I saw my parents exchange a glance. We could hear Milt speaking cautiously a moment later, and when he returned his face was a mask.

As he sat down my mother asked, "Who was it?"

"Oh—somebody."

"A girl? That one on the North Side?"

"Yes—Anne."

"How did she know you came home?"

Milt bent to cut his chicken. "Gee, I don't know. I guess she took a chance and called."

My parents exchanged another glance. Of course he was lying; he must have sent the girl a letter from the road, notifying her that he'd be in Chicago for the seder.

"Milt," our mother said with forgiveness in her voice, as well as gentle understanding in her eyes, "we don't see much of you now—with your traveling. Don't you think it would be nice to spend this evening with us at home here?"

"Gee, Ma." There was pain in Milt's voice, in his face. "You don't understand——"

My father reached for more wine, his wide face flushed. "The grapes were good this year," he blurted. He took a hearty swallow and speared another piece of veal. For a few moments there was silence around the table.

"Hey, look, I got the wishbone," Louis yelled. Turning, he gripped one part of it and I held on to the other. We pulled, there was a snap, and he got the bigger part. "I wish——!"

"Don't say it!" Ruth cried to Louis warningly.

We ate until we could eat no more. Under the table I could feel my belly stretched tight as a drum, I felt uncomfortable but knew that in another hour I'd feel better.

My mother went into the kitchen to prepare tea for the grown folks. She returned with cups of very hot tea, pieces of lemon resting in the saucers. After setting down the steaming cups before Milt, Ben, my father, and herself, she proceeded to slice the big, fluffy, yellow, Passover cake. There wasn't any more room left in my stomach, but as I witnessed Louis and Irving accepting portions of cake, I did likewise and stuffed myself with it, adding three macaroons to my share.

Then Milt went into his bedroom where his Gladstone bag rested on the floor. Returning, he gave Louis and me five small cakes of beautiful-smelling soap taken from various Iowa hotels;

he handed Irving a small, celluloid-handled pocket knife; he presented Ruth with a little genuine leather handbag; he gave our father a blue knitted necktie and Ben a shirt; and he held out a beautiful brown silk blouse to our mother.

Choking, our mother got up and kissed him. While Milt sat grinning, my father blew his nose, then took another big swallow of wine; his face was really overhealthy-looking by this time.

"All right," he remarked clearly, rising from the table. "This seems to be the night for presents!" He glanced at our mother, who nodded. "Well," he said, "everybody here knows that when they reach the age of twenty-one they're going to get a present—from Ma and me." He glanced around the table. "For years I've told you about it, how my parents gave their children presents when they reached twenty-one. It's a good tradition. It makes you think, uh, it makes you think of growing up, of, uh, life——"

Listening, we all grew silent. Usually he was never at a loss for words, but now he was stumbling.

"But because Milt—because he—our oldest son—has always been such a good boy, your mother and I decided not to wait until Milt is twenty-one, which won't be for another eight months. We're going to give him his gift on seder night——tonight."

To our surprise and delight, he drew a new round, solid gold watch from his pocket, holding it by its gold chain. My mother was crying a little, looking at us—God knows why. Milt moved his lips, choked up himself. As he reached forward for his present, we all clapped.

"And let me add," my father shouted above the excitement, looking at the rest of us, "that I'll break the rule for you, too. If anybody here accomplishes something big, like going on the road before he's twenty-one, or winning a prize, they'll get their gold watch before they're of age, too!"

We stamped and clapped, then crowded around Milt to inspect the brand-new present. To cover up his confusion, my father tossed off another glass or two of wine.

Then the feast was over. Blowing her nose and happy, my mother with Ruth's assistance, began clearing the table, and we all moved into the front room. Irving and Ben played a dozen of my father's favorite phonograph records, mostly scratchy Caruso discs which we had listened to hundreds of times. We sat patiently, hearing the scratchy bellowings of the world's greatest tenor. My eyelids had grown so heavy (it was nine o'clock already) I could hardly keep them open. Louis was already dozing in a chair, and Irving began yawning.

After the phonograph recital, my father interrogated Milt again concerning business conditions out of town, new accounts he had opened up, and the state of the crops.

"And what do the merchants think about the next elections?" he pressed Milt.

My mother merely sat quietly, staring hungrily at her oldest son who had been away from home for many weeks.

At last I noticed Milt growing more and more restive. Finally he got up, his eyes avoiding my mother's. "Well, I think I'll go and comb my hair."

He went into his bedroom and a few minutes later he came out, holding his hat. "I won't be gone long, just for an hour or so," he began lamely. My parents did not say anything. "If that blouse is too small or too big, Ma, I can always exchange it. I want you to try it on tomorrow—I want it to fit you just right."

He walked over guiltily and kissed my mother, who offered him her cheek. Her mouth was twisted as she attempted to understand the first crack opened in the wall of her large family. She followed him out with her eyes.

When the door closed behind Milt, my sister went to our upright piano and played her latest practice piece, twice. Then she returned to her chair and joined us in the uneasy evening silence. To make conversation, my father, who looked tired, began to talk about this year's good matzos, praising the factory that had made them.

"It pays to have a good friend like Mr. Kleinholtz. Just think, he went right to the ovens and got them hot for me!" Then he broke off and yawned, as if thinking of his grocery which he would have to open at six o'clock tomorrow morning for the railroad workers' trade.

In the silence, we could hear a Kedzie Avenue trolley swishing along the rails in the night. Suddenly my mother bent over cautiously and picked up Louis in her arms, preparatory to carrying him to his bed and undressing him. As she looked down at him gently, a tear glistened on her cheek. Louis was snoring lustily, like an exhausted bartender. After my mother carried him from the room, I grew restless.

Finally I stole toward the kitchen. I stood on a chair and lit the gas-mantle, which revealed the unwashed dishes in the sink. Then I got down and came over to the three unopened parcels of matzos, still tied with yellow, hairy cord. When I felt them I was keenly disappointed. They were no longer warm to my touch. They were cold now, like bundles of last week's newspapers.

THE SNOWBALL MAN AND HOLY WRIT

by LOUIS BERG

WHEN I WAS A BOY OF EIGHT I WENT TO HEDER, OR TO ITS EQUIVA-lent, in a little Virginia town. And when the day's session came to an end and the youngsters, free at last, ran whooping down the rickety stairway to the street, I followed more slowly after, being a serious-minded youth, and walked away from the rest down a side street where, pleasantly situated, was a little refreshment stand operated by a very old colored gentleman—a friend of mine.

His name I have forgotten, and his appearance also, although I can remember that he had a white frizzled beard, like Old Black Joe, and wore a frock coat even in the heat of the summer, for all the world like the pious old Jews of the Hevrah Mishnais. And I know that he was a kindly old soul; that his "snowballs" were the best in town; and that he dealt generously with his youthful customers, sparing neither ice nor flavoring to satisfy them.

A snowball is a rare delicacy. It consists of finely scraped ice, packed into a glass, over which is poured a syrupy flavoring.

It is sweet, and it takes a long time to consume, thereby fulfilling all the requirements of juvenile taste. At my friend's stand it cost only a penny, although there were others, more grasping, who charged two. As an added refinement, milk was sometimes added, but for this concoction double price was demanded, and it was generally beyond my means, being reserved for special occasions, or obtainable only through the exercise of considerable restraint on my part. That is to say, by refraining from a plain snowball on one day I could get one with milk on the next, which occurred to me even then as an excellent object lesson.

Plain or with milk, they were very delicious in hot weather, and since they could not be gulped down immediately but were sipped with a spoon, and each spoonful melted in the mouth while the cool liquid trickled down the throat, there was plenty of opportunity to linger around and to get acquainted with the proprietor. And since also the stand was set back from the road, and under the shade of a splendid magnolia tree belonging to a yard adjoining, and rich in odorous white blossoms, there was no hurry at all. I could sit on the wooden crate that was furnished me as a seat, and could linger as long as the snowball lasted, and longer, sipping my ice and discussing theology with the old negro, who was deeply religious, as the frock coat might indicate, and filled with curiosity concerning the alien rituals of the Jews.

Before long I began to be treated with special marks of favor. It was discovered that I was studying Hebrew, the holy language, the speech in which had asserted themselves the warriors and prophets of Israel, nay, the mother tongue of Christ himself; and the old man's admiration knew no bounds. I finally consented to bring him a book in the sacred script, and the old man bowed his head and looked long and awesomely at the strange characters, handling the somewhat battered old siddur, the prayer book, as if it were the revelation itself, and fragile in the bargain. He confided in me that it had been a long cherished ambition with him to learn the language in which the "Good Book" had been written, and he said no more. But when he made the snowball for me he very absent-mindedly added milk, and on my reminding him that I had only a penny he became somewhat confused.

"Guess it's yo' good luck," he acknowledged sheepishly, and lolled his tongue like a child detected in an act of mischief.

The next day, however, he repeated his error, and the next day, watching me with a sly expression that I caught as I contentedly sipped the doubly delicious refreshment at exactly half cost. I understood somehow that it was no mistake on his part; that for some mysterious reason I was being signally marked out for his favors, and also that my occult understanding of the Hebrew letterings had something to do with my good fortune. Whereupon my own respect for the Torah rose to a height that it has never since attained.

However, I said nothing, and philosophically enjoyed my luck as long as it should last. Perhaps I sensed that sooner or later an explanation would be forthcoming.

Finally the secret reason came out, and a pact was made, over which I smile tenderly to this day, between the boy of eight and the colored deacon of the First Baptist Church, who must have been close to eighty. I was to teach him to decipher the original Holy Writ, and in return could have the best in the house free of charge. In vain I objected, quite honestly, that my own knowledge was extremely limited.

"Ain't you learnin' all the time," he countered, "and can't I follow right behind?" Which was a logic that I did not care at the time to dispute. So the gentlemen's agreement was made, and nothing would please him but that the lessons should begin that evening.

His little stand was every night converted into his dwelling. There was a little cot in the rear of the room which during the day was concealed by a dingy calico curtain. On a shelf on the wall were the bottles of colored flavoring, green, red, and yellow, still in plain view; but the huge box upon which the ice was scraped was covered with a torn bit of canvas. A small ice-box, one chair, my familiar crate, and a small table, bare and unsteady, completed the furnishings of the room. By way of decoration were tacked to the wall several colored prints on religious subjects: Jesus entering Jerusalem on an ass; Abraham about to offer his son as a sacrifice; and one framed picture, but without a glass, depicting, as I remember to this day, several dark-skinned angels ascending to heaven with a little negro child. On the table was a huge Bible which, I discovered later, contained highly tinted illustrations.

The room was dimly lighted with a smoky kerosene lamp, which hung from the wall, the light being thrown from a tin reflector, in which your face was very oddly mirrored if you looked close. A musty odor hung in the room, disagreeably heightened by the smell of kerosene from the lamp.

I felt uneasy when I first entered, with the uncomfortable realization that I was violating an unwritten Southern code by accepting the hospitality of a negro, and he was equally embarrassed. He offered me the chair, while he himself took the crate for a seat; and my siddur was spread out on the table between us. The lamp cast flickering shadows that made for difficult reading, and we both sat with our heads bowed close to the book.

"The first letter you see here is Aleph," I began, "same as A." He repeated after me, and so on to the letter Ches, whose guttural sound he could not reproduce for the life of him. And the rest of the evening was spent in teaching him to properly enunicate the letter Ches, with only moderate success. We finally compromised on some weird sound of his own invention, and the lesson closed. Although I made no comment, I was inclined to be pessimistic, but he was almost childishly pleased. Then came my fee, which did not taste as pleasant to me as during the heat of the day.

Many a night was spent on the alphabet, which he never completely mastered. However, he continued to be highly satisfied with the progress he was making. I think he must have taken others into his confidence, for I remember passing his shack on one occasion when he was seated in front in earnest conversation with a confrere, as grave and elderly as himself. On that account I did not stop, but they both ceased their talk as I drew near, and bowed their heads in a friendly and respectful manner. I felt like a youthful gaon, and my manner with him took on professorial dignity.

Something happened during this time that impressed me

greatly. Since I treated the siddur with only slight reverence, there was a page torn, which one day he bribed me, with innumerable promises and humble pleading, to lend him. I permitted myself to be persuaded, but with the consciousness that it was somehow a sin.

This page he treasured mightily. Passing his shack on an off night (for I refused to give more than three lessons a week) I happened to look curiously in. He did not see me. He was bent over the table, with the torn page before him and apparently in rapt contemplation of the sacred print which for him must have contained a mysterious sense, the more to be revered because he could not understand it. I must have stared at him for fully five minutes, and then he turned and looked full at me, but without a sign of recognition or even an acknowledgment that I was there. I walked away hastily.

Meanwhile I was becoming tired of snowballs, with or without milk. I was satiated to distress and gulped them down more for fear of making him miserable than for any other reason. And I became more and more careless about the lessons. His place stifled me, and I skipped through the assignments, gulping eagerly as soon as I had left him of the air that was wonderfully sweet and fresh outside. How he remained in his shack, night after night, puzzled me greatly. I felt vaguely sorry for him, and soon it was only this sympathy that kept me at my task of teaching him the language of the sages.

For he made marvelously little progress. He invariably had forgotten, on the night of a lesson, what he had been taught in the lesson before. Never was a student more zealous and less apt. It was irritating, and it was pathetic. I would scold, and he would accept my scolding meekly. Patiently, laboriously, I would strain my voice in earnest attempt to impress forever on his mind "Bes-Aleph, Bo."

And never for a moment did he realize that he was making anything but glorious progress. His glee when he managed to hit upon a correct solution was a sight to behold. "Got him dat time," he would chortle; and grope painstakingly for the next combination.

I became proudly superior, and dictated to him in the most

outrageous terms. He accepted everything as natural and inevitable, and bore my complaints with touching humility. But I was growing weary, and increasingly aware of the stuffiness of the place.

Finally, in desperation, I made a grand announcement. "That's finished," I said. "Tomorrow night we will begin the translation of the Bible." I spoke in a stately manner, befitting the importance of the occasion.

It had been a hard night, and he had been troubled and apologetic. But now his face brightened, and he hastened, flustered and eager, to mix for me a snowball that I did not at all want. I ran out to join my friends, who were forever mystified as to the reason for my continual tardiness.

The next night I reminded myself and went rather grudgingly to keep the appointment. To my surprise the old man had donned his Sunday clothes, and was arrayed in his very best manner. His face shone as if it had been smeared in oils, as may indeed actually have been the case; and upon his head was a top hat, the first I had ever seen. In accordance with my injunction he retained this during the reading, for I would not have dreamed of letting him look upon the Law with his head uncovered.

There had been an attempt also to put the room in order. It seemed less dingy, and had been carefully swept. I noticed that the lamp globe had been polished and cast a much brighter light and that a clean cloth was on the table.

There was unusual gravity in his demeanor. I caught somewhat the spirit of the occasion, and it was with slow deliberation that I drew up my chair, and opened the book, no longer a siddur, but the Pentateuch, in Hebrew, with an English translation on the right hand margin. The lesson began.

"What is the first word?" I began, and even I realized the absurdity of asking. The task of deciphering it was as much beyond his powers as if indeed he had not labored those many nights.

He started resolutely enough, but was baffled. "Lemme see now, dass a Bes." "Right," I agreed, "and the next letter is Resh. What now?"

He stared blankly.

"B'reshis," I started desperately. "B'reshis," he repeated faithfully.

"That means, in the beginning. Now; boroh, he created; Elohim, God; Hooretz, the earth. Repeat now after me—B'reshis. . . ."

And carefully he followed after, repeating phrase for phrase the opening lines of the book of Genesis; and got no further than the opening lines. For suddenly the realization must have come to him that these were for a fact the words of the Bible, as he had many times read them before, but never in the original.

He was caught in a wave of religious fervor. "Dass it!" he cried, "Dass it, Lord!"

He began to wave his hands above his head. His eyes were blurred and watery. Suddenly he began to cry out, in an astonishingly clear and vibrant voice.

"Ah got religion," he yelled.

His body rocked to and fro. Now he was chanting. "O, mah Jesus, Lord, huh; Mah soul is free. As see de light, huh! and Jesus have set me free. Glory be to God, huh!" Babbling, incoherent phrases followed, rushing from his lips. "Glory be! praise God. Hallelujah! Ah'm sanctified, Lord Ah'm sanctified." He clapped his hands in ecstasy, and his body shook. Suddenly he stopped, and his body grew rigid. He stood fixed, with his hands high in the air, and his lips moved rapidly, but no sound came. His eyes rolled alarmingly; he was frothing slightly at the mouth.

I had been staring fascinated and uneasy. Now I grew frightened and ran away. Ran into the night, in genuine panic, and did not stop until I had passed from the dark street into a lighted way.

I did not return after that. I never saw him again. My interest in snowballs was completely dissipated, and my experience had frightened me so badly that I even avoided the street on which the stand was situated.

When I told my father about it, some time afterwards, he laughed a good deal more than was usual for him, and I think was a little touched too. He said: "Aren't you ashamed, Yungatz? A black negro takes the holy tongue more to heart than you do." Which reproach I did not think was altogether justified, for at that time I was both pious and studious, as Rebbe Neufeld, if he were still living, could testify.

MOLLY BRANDEIS TAKES HOLD

by EDNA FERBER

You could not have lived a week in Winnebago without being aware of Mrs. Brandeis. In a town of ten thousand, where every one was a personality, from Hen Cody, the drayman, in blue overalls (magically transformed on Sunday mornings into a suave black-broadcloth usher at the Congregational Church), to A. J. Dawes, who owned the water-works before the city bought it. Mrs. Brandeis was a super-personality. Winnebago did not know it. Winnebago, buying its dolls, and china, and Battenberg braid and tinware and toys of Mrs. Brandeis, of Brandeis' Bazaar, realized vaguely that here was some one different.

When you entered the long, cool, narrow store on Elm Street, Mrs. Brandeis herself came forward to serve you, unless she already was busy with two customers. There were two clerks—three, if you count Aloysius, the boy—but to Mrs. Brandeis belonged the privilege of docketing you first. If you happened in during a moment of business lull, you were likely to find her reading in the left-hand corner at the front of the store, near the shelf where were ranged the dolls' heads, the pens, the pencils, and school supplies.

You saw a sturdy, well-set-up, alert woman, of the kind that looks taller than she really is; a woman with a long, straight, clever nose that indexed her character, as did everything about

her, from her crisp, vigorous, abundant hair to the way she came
down hard on her heels in walking. She was what might be called
a very definite person. But first you remarked her eyes. Will you
concede that eyes can be piercing, yet velvety? Their piercingness
was a mental quality, I suppose, and the velvety softness a physical
one. One could only think, somehow, of wild pansies—the brown
kind. If Winnebago had taken the trouble to glance at the title
of the book she laid face down on the pencil boxes as you entered,
it would have learned that the book was one of Balzac's, or, perhaps, Zangwill's, or Zola's. She never could overcome that habit
of snatching a chapter here and there during dull moments. She
was too tired to read when night came.

There were many times when the little Wisconsin town lay
broiling in the August sun, or locked in the January drifts, and
the main business street was as silent as that of a deserted village.
But more often she came forward to you from the rear of the
store, with bits of excelsior clinging to her black sateen apron.
You knew that she had been helping Aloysius as he unpacked a
consignment of chamber sets or a hogshead of china or glassware,
chalking each piece with the price mark as it was dug from its
nest of straw and paper.

"How do you do!" she would say. "What can I do for you?"
And in that moment she had you listed, indexed, and filed, were
you a farmer woman in a black shawl and rusty bonnet with a
faded rose bobbing grotesquely atop it, or one of the patronizing
East End set who came to Brandeis' Bazaar because Mrs. Brandeis'
party favors, for one thing, were of a variety that could be got
nowhere else this side of Chicago. If, after greeting you, Mrs.
Brandeis called, "Sadie! Stockings!" (supposing stockings were
your quest), you might know that Mrs. Brandeis had weighed you
and found you wanting.

There had always been a store—at least, ever since Fanny
could remember. She often thought how queer it would seem to
have to buy pins, or needles, or dishes, or soap, or thread. The
store held all these things, and many more. Just to glance at the
bewildering display outside gave you promise of the variety
within. Winnebago was rather ashamed of that display. It was
before the day of repression in decoration, and the two benches

in front of the windows overflowed with lamps, and water sets, and brooms, and boilers and tinware and hampers. Once the Winnebago *Courier* had had a sarcastic editorial about what they called the Oriental bazaar (that was after the editor, Lem Davis, had bumped his shin against a toy cart that protruded unduly), but Mrs. Brandeis changed nothing. She knew that the farmer women who stood outside with their husbands on busy Saturdays would not have understood repression in display, but they did understand the tickets that marked the wares in plain figures— this berry set, $1.59; that lamp, $1.23. They talked it over, outside, and drifted away, and came back, and entered, and bought.

She knew when to be old-fashioned, did Mrs. Brandeis, and when to be modern. She had worn the first short walking skirt in Winnebago. It cleared the ground in a day before germs were discovered, when women's skirts trailed and flounced behind them in a cloud of dust. One of her scandalized neighbors (Mrs. Nathan Pereles, it was) had taken her aside to tell her that no decent woman would dress that way.

"Next year," said Mrs. Brandeis, "when you are wearing one, I'll remind you of that." And she did, too. She had worn shirt-waists with a broad "Gibson" shoulder tuck, when other Winnebago women were still encased in linings and bodices. Do not get the impression that she stood for emancipation, or feminism, or any of those advanced things. They had scarcely been touched on in those days. She was just an extraordinarily alert woman, mentally and physically, with a shrewd sense of values. Molly Brandeis never could set a table without forgetting the spoons, or the salt, or something, but she could add a double column of figures in her head as fast as her eye could travel.

There she goes, running off with the story, as we were afraid she would. Not only that, she is using up whole pages of description when she should be giving us dialogue. Prospective readers, running their eyes over a printed page, object to the solid block formation of the descriptive passage. And yet it is fascinating to weave words about her, as it is fascinating to turn a fine diamond this way and that in the sunlight, to catch its prismatic hues. Besides, you want to know—do you not?—how this woman who reads Balzac should be waiting upon you in a little general store in Winnebago, Wisconsin?

In the first place, Ferdinand Brandeis had been a dreamer, and a potential poet, which is bad equipment for success in the business of general merchandise. Four times, since her marriage, Molly Brandeis had packed her household goods, bade her friends good-by, and with her two children, Fanny and Theodore, had followed her husband to pastures new. A heart-breaking business, that, but broadening. She knew nothing of the art of buying and selling at the time of her marriage, but as the years went by she learned unconsciously the things one should not do in business, from watching Ferdinand Brandeis do them all. She even suggested this change and that, but to no avail. Ferdinand Brandeis was a gentle and lovable man at home; a testy, quick-tempered one in business.

That was because he had been miscast from the first, and yet had played one part too long, even though unsuccessfully, ever to learn another. He did not make friends with the genial traveling salesmen who breezed in, slapped him on the back, offered him a cigar, inquired after his health, opened their sample cases and flirted with the girl clerks, all in a breath. He was a man who talked little, listened little, learned little. He had never got the trick of turning his money over quickly—that trick so necessary to the success of the small-town business.

So it was that, in the year preceding Ferdinand Brandeis' death, there came often to the store a certain grim visitor. Herman Walthers, cashier of the First National Bank of Winnebago, was a kindly-enough, shrewd, small-town banker, but to Ferdinand Brandeis and his wife his visits, growing more and more frequent, typified all that was frightful, presaged misery and despair. He would drop in on a bright summer morning, perhaps, with a cheerful greeting. He would stand for a moment at the front of the store, balancing airily from toe to heel, and glancing about from shelf to bin and back again in a large, speculative way. Then he would begin to walk slowly and ruminatively about, his shrewd little German eyes appraising the stock. He would hum a little absent-minded tune as he walked, up one aisle and down the next (there were only two), picking up a piece of china there, turning it over to look at its stamp, holding it up to the light, tapping it a bit with his knuckles, and putting it down carefully before going musically on down the aisle to the water sets, the lamps, the stockings, the hardware, the toys. And so, his hands behind his back, still humming, out the swinging screen door and into the sunshine of Elm Street, leaving gloom and fear behind him.

One year after Molly Brandeis took hold, Herman Walthers' visits ceased, and in two years he used to rise to greet her from his little cubbyhole when she came into the bank.

Which brings us to the plush photograph album. The plush photograph album is a concrete example of what makes business failure and success. More than that, its brief history presents a complete characterization of Ferdinand and Molly Brandeis.

Ten years before, Ferdinand Brandeis had bought a large bill of Christmas fancy-goods—celluloid toilette sets, leather collar boxes, velvet glove cases. Among the lot was a photograph album in the shape of a huge acorn done in lightning-struck plush. It was a hideous thing, and expensive. It stood on a brass stand, and its leaves were edged in gilt, and its color was a nauseous green and blue, and it was altogether the sort of thing to grace the chill and funereal best room in a Wisconsin farmhouse. Ferdinand Brandeis marked it at six dollars and stood it up for the Christmas trade. That had been ten years before. It was too expensive, or too pretentious, or perhaps even too horrible for the bucolic purse. At any rate, it had been taken out, brushed, dusted, and placed on its stand every holiday season for ten years. On the day after Christmas it was always there, its lightning-struck plush face staring wildly out upon the ravaged fancy-goods counter. It would be packed in its box again and consigned to its long summer's sleep. It had seen three towns, and many changes. The four dollars that Ferdinand Brandeis had invested in it still remained unturned.

One snowy day in November (Ferdinand Brandeis died a fortnight later) Mrs. Brandeis, entering the store, saw two women standing at the fancy-goods counter, laughing in a stifled sort of way. One of them was bowing elaborately to a person unseen.

Mrs. Brandeis was puzzled. She watched them for a moment, interested. One of the women was known to her. She came up to them and put her question, bluntly, though her quick wits had already given her a suspicion of the truth.

"What are you bowing to?"

The one who had done the bowing blushed a little, but giggled too, as she said, "I'm greeting my old friend, the plush album. I've seen it here every Christmas for five years."

Ferdinand Brandeis died suddenly a little more than a week later. It was a terrible period, and one that might have prostrated a less resolute and balanced woman. There were long-standing debts, not to speak of the entire stock of holiday goods to be paid for. The day after the funeral Winnebago got a shock. The Brandeis house was besieged by condoling callers. Every member of the little Jewish congregation of Winnebago came, of course, as they had come before the funeral. Those who had not brought cakes, and salads, and meats, and pies, brought them now, as was the invariable custom in time of mourning.

Others of the townspeople called, too; men and women who had known and respected Ferdinand Brandeis. And the shock they got was this: Mrs. Brandeis was out. Anyone could have told you that she should have been sitting at home in a darkened room, wearing a black gown, clasping Fanny and Theodore to her, and holding a black-bordered handkerchief at intervals to her reddened eyes. And that is what she really wanted to do, for she had loved her husband, and she respected the conventions. What she did was to put on a white shirtwaist and a black skirt at seven o'clock the morning after the funeral.

The store had been closed the day before. She entered it at seven forty-five, as Aloysius was sweeping out with wet sawdust and a languid broom. The extra force of holiday clerks straggled in, uncertainly, at eight or after, expecting an hour or two of undisciplined gossip. At eight-ten Molly Brandeis walked briskly up to the plush photograph album, whisked off its six-dollar price mark, and stuck in its place a neatly printed card bearing these figures: "To-day—79¢!" The plush album went home in a farmer's wagon that afternoon.

Right here there should be something said about Fanny

Brandeis. And yet, each time I turn to her I find her mother
plucking at my sleeve. There comes to my mind the picture of
Mrs. Brandeis turning down Norris Street at quarter to eight
every morning, her walk almost a march, so firm and measured
it was, her head high, her chin thrust forward a little, as a fighter
walks, but not pugnaciously; her short gray skirt clearing the
ground, her shoulders almost consciously squared. Other Winnebago women were just tying up their daughters' pigtails for
school, or sweeping the front porch, or watering the hanging
baskets. Norris Street residents got into the habit of timing themselves by Mrs. Brandeis. When she marched by at seven forty-five
they hurried a little with the tying of the hair bow, as they
glanced out of the window. When she came by again, a little
before twelve, for her hasty dinner, they turned up the fire under
the potatoes and stirred the flour thickening for the gravy.

Mrs. Brandeis had soon learned that Fanny and Theodore
could manage their own school toilettes, with, perhaps, some
speeding up on the part of Mattie, the servant girl. But it needed
her keen brown eye to detect corners that Aloysius had neglected
to sweep out with wet sawdust, and her presence to make sure
that the counter covers were taken off and folded, the outside
show dusted and arranged, the windows washed, the whole store
shining and ready for business by eight o'clock. So Fanny had
even learned to do her own tight, shiny, black, shoulder-length
curls, which she tied back with a black bow. They were wet, meek,
and tractable curls at eight in the morning. By the time school
was out at four they were as wildly unruly as if charged with
electric currents—which they really were, when you consider the
little dynamo that wore them.

Mrs. Brandeis took a scant half hour to walk the six blocks
between the store and the house, to snatch a hurried dinner, and
traverse the distance to the store again. It was a program that
would have killed a woman less magnificently healthy and determined. She seemed to thrive on it, and she kept her figure and
her wit when other women of her age grew dull, and heavy, and
ineffectual. On summer days the little town often lay shimmering
in the heat, the yellow road glaring in it, the red bricks of the

high school reflecting it in waves, the very pine knots in the side-walks gummy and resinous with heat, and sending up a pungent smell that was of the woods, and yet stifling. She must have felt an almost irresistible temptation to sit for a moment on the cool, shady front porch, with its green-painted flower boxes, its hanging fern baskets and the catalpa tree looking boskily down upon it.

But she never did. She had an almost savage energy and determination. The unpaid debts were ever ahead of her; there were the children to be dressed and sent to school; there was the household to be kept up; there were Theodore's violin lessons that must not be neglected—not after what Professor Bauer had said about him.

You may think that undue stress is being laid upon this driving force in her, upon this business ability. But remember that this was fifteen years or more ago, before women had invaded the world of business by the thousands, to take their place, side by side, salary for salary, with men. Oh, there were plenty of women wage earners in Winnebago, as elsewhere; clerks, stenographers, school teachers, bookkeepers. The paper mills were full of girls, and the canning factory too. But here was a woman gently bred, untrained in business, left widowed with two children at thirty-eight, and worse than penniless—in debt.

And that was not all. As Ferdinand Brandeis' wife she had occupied a certain social position in the little Jewish community of Winnebago. True, they had never been moneyed, while the others of her own faith in the little town were wealthy, and somewhat purse-proud. They had carriages, most of them, with two handsome horses, and their houses were spacious and veranda-encircled, and set in shady lawns. When the Brandeis family came to Winnebago five years before, these people had waited, cautiously, and investigated, and then had called. They were of a type to be found in every small town; prosperous, conservative, constructive citizens, clannish, but not so much so as their city cousins, mingling socially with their Gentile neighbors, living well, spending their money freely, taking a vast pride in the education of their children. But here was Molly Brandeis, a Jewess, setting out to earn her living in business, like a man. It was a thing to stir Congregation Emanu-el to its depths. Jewish women, they would tell you, did not work thus. Their husbands worked for them, or their sons, or their brothers.

"Oh, I don't know," said Mrs. Brandeis, when she heard of it. "I seem to remember a Jewess named Ruth who was left widowed, and who gleaned in the fields for her living, and yet the neighbors didn't talk. For that matter, she seems to be pretty well thought of, to this day."

But there is no denying that she lost caste among her own people. Custom and training are difficult to overcome. But Molly Brandeis was too deep in her own affairs to care. That Christmas season following her husband's death was a ghastly time, and yet a grimly wonderful one, for it applied the acid test to Molly Brandeis and showed her up pure gold.

The first week in January she, with Sadie and Pearl, the two clerks, and Aloysius, the boy, took inventory. It was a terrifying thing, that process of casting up accounts. It showed with such starkness how hideously the Brandeis ledger sagged on the wrong side. The three women and the boy worked with a sort of dogged cheerfulness at it, counting, marking, dusting, washing. They found shelves full of forgotten stock, dust-covered and profitless. They found many articles of what is known as hard stock, akin to the plush album; glass and plated condiment casters for the dining table, in a day when individual salts and separate vinegar cruets were already the thing; lamps with straight wicks when round wicks were in demand.

They scoured shelves, removed the grime of years from boxes, washed whole battalions of chamber sets, bathed piles of plates, and bins of cups and saucers. It was a dirty, back-breaking job, that ruined the finger nails, tried the disposition, and caked the throat with dust. Besides, the store was stove-heated and, near the front door, uncomfortably cold. The women wore little shoulder shawls pinned over their waists, for warmth, and all four, including Aloysius, sniffled for weeks afterward.

That inventory developed a new, grim line around Mrs. Brandeis' mouth, and carved another at the corner of each eye. After it was over she washed her hair, steamed her face over a bowl of hot water, packed two valises, left minute and masterful

instructions with Mattie as to the household, and with Sadie and
Pearl as to the store, and was off to Chicago on her first buying
trip. She took Fanny with her, as ballast. It was a trial at which
many men would have quailed. On the shrewdness and judgment
of that buying trip depended the future of Brandeis' Bazaar,
and Mrs. Brandeis, and Fanny, and Theodore.

Mrs. Brandeis had accompanied her husband on many of his
trips to Chicago. She had even gone with him occasionally to the
wholesale houses around La Salle Street, and Madison, and Fifth
Avenue, but she had never bought a dollar's worth herself. She
saw that he bought slowly, cautiously, and without imagination.
She made up her mind that she would buy quickly, intuitively.
She knew slightly some of the salesmen in the wholesale houses.
They had often made presents to her of a vase, a pocketbook, a
handkerchief, or some such trifle, which she accepted reluctantly,
when at all. She was thankful now for these visits. She found
herself remembering many details of them. She made up her
mind, with a canny knowingness, that there should be no presents
this time, no theater invitations, no lunches or dinners. This was
business, she told herself; more than business—it was grim war.

They still tell of that trip, sometimes, when buyers and job-
bers and wholesale men get together. Don't imagine that she came
to be a woman captain of finance. Don't think that we are to see
her at the head of a magnificent business establishment, with buyers and department heads below her, and a private office done
up in mahogany, and stenographers and secretaries. No, she was
Mrs. Brandeis, of Brandeis' Bazaar, to the end. The bills she
bought were ridiculously small, I suppose, and the tricks she
turned on that first trip were pitiful, perhaps. But they were
magnificent too, in their way. I am even bold enough to think
that she might have made business history, that plucky woman, if
she had had an earlier start, and if she had not, to the very end,
had a pack of unmanageable handicaps yelping at her heels, pulling at her skirts.

It was only a six-hour trip to Chicago. Fanny Brandeis' eyes,
big enough at any time, were surely twice their size during the
entire journey of two hundred miles or more. They were to have
lunch on the train! They were to stop at an hotel! They were to

go to the theater! She would have lain back against the red plush seat of the car, in a swoon of joy, if there had not been so much to see in the car itself, and through the car window.

"We'll have something for lunch," said Mrs. Brandeis when they were seated in the dining car, "that we never have at home, shall we?"

"Oh, yes!" replied Fanny in a whisper of excitement. "Something—something queer, and different, and not so very healthy!"

They had oysters (a New Yorker would have sniffed at them), and chicken potpie, and asparagus, and ice cream. If that doesn't prove Mrs. Brandeis was game, I should like to know what could! They stopped at the Windsor-Clifton, because it was quieter and less expensive than the Palmer House, though quite as full of red plush and walnut. Besides, she had stopped at the Palmer House with her husband, and she knew how buyers were likely to be besieged by eager salesmen with cards, and with tempting lines of goods spread knowingly in the various sample-rooms.

Fanny Brandeis was thirteen, and emotional, and incredibly receptive and alive. It is impossible to tell what she learned during that Chicago trip, it was so crowded, so wonderful. She went with her mother to the wholesale houses and heard and saw and, unconsciously, remembered. When she became fatigued with the close air of the dim showrooms, with their endless aisles piled with every sort of ware, she would sit on a chair in some obscure corner, watching those sleek, over-lunched, genial-looking salesmen who were chewing their cigars somewhat wildly when Mrs. Brandeis finished with them. Sometimes she did not accompany her mother, but lay in bed, deliciously, until the middle of the morning, then dressed, and chatted with the obliging Irish chamber maid, and read until her mother came for her at noon.

Everything she did was a delightful adventure; everything she saw had the tang of novelty. Fanny Brandeis was to see much that was beautiful and rare in her full lifetime, but she never again, perhaps, got quite the thrill that those ugly, dim, red-carpeted, gas-lighted hotel corridors gave her, or the grim bed-room, with its walnut furniture and its Nottingham curtains. As for the Chicago streets themselves, with their perilous corners (there were no czars in blue to regulate traffic in those days) older and more sophisticated pedestrians experienced various emotions while negotiating the corner of State and Madison.

That buying trip lasted ten days. It was a racking business, physically and mentally. There were the hours of tramping up one aisle and down the other in the big wholesale lofts. But that brought bodily fatigue only. It was the mental strain that left Mrs. Brandeis spent and limp at the end of the day. Was she buying wisely? Was she over-buying? What did she know about buying, anyway? She would come back to her hotel at six, sometimes so exhausted that the dining-room and dinner were unthinkable. At such times they would have dinner in their room— another delicious adventure for Fanny. She would try to tempt the fagged woman on the bed with bits of this or that from one of the many dishes that dotted the dinner tray. But Molly Brandeis, harrowed in spirit and numbed in body, was too spent to eat.

But that was not always the case. There was that unforgettable night when they went to see Bernhardt the divine. Fanny spent the entire morning following standing before the bedroom mirror, with her hair pulled out in a wild fluff in front, her mother's old marten-fur scarf high and choky around her neck, trying to smile that slow, sad, poignant, tear-compelling smile; but she had to give it up, clever mimic though she was. She only succeeded in looking as though a pin were sticking her somewhere. Besides, Fanny's own smile was a quick, broad, flashing grin, with a generous glint of white teeth in it, and she always forgot about being exquisitely wistful over it until it was too late.

I wonder if the story of the china religious figures will give a wrong impression of Mrs. Brandeis. Perhaps not, if you will only remember this woman's white-lipped determination to wrest a livelihood from the world, for her children and herself. They had been in Chicago a week, and she was buying at Bauder & Peck's. Now Bauder & Peck, importers, are known the world over. It is doubtful if there is one of you who has not been supplied, indirectly, with some imported bit of china or glassware, with French opera glasses or cunning toys and dolls, from the great New York and Chicago showrooms of that company.

Young Bauder himself was waiting on Mrs. Brandeis, and he was frowning because he hated to sell women. Young Bauder was being broken into the Chicago end of the business, and he was not taking gracefully to the process.

At the end of a long aisle, on an obscure shelf in a dim corner, Molly Brandeis' sharp eyes espied a motley collection of dusty, grimy china figures of the kind one sees on the mantel in the parlor of the small-town Catholic home. Winnebago's population was two-thirds Catholic, German and Irish, and very devout.

Mrs. Brandeis stopped short. "How much for that lot?" She pointed to the shelf. Young Bauder's gaze followed hers, puzzled. The figures were from five inches to a foot high, in crude, effective blues, and gold, and crimson, and white. All the saints were there in assorted sizes, the Pieta, the cradle in the manger. There were probably two hundred or more of the little figures.

"Oh, those!" said young Bauder vaguely. "You don't want that stuff. Now, about that Limoges china. As I said, I can make you a special price on it if you carry it as an open-stock pattern. You'll find——"

"How much for that lot?" repeated Mrs. Brandeis.

"I really don't know. Three hundred, I should say. But——"

"I'll give you two hundred," ventured Mrs. Brandeis, her heart in her mouth and her mouth very firm.

"Oh, come now, Mrs. Brandeis! Bauder & Peck don't do business that way, you know. We'd really rather not sell them at all. The things aren't worth much to us, or to you, for that matter. But three hundred——"

"Two hundred," repeated Mrs. Brandeis, "or I cancel my order, including the Limoges. I want those figures."

And she got them. Which isn't the point of the story. The holy figures were fine examples of foreign workmanship, their colors, beneath the coating of dust, as brilliant and fadeless as those found in the churches of Europe. They reached Winnebago duly, packed in straw and paper, still dusty and shelf-worn. Mrs. Brandeis and Sadie and Pearl sat on up-ended boxes at the rear of the store, in the big barn-like room in which newly arrived goods were unpacked. As Aloysius dived deep into the crate and brought up figure after figure, the three women plunged them into warm and soapy water and proceeded to bathe and scour the entire school of saints, angels, and cherubim. They came out brilliantly fresh and rosy.

All the Irish ingenuity and artistry in Aloysius came to the surface as he dived again and again into the great barrel and brought up the glittering pieces.

"It'll make an elegant window," he gasped from the depths of the hay, his lean, lengthy frame jack-knifed over the edge. "And cheap." His shrewd wit had long ago divined the store's price mark. "If Father Fitzpatrick steps by in the forenoon I'll bet they'll be gone before nighttime to-morrow. You'll be letting me do the trim, Mrs. Brandeis?"

He came back that evening to do it, and he threw his whole soul into it, which, considering his ancestry and temperament, was very high voltage for one smalltown store window. He covered the floor of the window with black crepe paper, and hung it in long folds, like a curtain, against the rear wall. The gilt of the scepters, and halos, and capes showed up dazzlingly against this background. The scarlets, and pinks, and blues, and whites of the robes appeared doubly bright. The whole made a picture that struck and held you by its vividness and contrast.

Father Fitzpatrick, very tall and straight, and handsome, with his iron-gray hair and his cheeks pink as a girl's, did step by next morning on his way to the postoffice. It was whispered that in his youth Father Fitzpatrick had been an actor, and that he had deserted the footlights for the altar lights because of a disappointment. The drama's loss was the Church's gain. You should have heard him on Sunday morning, now flaying them, now swaying them! He still had the actor's flexible voice, vibrant, tremulous, or strident, at will. And no amount of fasting or praying had ever dimmed that certain something in his eye—the something which makes the matinee idol.

Not only did he step by now; he turned, came back; stopped before the window. Then he entered.

"Madam," he said to Mrs. Brandeis, "you'll probably save

more souls with your window display than I could in a month of hell-fire sermons." He raised his hand. "You have the sanction of the Church." Which was the beginning of a queer friendship between the Roman Catholic priest and the Jewess shopkeeper that lasted as long as Molly Brandeis lived.

By noon it seemed that the entire population of Winnebago had turned devout. The figures, a tremendous bargain, though sold at a high profit, seemed to melt away from the counter that held them.

By three o'clock, "Only one to a customer!" announced Mrs. Brandeis. By the middle of the week the window itself was ravished of its show. By the end of the week there remained only a handful of the duller and less desirable pieces—the minor saints, so to speak. Saturday night Mrs. Brandeis did a little figuring on paper. The lot had cost her two hundred dollars. She had sold for six hundred. Two from six leaves four. Four hundred dollars! She repeated it to herself, quietly. Her mind leaped back to the plush photograph album, then to young Bauder and his cool contempt. And there stole over her that warm, comfortable glow born of reassurance and triumph. Four hundred dollars. Not much in these days of big business. We said, you will remember, that it was a pitiful enough little trick she turned to make it, though an honest one. And—in the face of disapproval—a rather magnificent one too. For it gave to Molly Brandeis that precious quality, self-confidence, out of which is born success.

By spring Mrs. Brandeis had the farmer women coming to her for their threshing dishes and kitchenware, and the West End Culture Club for their whist prizes. She seemed to realize that the days of the general store were numbered, and she set about making hers a novelty store. There was something terrible about the earnestness with which she stuck to business. She was not more than thirty-eight at this time, intelligent, healthy, fun-loving. But she stayed at it all day. She listened and chatted to every one, and learned much. There was about her that human quality that invites confidence.

She made friends by the hundreds, and friends are a business asset. Those blithe, dressy, and smooth-spoken gentlemen known as traveling men used to tell her their troubles, perched on a stool near the stove, and show her the picture of their girl in the back of their watch, and asked her to dinner at the Haley House. She listened to their tale of woe, and advised them; she admired the picture of the girl, and gave some wholesome counsel on the subject of traveling men's lonely wives; but she never went to dinner at the Haley House.

It had not taken these debonair young men long to learn that there was a woman buyer who bought quickly, decisively, and intelligently, and that she always demanded a duplicate slip. Even the most unscrupulous could not stuff an order of hers, and when it came to dating she gave no quarter. Though they wore clothes that were two leaps ahead of the styles worn by the Winnebago young men—their straw sailors were likely to be saw-edged when the local edges were smooth, and their coats were more flaring, or their trousers wider than the coats and trousers of the Winnebago boys—they were not, for the most part, the gay dogs that Winnebago's fancy painted them. Many of them were very lonely married men who missed their wives and babies, and loathed the cuspidored discomfort of the small-town hotel lobby. They appreciated Mrs. Brandeis' good-natured sympathy, and gave her the long end of a deal when they could. It was Sam Kiser who had begged her to listen to his advice to put in Battenberg patterns and braid, long before the Battenberg epidemic had become widespread and virulent.

"Now listen to me, Mrs. Brandeis," he begged, almost tearfully. "You're a smart woman. Don't let this get by you. You know that I know that a salesman would have as much chance to sell you a gold brick as to sell old John D. Rockefeller a gallon of oil."

Mrs. Brandeis eyed his samples coldly. "But it looks so unattractive. And the average person has no imagination. A bolt of white braid and a handful of buttons—they wouldn't get a mental picture of the completed piece. Now, embroidery silk——"

"Then give 'em a real picture!" interrupted Sam. "Work up one of these water-lily pattern table covers. Use No. 100 braid and the smallest buttons. Stick it in the window and they'll tear their hair to get patterns."

She did it, taking turns with Pearl and Sadie at weaving the great, lacy square during dull moments. When it was finished they placed it in the window, where it lay like frosted lace, exquisitely graceful and delicate, with its tracery of curling petals and feathery fern sprays. Winnebago gazed and was bitten by the Battenberg bug. It wound itself up in a network of Battenberg braid, in all the numbers. It bought buttons of every size; it stitched away at Battenberg covers, doilies, bedspreads, blouses, curtains. Battenberg tumbled, foamed, cascaded over Winnebago's front porches all summer. Listening to Sam Kiser had done it.

She listened to the farmer women too, and to the mill girls, and to the scant and precious pearls that dropped from the lips of the East End society section. There was something about her brown eyes and her straight, sensible nose that reassured them so that few suspected the mischievous in her. For she was mischievous. If she had not been I think she could not have stood the drudgery, and the heartbreaks, and the struggle, and the terrific manual labor.

She used to guy people, gently, and they never guessed it. Mrs. G. Manville Smith, for example, never dreamed of the joy that her patronage brought Molly Brandeis, who waited on her so demurely. Mrs. G. Manville Smith (née Finnegan) scorned the Winnebago shops, and was said to send to Chicago for her hairpins. It was known that her household was run on the most niggardly basis, however, and she short-rationed her two maids outrageously. It was said that she could serve less real food on more real lace doilies than any other housekeeper in Winnebago. Now, Mrs. Brandeis sold Scourine two cents cheaper than the grocery stores, using it as an advertisement to attract housewives, and making no profit on the article itself. Mrs. G. Manville Smith always patronized Brandeis' Bazaar for Scourine alone, and thus represented pure loss. Also she my-good-womaned Mrs. Brandeis. That lady, seeing her enter one day with her comic, undulating gait, double-actioned like a giraffe's, and her plumes that would have shamed a Knight of Pythias, decided to put a stop to these unprofitable visits.

She waited on Mrs. G. Manville Smith, a dangerous gleam in her eye.

"Scourine," spake Mrs. G. Manville Smith.

"How many?"

"A dozen."

"Anything else?"

"No. Send them."

Mrs. Brandeis, scribbling in her sales book, stopped, pencil poised. "We cannot send Scourine unless with a purchase of other goods amounting to a dollar or more."

Mrs. G. Manville Smith's plumes tossed and soared agitatedly. "But my good woman, I don't want anything else!"

"Then you'll have to carry the Scourine."

"Certainly not! I'll send for it."

"The sale closes at five." It was then 4:57.

"I never heard of such a thing! You can't expect me to carry them."

Now, Mrs. G. Manville Smith had been a dining-room girl at the old Haley House before she married George Smith, and long before he made his money in lumber.

"You won't find them so heavy," Molly Brandeis said smoothly.

"I certainly would! Perhaps you would not. You're used to that sort of thing. Rough work, and all that."

Aloysius, doubled up behind the lamps, knew what was coming, from the gleam in his boss's eye.

"There may be something in that." Molly Brandeis returned sweetly. "That's why I thought you might not mind taking them. They're really not much heavier than a laden tray."

"Oh!" exclaimed the outraged Mrs. G. Manville Smith. And took her plumes and her patronage out of Brandeis' Bazaar forever.

That was as malicious as Molly Brandeis ever could be. And it was forgivable malice.

GRANDFATHER TZALEL

by CHARLES ANGOFF

HE WAS REALLY OUR GREAT-GRANDFATHER, BUT WE ALWAYS CALLED him Zayde Tzalel, or Grandfather Tzalel. It may have been because he was so much younger, by about fifteen years, than his wife, Alte Bobbe, or because he seemed so much stronger than we imagined a great-grandfather should be. Anyway, he didn't mind. The only thing he minded from us, his great-grandchildren, all of whom he taught Hebrew language and literature, was when we called him Charlie. When he heard that he would snap at us, "I'm not a pork-eating Charlie." We didn't call him Charlie often, because he had a mighty wallop, which he trained on us for much lesser offenses, such as not knowing a fine point of Hebrew grammar or coming to class without a hat.

He was a strict disciplinarian and he pushed us hard, but he treated me fairly leniently, because I was his oldest great-grand-child and he had a high regard for my mother, his oldest grandchild. Even so I didn't escape occasional corporal punishment, particularly in the spring when my mind was more occupied with the ups and downs of the Boston Red Sox and the Boston Braves than with the Lamentations of Jeremiah. As he used to dig his enormous right hand into my shoulder—one of his favorite forms of correction—he would say, "Ah, the atheistical baseball! And such a nice boy from such a nice mother! You'll never know how much this pains me till you have great-grandchildren of your own." I was then about eleven or twelve, and I didn't sympathize with him.

Just the same, I liked him. He used to tell the stories of the Bible and the great rabbis with enthusiasm and always he made Jewish history exciting and romantic. I remember how deeply I fell in love with Esther, after he told us the wonderful things she did for her people. I confided to a classmate, "That's the kind of girl I'm going to marry." He said, "Me, too."

Zayde Tzalel fascinated me for other reasons. I gathered from the talk at home that nobody knew precisely where he lived. When asked, he would merely say, "Oh, I live on the fourth floor back, on Leverett Street," which was a long, winding thoroughfare. When pressed for further information he would say, "But I told you. Near a drug store." Neither did anybody know exactly how he managed to get along. He had all kinds of jobs at various times, but not one of them paid very much. From teaching he got very little money. He wouldn't accept payment for teaching his great-grandchildren. "That would be a sin," he said. For every other child he would take only twenty-five cents a week, and he regretted even that. He said, "A teacher in Israel should spread the light free. But so long as we Jews haven't got our own land back, a teacher has to charge something. The good Lord understands." He couldn't have made more than three dollars a week from teaching, and in the summer, when there were no classes, he made nothing.

Occasionally he taught thirteen-year-old children their bar-mitzvah speeches, but since he wasn't a pusher he didn't have many bar-mitzvah, and as usual he charged very little, seldom more than five dollars for a month or more of arduous labor. Other bar-mitzvah teachers charged twenty-five dollars and fifty dollars and even one hundred dollars. On Rosh Hashanah and Yom Kippur he would sometimes get a job as cantor in a synagogue, which would pay him about twenty-five dollars. He had an excellent baritone voice and could easily have got for himself a steady position as a cantor. His children often asked him why he didn't try to get such a job. Zayde Tzalel would smile and say, "Oh, steady jobs are for other people."

These were thrilling words to a youngster who was already under the spell of Theodore Roosevelt and his Rough Riders. Zayde Tzalel was a lone wolf, and all lone wolves were magnificent to me. Apparently he was too much of a lone wolf, because his children used to complain that he didn't pay enough attention to his wife, Alte Bobbe, and that he didn't tell them more about himself and ask them to make things easier for him. But these complaints did not change him. Alte Bobbe always defended him. "He is a good man," she said. "He has his own ways." He visited her once a week, and she treated him almost like a son. He was her third husband, and she had five children by him. I believe she gave him some money, which she saved up from the small allowances given her by her children and grandchildren. She also brought him food and old clothes, meeting him at his favorite synagogue on Phillips Street, then a slum neighborhood and now part of Boston's Bohemia. Perhaps she also knew where he lived; if she did, she never told anybody. She respected his "ways." If anyone in the family wanted to see him for any reason, he or she would have to go to the same synagogue, where he was to be found almost every day at prayer time in the morning and evening.

Zayde Tzalel was very pious, even more so than Alte Bobbe. He did not approve of anybody working on the Sabbath, and he would listen to no excuses. For a while, it seems, he lived in a suburb of Boston, about seven miles away from the center of the city, but that didn't stop him from getting to his synagogue on Phillips Street every Saturday. Of course, he didn't ride into town. That was a sin. He walked into town, getting up at six in the morning in time for the services at eight. Since he had a poor sense of direction, he followed the street-car tracks, walking close by them. Policemen and street-car motormen on that route got to know him. He walked that distance in all sorts of weather, rain, snow, hail, intense heat, severe cold.

In the realms of dress and health, he had his own ideas. He always wore a frock coat, maintaining that in an ordinary coat or jacket he felt undressed. He also was strenuously opposed to low-cut shoes. He said that high shoes were the only ones suitable to an adult. "I'm no baby," he exclaimed when one of his children tried to make him change. He carried spoons, knives, forks, needles, and thread in his pockets. The only reason I heard him give for this was, "I like to have everything with me."

He looked upon doctors as ignoramuses. "Moses lived to be 120 years without a doctor," he said. He was almost six feet tall and solidly built. In the Russian Army, where he was conscripted for four years, he was in the heavy artillery. He laughed at tooth paste, tooth brushes, and all dentistry. "There's nothing wrong with the teeth that a little water can't wash out or onions or garlic can't cure," he held. He never needed onions or garlic himself, except once, when a wisdom tooth went bad on him. He must have eaten three dozen onions and many more dozen pieces of garlic in the attempt to stop the pain. Finally, his children prevailed upon him to go to a dentist. The dentist pulled the tooth out only after great difficulty. He said he had never seen so deep-rooted a tooth. But for years Zayde Tzalel said he could have saved that tooth if the children had allowed him to use more garlic. In any case, all his other teeth were sound, and he took them with him to his grave.

As for the hair on his head, he thought that fresh air was very injurious to it, as were water and soap. All he ever did was sprinkle his hair with faucet water, at the same time making a strange noise with his mouth: "Bl-bl-br-br-br, bl-bl-br-br-br." Being a very orthodox Jew he had his head covered nearly all the time with a skull-cap, and with both a skull-cap and a hat when he was outside. On his death-bed—he died at the age of eighty-odd; he was vague about the year of his birth—he had all his hair, with only a touch of gray. His thick, medium-length beard didn't have many more gray hairs.

Like Alte Bobbe he put great store by chicken soup, black bread, and tea. Occasionally he'd get stomach trouble, and he'd cure it quickly with five, six glasses of quadruple strength tea. Colds, rashes, strange pains anywhere he'd cure with onions and garlic—eating them and putting them on the affected parts in poultices. He held that onions and garlic, when used as poultices, are probably more effective when heated slightly, but he said that heat in such cases was a matter of taste: he was not willing to be dogmatic on the point. In the case of colds in young children he had a special remedy: a stocking, rubbed with soap, wound around the neck. Usually it worked in a couple of days; if it didn't he resorted to the "stronger" remedy of onions and garlic. He treated me against my will with all these remedies— the soaped stocking, onions and garlic—many times, and I am living testimony to their efficacy.

The only salvation of us youngsters was that he didn't visit our individual families very often. When he did we'd run out of the house if anything ailed us, for fear he'd get to work with the stocking, onions, and garlic. On these visits he'd inquire if there was any work he could do: a little carpentry perhaps, or a little plumbing. He was handy at a number of such trades and knew where to get the necessary tools. He never asked for or expected payment; he looked upon this work as his duty to his children and grandchildren. But it was customary to give him a huge bowl of chicken soup, several thick slices of black bread, and several glasses of tea. Then he'd disappear for weeks and months.

He used snuff, which he carried in a tin box, and there always were tell-tale brown splotches on his mustache and the upper part of his beard. But he didn't smoke. Whiskey he drank only at weddings and circumcisions. The one alcoholic drink he really liked was wine. He used to make several barrels of wine himself every year, enough time ahead for it to be ready for Passover. A couple of days before he'd bring a gallon to the families of his children and grandchildren. He'd bring another gallon in the event of a birth or a wedding. He claimed that wine was the only liquor an orthodox Jew could drink without any qualms, and would quote dozens of passages from the Bible to prove it. The sight of an intoxicated man disgusted him. "Only atheists, Poles, and Rumanian hooligans get drunk," he said. On rare occasions, after a couple of glasses of wine, he'd sing to us younger ones beautiful old Russian folk songs and Yiddish lullabies.

The death of his wife, Alte Bobbe, was a severe blow to him. He seemed to lose his strength overnight, and he became stoop-shouldered and absent-minded. He stopped coming to my grandmother's house as often as he used to, and for months members of the family would have to go to the Phillips Street synagogue if they wanted to see him. They pleaded with him to come live with any one of them, but he refused. In time, he made one request of them: that they should not bury him beside Alte Bobbe. His reason was this: "I noticed that just before she died, she lifted the sheet over her face and passed away. It says in the Talmud that only the holiest people do that. I am not worthy to lie beside her." They promised him that they would do as he wished.

One day an old crony of his came to my grandmother's house and said Zayde Tzalel was in the hospital. He had caught a severe cold while walking in the snow the preceding Saturday to hear a new cantor at a synagogue some two miles away, and the cold had developed into pneumonia. He died two days later. The family thought he had led a lonely life, but at the funeral some twenty strange people showed up: policemen, street-car motormen, sanitation department employees, and synagogue friends. He had been good to all of them, having given them wine and matzohs on Passover, and done them other kindnesses. A few of them came around afterwards, then they disappeared. The last one to show up was a street cleaner, who returned to my grandmother one dollar which Zayde Tzalel had lent him months before. "He never asked me for it," said the street cleaner, "but I didn't forget."

A PARABLE OF PEACE AND WAR

by ROBERT NATHAN

MR. EDWARD HERRINGWAY, AN ASSISTANT KEEPER AT THE ZOO, stepped out of the honeybear's cage, carrying a pail of water in his hand. As he turned to fasten the gate, his attention was drawn to a commotion among the seals; he stepped forward, to peer in that direction, leaving the cage closed, but not locked. Thereafter, he forgot about it, and continued on toward the grizzlies.

The honeybear, a brown friendly little fellow, came to the door of his cage to watch Mr. Herringway go off. The door rattled a little, and he gave it an enquiring tap with his long claws. It seemed to be loose . . .

Ten minutes later, the cage was empty, and the honeybear was hiding in the shadows of the Sixty-Fifth Street tunnel, thinking things over.

He had no burning desire for freedom, but he had a great deal of curiosity. He did not wish to bother anybody; fortunately, there did not seem to be anyone about. The path went north, through shadows and under lamplight; there were trees on either side, and grassy hills; and it disappeared in the misty distance. It looked interesting, and he decided to follow it.

From Sixty-fifth to Seventy-second Street, his progress was slow, but joyful, and without incident. He climbed a tree, but there was nothing there, and he came down again. He examined a little summer house made of wood; it was empty, and smelled of children; he broke off a bit of flowering bush, and tried the taste.

At Seventy-second Street he crossed the drive, and started down the hill. It was here, and at this moment, that Amy saw him, his silhouette looming above her as she stood beside the lake, where she had gone to carry home some water to her mother. For a second, while her heart stopped beating, she stared in horror at the ominous bulk between her and the sky; then, with a gasp, she turned, and tore for the Museum.

Micah heard her squeaks while she was still some distance away, and ran forward to help her. Breathless and trembling, she threw herself upon his bosom. "It has come," she announced in a tragic voice; "the war is here. The enemy is behind me, laying waste the world." "I had better sound the alarm," said Micah, "for I imagine that the battle is about to begin."

And he went to report the news to his Colonel.

Tapiola received the message in silence, and with a calm mien. He ordered the regiment paraded; and when they were drawn up in line, he appeared before them with a serious air, and addressed them as follows:

"Officers and men of the Twenty-Seventh . . . the moment for which we have been waiting has arrived. The enemy has crossed the drive in force, and his advance units have reached the west shore of the lake. This attack comes in the dark hours of the night, and at a time when I was not expecting it, but it does not find me unprepared. I have studied the map, and I think I can say that I have made the best possible disposition of the forces at my command. You, Henry, will go aloft, to bomb the foe at the Seventy-Eighth Street underpass, and Micah will go with you, to oppose him on the ground. Richard will inspire us from a tree; and Jeremiah will mind the spike. I myself shall observe the battle from the base of the obelisk. The order of the day is Victory; but that does not mean that the war is over. Go now to your positions, my friends, and prepare to do battle for the honor of the regiment.

"There will be bandages and refreshments in the rear."

So saying, and with a grave and martial bearing, he turned away.

"I do not feel very much like singing," said Richard; "my stomach is upset from so much worry."

"In that case," said Tapiola, "you may come with me to the obelisk, and carry messages to the forward units of the command."

"I do not think that I can fly," said Richard; "my bowels are so loose."

"Richard," exclaimed Tapiola, losing his temper, "I do not care what you do, but please do not bother me about your bowels."

"At least I am honest," said Richard, "and do not pretend to be braver than I feel."

Standing before the spike, erect and sober, Jeremiah bade farewell to his grandson. "Good-by, Micah," he said; "I do not know what you will find where you are going, but if it is large, try to get behind it. For in the dark, it is sometimes possible to surprise a foe, and defeat him from a safe distance. Do not be afraid to use your wits, as in the case of the Midianites and the Amalekites, whom Gideon smote in the valley of Jezreel. He had but three hundred, against a host; but he divided them, and gave them trumpets and pitchers, with which to make a great sound. The Midianites and Amalekites were surprised at this maneuver;

and the host fled as far as Bethshittah, in considerable confusion."

"Alas," said Micah, "I am only one and not three hundred, and I have neither trumpet nor pitcher."

"I should have provided them," said Jeremiah with a sigh. "I do not suppose that you have a sling shot, and a smooth pebble?"

"I have nothing but my teeth," said Micah, "and a stout heart."

"Well," said Jeremiah, whose own teeth were yellow and dull with age, "that is all your ancestors had."

But as his grandson turned to go, he drew him close once more, and embraced him. "I do not know if I did right to let you join this war, my child," he said, "and if anything happens to you, I shall regret it."

"Do not be afraid, Grandfather," said Micah bravely, "for God will protect me."

"He hath established the world by His wisdom," said Jeremiah gravely, "and perhaps He will."

With these words, he returned to his spike, and Micah marched away toward the south, with Henry circling protectively above him.

At the underpass they halted, while Henry flew up onto the parapet, to reconnoiter. Presently he flew down again; and Micah whispered, "Did you see anything?"

"Yes," said Henry, speaking low; "the enemy is approaching."

"What does he look like?" asked Micah eagerly.

"He is a horrid looking object," said Henry.

"I am a little nervous," he admitted, as he sharpened his beak upon a stone.

Finding a slight depression in which to hide, Micah set himself to wait. His heart was beating strongly, and his mouth was dry, but he was not afraid. It seemed to him that the climax of his life was at hand, and that before the morning broke, everything would be changed for him. He saw himself returning home after the battle, a Corporal and a hero; and he imagined the serious talks that he would have with Amy when the war was over. His mother's face appeared before him in the darkness, and he smiled at her. "You will have no reason to be ashamed of me," he said. At the same time, he felt a lump in his throat, and his eyes grew moist, against his will.

The night hung clear and still above the earth, the lamps of the Park making a misty glow here and there in the darkness. All was silent; beyond, in the city, something hooted, dim and far away. "Can you see anything?" asked Micah, shivering a little in the cold night air. "I think he is coming nearer," said Henry.

A moment later he remarked in a firm voice, "It is time." And with a single cry, "Matilda," he rose upon his wings, and launched himself at the honeybear, who, taken by surprise, fell over onto his back. At the same time, Micah scrambled from his trench, and charging across the intervening ground, closed his eyes, and gave the honeybear a sharp nip on the leg.

On the hill by the obelisk, Tapiola and Richard were waiting for news of the battle. "I do not hear anything," said Tapiola. "Our troops are not yet engaged." And as he strained to see through the darkness, he thought: Only a few days ago, I was leading a literary life at Mrs. Poppel's. Now I am here, on a hill in the night, fighting for freedom. But perhaps there is not as much difference as I thought; for whether one is on a hill, or under a sofa, the important thing is, what is one doing there? Battles and books have changed the course of history before this, the one as much as the other. Perhaps it would have been wiser for me to stay at home, to help Mrs. Poppel. But the truth is, that to the poet, a single blow is more satisfying than a poem. And so, I was carried away . . . I am not sure that I was right. For who now will play with my ball, and my little bone made of rubber, amusing the guests, and creating an atmosphere of joy? Those things also are necessary to civilization. My little basket will stand empty in its corner, a mute reminder of my heroism, and my fate; but in the years to come, my absence will be felt in the publishing business. There is another courage, besides that of the soldier; it is to stay at home, doing the work at hand, without glory and without acclaim.

Dear Mrs. P., if I do not return, believe that I have laid down my life to enable you to publish the works of Mr. Nathan, Mme. Undset, and Thomas Mann.

Turning to Richard, he exclaimed: "See that my remains are wrapped in my eiderdown quilt, for death is a cold and lonely land, and I shall want to take with me all the warmth and friendliness my heart can carry."

"Very well," said Richard unhappily, "but it seems a great pity, for there is only the one quilt, and winter is coming."

"You will be home before winter," said Tapiola; "the war is almost over."

"I am glad to hear it," said Richard, "for I am considering an offer in the theater."

"I thought that you intended to retire," said Tapiola in surprise, "and lead a spiritual life."

"That is true," said Richard, "and I have not changed my mind; but I think that it is possible to lead a more spiritual life after having been a great success."

At this moment, the sound of fighting was wafted to them from the underpass, where the attack had begun. "Hark," said Tapiola; "the battle is joined. Our advance forces are in action."

"That sounds like Micah to me," said Richard, as a shrill squeal split the air; "he is in trouble."

"Then we had better go at once to his assistance," said Tapiola.

"Let us wait for another squeal," said Richard.

A second cry, louder, and full of anguish, rose through the darkness from the underpass. "Come," said Tapiola; "we dare delay no longer, or the battle will be lost." And taking a deep breath, he cried, "Forward, the Twenty-Seventh."

And with the added cry of "Victory and Mrs. Poppel," he dashed slowly down the hill.

"I will go and see what Jeremiah is doing," said Richard.

The canary found the Quartermaster General pacing nervously up and down in front of his spike. "How goes the battle?" he asked, as soon as he caught sight of Richard; "I have heard some very distressing sounds."

"All is lost," replied Richard despondently; "I fear that your grandson has perished."

"And Tapiola?" demanded Jeremiah loudly; "where is he, and where are the reserves?"

"He has gone to see for himself," said Richard. "As for the reserves, I believe that they are us."

"Then what are we waiting for?" cried Jeremiah; "let us attack at once, and save what we can."

"Very well," said Richard gloomily, "if you think so; but if we lose the reserves, we shall have nothing left at all."

"Are you afraid?" cried Jeremiah.

"Yes," said Richard.

"Then I implore you to be brave," said Jeremiah.

"Honesty like mine also takes courage," said Richard.

"It is too late to debate the point," said Jeremiah, with a groan; "let us go."

He had no sooner spoken, than Amy ran up to them, her face bright with resolve. "Let me go with you," she cried, "to help, in my poor way."

"Are you not frightened?" asked Jeremiah tenderly.

"No," she said proudly, "for my heart is bigger than my fears."

And she added: "It is the women who must bind up the wounds of this war."

Taking the bandages, she followed Jeremiah, who led the way with the spike, while Richard flew up into a tree, to act as observer.

As Jeremiah had feared, they were too late; when they arrived at the underpass, the battle was already over. Weary of the conflict, which he had not expected, and did not enjoy, the honey-bear had retired, nursing his paw where Micah had bitten it. Seated upon the battlefield, which now was theirs, the victors attempted to get their breath, Tapiola upon his haunches with his tongue hanging out, and Henry amidst a fluff of loose feathers in the grass. But Micah lay upon his side with his eyes closed, and the life blood draining from two great wounds in his belly.

They gathered about him in silence, while Amy attempted to stanch the blood, and Jeremiah strove to master his grief. Richard was the first to speak; with an expression of anguish, he remarked, "This is the end of my hopes; my career in the theater is finished." And seeking out Henry, he said to him with a dejected air, "Now I have learned the futility of worldly ambitions."

Amy had Micah's weary head pillowed on her lap. "Micah," she said, "can you hear me? It is I, Amy, your friend. I am here to hold you. The battle is over, and you have won a great victory. I am so proud of you . . . But do not try to move. Rest, now; the war is ended."

"Amy," said Micah, opening his eyes, "is it you? Do not go away." And he added simply, "I did the best I could."

Turning his head, he saw Jeremiah in the crowd around him. "You too, Grandfather?" he said wonderingly. "God did His best for me."

But a spasm of pain shook him, and he cried, "It hurts."

Jeremiah knelt beside him, smiling, while the tears ran down his cheeks. "Micah, my little one," he said gently, "you must try to bear it bravely. It will not hurt for long."

Micah's eyes searched his grandfather's face. "Am I dying, Grandfather?" he asked at length; and Jeremiah inclined his head. The young soldier took a deep breath. "Talk to me, then," he whispered.

"Micah," said Jeremiah, "you are going into a cool and lovely land. There the sweet colors of the evening live, the deep blue sky of night. Where you are going, it is wide and clear and beautiful and free; there is no sadness there, and no regret. The stars will shine around you, making a peaceful glory; and you will hear the friendly winds forever speaking with quiet voices. You will be happy there, Micah, my son."

"Will it not be lonely, Grandfather?" asked Micah.

"No," said Jeremiah; "for love goes with you, and will never leave you. It is in your heart, Micah, my son. And we who stay behind you here, will join you in a little while . . . in a little while."

"Yes, Grandfather," said Micah, smiling. And he added, with a sigh, "I wish I were a Corporal."

Deeply moved, Tapiola stepped forward, and in a low voice remarked, "Then receive your promotion now, upon this very field your bravery has won for us." So saying, he embraced Micah, and declared, "From now on, you are a Corporal."

Micah beckoned Jeremiah to bend closer. "Tell Mother," he whispered; "she will be so proud." His eyes, which shone with pain and with surprise, grew dim. "See, it is morning," he said; "the night is over." And later, "It is the peaceful day."

They were his last words. Tapiola covered him with the quilt, and ordered the silk banner of the regiment to be laid across it. On a low branch above the bier, Richard sang a last farewell; and Henry read from the Psalms:

> The Lord is my Shepherd; I shall not want.
> He maketh me to lie down in green pastures.
> He leadeth me beside still waters.

Jeremiah stood above his grandson, with bent head. "Farewell, Micah, my son," he said. "Now you are free, of pain and sadness; and no loss can touch you. It is for us to weep, who still are captive here; who see the sun by day and the moon by night, and strive to comfort our hearts with small changes. But for you there is the wide and endless sky, and the peace that passeth understanding." And as he mourned, he repeated to himself the words, "Turn again our captivity, O Lord, as the streams in the South."

Slowly and sadly, Tapiola turned away. "The war is over," he said. "It is time to go home."

And as he passed beneath the tree on which Richard was sitting, he added under his breath,

"We have lost the flower of our youth."

On his branch, Richard looked down at him with an exasperated expression. "What else did you expect?" he asked.

MUSIC IN THE AIR

by ARTHUR KOBER

Mrs. KAHN AND MRS. LESHINSKY STIRRED THEIR CUPS OF TEA AS they watched Sister Gross, their fellow committee-member, cut the sponge cake she had prepared for them. Mrs. Gross was very nervous; she didn't mind Mrs. Kahn, who would have been satisfied with tea served in a glass, but she certainly feared Mrs. Leshinsky, the wife of the landlord and the chair-lady of the committee.

"That stuck-upnick fomm the lodge, Sister Leshinsky," she once told her husband, "she's a regella Yenkee. Let her go two blocks fomm her house and she must put on by her the hat. Two blocks let her go! And all the time she must have on by her the gorset. A regella Yenkee!"

Mrs. Kahn accepted the platter of cake with a nod. She was an agreeable old lady who had to be asked only once to take off her hat. But no amount of urging from Mrs. Gross could force the frozen-faced Mrs. Leshinsky to remove the flowered bird's nest perched so perilously on her head.

Mrs. Gross cut a tremendous chunk of cake, placed it on a doilied platter and handed it to Mrs. Leshinsky.

"Go on, taste this spuntch cake if you wanna eat something delicious. It will melt by you in mouth. Go on."

Mrs. Leshinsky took the extended platter, eyed the cake for several seconds and said, "Looks very good the cake. You got maybe a fork?"

"Parm me, Sister Leshinsky," said the agitated Mrs. Gross, and flew into the kitchen.

"Forks!" she said to herself as she quickly wiped several of

84

them. "In the old country the fingiss was good enough fa her to use. Now alluva sudden is fency-shmency with forks."

She came rushing back with the utensils. "You must parm me the forks," she apologized. "Is my mind on the committee mitting I foggot the forks. You must parm me."

Mrs. Leshinsky drew back her lips in what was intended to be a smile. She dug into the cake. Ma Gross watched her apprehensively.

"Mmm, is good the cake," she said, approvingly. "You must use lotsa ecks fa such a cake."

Mrs. Gross refused to be the victim of Mrs. Leshinsky's curiosity. "I use plenty ecks, believe me," she replied. "Lest wikk came by us in house fa soppur my son. Oiving, and his wife, Gussie, and mine granndutter, Shoiley, and I baked a spuntch cake so big." She indicated the size with her hands. "And I put the cake on table, and one-two-three right away was gone the whole cake, and they was licking by them the fingiss, *kenehorreh*. But a whole cake they ate op, one-two-three!"

"Is very good, Sister Gross," said Mrs. Kahn. "Maybe you'll bake fa us a couple cakes fa the ball."

This reminded Mrs. Leshinsky of the matter they had been discussing—the music for the ball.

"Sisters," she said as she reached for a white slip of paper, "I got it here an estimate fomm Peffesseh Goldfobb. He got a fine bend music, fife pieces the bend, and believe me, Sisters, not evvey day you find such boggains like Peffesseh Goldfobb and his fife pieces music." She placed her tortoise-shell glasses on her nose and consulted the estimate. "He says here, till twelffa clock is each man fife dolless and the Peffesseh is ten dolless. And after twelffa clock——" She studied the figures and frowned. "Say, after twelffa clock is time awreddy to go home."

Mrs. Gross reached for Professor Goldfarb's estimate and glanced at it. "Such fency prices he chonngiss." And then added, timidly, "Is no boggain to me such prices."

Mrs. Leshinsky spoke tolerantly as if addressing a child. "Sister Gross," she began, "is by us in house all the time potties. Is not an engagement potty fa my cousin Bertram's dutter, is a bar-mitzvah potty fa my nephew, Reuben. Is all the time music

by us in house—special fa potties. Believe me, Sister Gross," and
she held up the estimate, "this I guarantee is a boggain in bend
music," She turned to Mrs. Kahn for support. "No, Mrs. Kahn?"

Mrs. Kahn grinned, shrugged her shoulders, said, "I know
fomm such things?" and held out her empty cup to Mrs. Gross,
who, highly impressed by her landlady's social activities, was ready
to accept the Professor's charges.

"More tea?" asked the hostess of Mrs. Kahn.

"Why not?" replied the guest, and then added, somewhat
ruefully, "By me a cup tea is oney haffa gless."

It was at this point that Pa Gross came home. He walked into
the room, looked around and then boomed, "Hello, hello, hello!
Company we got! Hello, Mrs. Kahn. Hello, Mrs. Leshinsky. Take
off the hat and don't make yesself such a stranger——" His eye
fell on the cake. "Aha, spuntch cake we got!" He reached for a
piece.

"Slop, not with the fingiss!" his wife admonished, quickly
wiping a used fork and handing it to him. He then saw the cups
and saucers, and turned to his wife in surprise. "The new dishes
you using?" he asked.

Ma Gross glared at him. "Listen to him! The new dishes! It
maybe says on the label, 'new dishes'? Is maybe mockt on the cups
and the saucers, 'new dishes'?" She turned to Mrs. Leshinsky.
"Three-four years I got the dishes and by him is new dishes yet."

"So awright." Pa was ready to drop the subject. "So give
awready a person a gless tea."

His wife threw him a scornful glance and started to pour a
cup of tea. He took it, looked at it, shook his head from side to
side and muttered, "Fency-shmency—alluva sudden in a cup!"

"Well, ladies," said the businesslike Mrs. Leshinsky, "so what
is gung to be with the music fa the ball? Peffesseh Goldfobb, he
is waiting fa an answer, yes udder no. He got another job music
the same night, so we got to give him quick an answer. Nu, ladies,
fife dolless a man and ten dolless fa the Peffesseh. Yes udder no?"

Mr. Gross, who was skillfully maneuvering the spoon and
lemon in his raised cup, looked up.

"Who is this Peffesseh, this boss, he must get it ten dolless

and the woiking man oney fife? A whole night a fiddleh makes
with the fiddle, and the Peffesseh stends and makes with a stick
and he gets awready ten dolless. Wat'sa metta, this Peffesseh got
maybe a furtinn-kerret gold stick in hend? What'sa metta, the
Peffesseh is awready the whole bend he should chonge so much?"

The nervous Mrs. Gross quickly cut another slice of cake and
offered it to Mrs. Leshinsky. "Have a piece cake. Is delicious."

Mrs. Leshinsky ignored her hostess and fixed Pa Gross with
a cold eye. "By you is nothing the Peffesseh stends up a whole
night without sitting donn? The fiddleh, he got a chair, he sits
donn, he makes hisself comftible. Is by him a couple minutes
fiddle music and a couple minutes is by him not fiddle music. But
the Peffesseh, he is all the time making with the stick and stend-
ing up on his two feet. And by him is all the time a Prince Albert
udder a full dress suit, and with a Prince Albert udder a full dress
suit is all the time a stotch shirt. So is coming in bills fomm
laundry all the time. Believe me, ten dolless fa the Peffesseh is
like doit."

"Oho," Pa retorted, "is awready ten dolless by you doit! So
if ten dolless is by you doit, why you don't fix by us in kitchen
fa a couple dolless the sink is all the time running the water?"

"Dope!" Mrs. Gross shouted. "Somebody esk you to stick in
your two cents in committee-mitting?"

Mrs. Leshinsky rose and froze Pa Gross with her haughtiest
glance. "The mitting fomm the ladies eggsilry is finndished." She
turned to Mrs. Gross, who was seeing her to the door. "So goodbye, Sister Gross. Thenks fa the spuntch cake and fa the tea."

"Comes me a thenks yet," said Mrs. Gross. Mrs. Kahn rose
soon after Mrs. Leshinsky had departed. "My Mister is waiting,"
she said.

"So when you coming to the house again?" asked Mrs. Gross.

"I'll come when I'll come," she replied.

"Don't make yesself such a stranger," said Mrs. Gross. "And
next time bring with you the Mister."

Mrs. Gross waited until the door had slammed before turning on her husband.

"Dope! Schlemiel! Who spoke to you? Who esked you? Somebody came to you with fifdy cents in hend and said, 'Please, Mr. Advice Man, gimme quick fa fifdy cents advice'?"

"Fa heaven's sakes, what I done so terrible?" he wanted to know.

" 'The new dishes you using?' " she mimicked. "What'sa metta, you can't hold you the tongue a couple minutes in front Mrs. Leshinsky?"

"So who is this Mrs. Leshinsky awready?" he shouted.

"She is by us the chair-lady!" Ma shouted back.

"And by me she is the lendlady! And by us in house is running the water in kitchen. Let her fix betta the sink. No! She much make with peffessehs and with music and with fency-shemency talk!"

Mr. Gross noticed that his wife was pouring a glass of tea for herself. "Listen," he exclaimed, "I'm not Mr. Leshinsky, the lendlord. So give me, too, some tea in a gless."

Mrs. Gross prepared a glass of tea for him. Pa reached for a lump of sugar, dug deeply into it with his teeth, swallowed some tea and listened. The silence was punctuated by the steady drip, drip, drip of water hitting the kitchen sink. His eye caught his wife's. "That stuck-upnick!" he snorted, and returned to his tea. The kitchen noises were soon drowned by Pa's loud sipping.

THE DANCE

by MEYER LEVIN

LATELY SOMETHING HAD CHANGED ABOUT THE BIG TEN. NATURALLY the fellows couldn't come around so much. Harry Perlin was down at Urbana, Mitch and Joe lived South, lots of the boys were studying law or working nights. But even the regular Friday meetings had changed.

At the start the idea had been to have a serious side to the club, and a social side too. At each meeting, one of the members was to give a talk. Rudy Stone had given that first talk on the microscope, then Harry Perlin had demonstrated radio, and Mitch Wilner had given a talk on "The History of Medicine." Joe had given a chalk talk that had gone over big.

The membership was limited to ten, but as some of the fellows went away to school the question came up as to whether they could have substitute members. Meyer Rosenberg and Chink Spingold got in, they were nice enough fellows, but nothing special. Once, when there was hardly a quorum present, the rule of ten was voted down, and more new members were admitted. Pretty soon a whole crowd of neighborhood kids got the habit of dropping around.

All that seemed to go on now was dancing and kibitzing. Sol Meisel had won that silver cup for bike racing, and brought it down to the place. A couple of pennants appeared on the walls. One night, for a social, they even strung yellow and green crape paper streamers across the ceiling. Joe Freedman, chairman of the decoration committee, was sore.

Then the question of a dance came up. The idea was to run a dance and make some money. Lou Green suggested that it be held during Christmas week.

Confusion began. Should it be a prom or should it be a hop? Could they make more money charging two bucks' tax for a swell affair in a hotel or selling dollar tickets for a hop in one of the park refectories? Runt Plotkin said he knew a politician and maybe could get the refectory free. Sam Eisen said he didn't see what the Big Ten needed to run a dance for anyway. What did they need money for? And the chances were they'd come out in the hole.

All that went on was business about the dance. Should the tickets be engraved or just printed. A long debate on whether to say Admission, or Tax, $1.00. A six-piece orch or a four-piece.

Sam Eisen was getting more and more disgusted. The Big Ten had started out to be something different but look at it now!

At the meeting a week before the dance, Lou Margolis took up the question of ticket sales.

"Well, so far we didn't do so good. It looks like the dance will be a kind of private affair," he cracked. The trouble was a few of the fellows were doing all of the work. If every member would do his share . . . And he began calling each member by name for a report. When he came to Sam he said:

"I've got you down for five. Is that right?"

"Yep."

Lou wanted to know how many of those were actually sold.

"None," Sam said. There was an awkward laugh.

"How about a little co-operation, Sam?" Lou said. "We've got to sell these tickets or we'll be in the hole."

"The dance wasn't my idea," Sam said, controlling himself.

Lou kidded: "I know where you can sell a couple of bids right now. How about selling a couple to Sam Eisen?"

"I don't think I'll be there," Sam said.

There was a cold wait.

"Well, if that's the way you feel about it . . ."

Sam got up. He couldn't stand it any more. His big bustout was coming. "Listen," he said in a tight, low voice, "I don't know what's happened to this club but it isn't what it started out to be. It started out to be something worthwhile. We were going to get together a bunch of fellows who meant something. We had a purpose. Well, it just seems to me that it's changed, that's all. We're no better than the Aces and the Deuces and all those bums that hang around the sidewalks and whistle and shake a leg. I'm not against having a good time. You fellows know me too. I don't mean to ignore the social and the athletic side. But it just seems to me that the spirit here has changed. I'm not accusing anybody. Maybe I just don't get the idea. But look at us! A bunch of sheiks, come around and wisecrack and tell a couple of raw jokes and— aw, what's the use! I don't belong in this kind of a club, that's all. The best thing for me is to get out."

He was making a fool of himself. Now that he came to ac- cuse—what was there to accuse? He became choked up with anger, rage at not being able to tell them, tell them. . . .

He stood for a moment as if ready to answer any arguments. Then he moved past a row of knees toward the door. Maybe he had been hot-headed. But everything that was wrong in his life seemed to have brought him to that speech. The arguments at home, now the coat-makers were on strike again and his mother kept nipping, nipping, nipping at his father, other men went and made money during a strike; his dissatisfaction at the law school, his uncertainty; and his troubled, girl-wanting nights; everything seemed to converge into this explosion against the bunch.

The fellows took it strangely. There was a burning quiet. As Sam got to the door Lou Margolis said sharply:

"Are we to take this as a resignation from the club?"

"Yes," Sam barked out, but with a feeling of defeat.

Rudy Stone hurried over to the door.

"There is something in what you say, Sam." Rudy's calm smile reassured, and yet hurt him. He didn't mean to be against fellows like Rudy. "Only you have to remember there is another side to the question. If the fellows want this to be a social club, that's their affair. There's nothing wrong with having a good time once in a while."

"Oh, that's all right," Sam stumbled. "I just figured I didn't belong here any more. It's nothing personal."

"Sure, no hard feelings, huh?" Rudy said, extending his hand. He was so understanding and friendly Sam felt a little ashamed of himself, and yet deep down he was sore at that too, because he knew he was basically in the right.

"Well," Rudy quoted, "if we can't be the same old sweethearts, we can still be the same old friends. Stop in at the store some time, you squidyalum!"

It was snowing. Large watery flakes melted on Sam's face like tears. He was still breathing hard. He felt sore at the whole world.

When Sam was gone, Lou Margolis said: "Any further business?" Runt Plotkin offered to take care of the checkroom at the dance. The meeting dribbled on for a while, and then was adjourned. It broke up into knots, while the fellows talked about Sam Eisen. Lou Green said the trouble with him was that unless he ran things he couldn't be satisfied.

Sol Meisel didn't know what Sam was bellyaching about. It was as if Sam had suddenly jumped up and started to punch everybody around him, for no reason.

"He'll end up with high blood pressure," Mitch said.

Of course the dance would go through as scheduled. Only after that things seemed vague. It was almost like Sam had said: the club had no purpose any more.

In a couple of days, Harry Perlin came up from Urbana. He was sorry to hear about Sam Eisen. But he jumped right in to pull the dance out of the hole. Come on, fellows, we can still put this over. He went into every store on Roosevelt Road to get ads for the program. He got Rosen's barber shop and Kantor's delicatessen, and a half-page from Elfman's funeral parlor—from old man Elfman himself, who said: "You're a hustler all right!" Then he got a fellow in the Aces, and one in the Bluebirds, and one in the Y.M.H.A. to sell tickets to those clubs. He got Mort Abramson to sell tickets. Mort was very sympathetic and helpful when he heard the club was going in the hole. "Why don't you stick 'em with a wardrobe tax?" he suggested. "Once they've got there they have to pay it. The Bluebirds stuck everybody half a buck at their last affair." But Pearly thought a thing like that would give the club a bad rep. Besides, Runt Plotkin already had the checkroom concession.

Three weeks in advance, Harry had written up to ask Aline to the hop, but she hadn't answered his letter for two weeks and then she said she was sorry but she had promised to go with Rudy. So Pearly was stagging, and could take care of the door.

At eight o'clock Harry Perlin was on the spot. He began to worry would the orch come on time? Would the checkroom boys come on time? He made useless telephone calls. Nobody was home, nobody knew anything.

At last Runt's two brothers shambled in. They hadn't even brought checkroom tags. Harry Perlin nearly had a hemorrhage. Mygod, he had never seen an affair so mismanaged. He began tearing paper into slips and writing sets of numbers on them. The

Polack janitor saw what he was doing and produced a set of numbered metal checks.

"Boss, you saved my life!" Harry cried. The boys started
sliding on the floor, and that reminded Harry there was no floor-
wax. The janitor appeared with a can of rosin, saving his life
again. He'd have to give that Polack a buck if it came out of his
own pocket.

"I worry too much," Harry thought. "That's the trouble with
me.". . .

Runt hung around the checkroom. He found a cigar-box
under the counter. "Take out the dimes and nickels," he instructed Hymie. "Just leave the quarters. Get the idea?" He figured everybody except himself in the family was dumb.

His kid brothers wouldn't dare hold out more than a couple
of bones from the tips and even at that he should clear at least
five bucks.

Lou Green was stagging too. He was kind of like a tail without a kite, as his sidekick, Lou Margolis, had given Rose Heller a
break, taking her to the dance. So Lou stood with Runt Plotkin
near the ballroom entrance, making sarcastic comments about
Aline Freedman's bow legs, or tossing out knowing remarks to
certain couples as they passed.

A lot of the Bluebirds were around, stagging, and Harry
Perlin was a little scared that the Bluebirds might get funny. But
Runt said he'd take care of things, he'd talk to the boys, and
every few moments he scurried off and took someone aside and
consulted, mysteriously, importantly.

> Sun shines east,
> Sun shines west . . .

Alvin Fox had a mustache! Call that a mustache, Lil Klein
scorned, it's a misplaced eyebrow. And where did he get that girl!

Squiffs of laughter rippled through the Ladies' Restroom.
But trust Alvin always to spring a sensation! The girl looked
hardly fifteen. Her bony knees on stork-like legs stuck out under
the scalloped hem of her girlish party dress. And with a cluster

of Mary Pickford curls against the nape of her neck! She's putting on an act, was the opinion. Well, no matter how young she is, she's old enough to know better. It's a wonder she didn't wear a pink sash!

> But I know where
> The sun shines best.

In warmth, in wariness, the girls clustered in their bunch for the last whisper and reconnoiter, before entering the ballroom. The hastily exchanged last-minute bulletins on who had come with who. The shocks of relief and of agony, of friendship and betrayal—Aline said she was just going to wear her old blue sateen and look at her in that stunning silver thing with the swishing fringe around the tunic! It must be new! Celia just has on that rose thing she wore at the Sherman. All the girls affected a carelessness, a littleness toward this dance. They were careful to let each other know of the real affairs they were attending during the holidays—at the Edgewater, and the Del Roi, and the Black-stone! And still, there was a special air, a sort of hominess about this little hop, because it was the boys' dance, and it was sort of up to the girls to see that it went off all right. After all, they were their boys, trying to be social . . . And whoever a fellow took here, there was a sort of meaning to it.

> In the land of Sandomingo . . .

Rose was scared. First she put makeup on her cheeks, then she rubbed it all off. She hardly ever used makeup and, when she tried to use it, she got flaring round red spots on her cheeks. "Oh, I look like a clown!" she cried in agony to Aline, who was lending her the rouge.

"Oh, take it easy!" Aline soothed. Poor Rose was just in a fit of excitement because Lou Margolis had finally given her a tumble. Why couldn't she take it easy? It was just Lou's system to go with the girls in turn, never going with anyone twice in succession. Oh, he was wise.

> Lived a little oh by jingo . . .

But Rose, the poor kid, still had her crush on Lou, and she thought this was her real chance. "Oh, kid, what'll I do!" she finally broke down, pleading with her chum Aline. "What'll I talk to him about! I—I——"

Aline nearly had a fit. Why, Rose was the cleverest girl in the bunch, she had a tongue in her like nobody's business, she was always keeping the girls in stitches, and here she was afraid she wouldn't be able to keep a fellow interested. "Well, you know," Aline said, "there's nothing to it. No matter who the fellow was, you can always make him think you're the most interesting girl in the world by making him talk about himself. Just ask him what he's doing, and be interested in what he's doing, and he'll talk a streak. That's my system and it never fails."

Rose was staring at her like a drowning woman.

"Oh, don't be a blimp. Why, Rose, you can talk better than any of us." It was really simple. All you needed was a couple of catchwords, like Oh, yeah? and That's the cats, and Is that nice? or What makes you so quiet? and when in danger, you could always dance.

> Oh by gee by gosh by joe by gee,
> Oh by jiminy you're the girl for me . . .

She was the youngest and most brilliant student at Madison, Alvin let it get around. As if his bringing her was a sort of proof of his own brilliance. Her name was Nora Rosen and she was a North Side girl, no, no relation to Rosen's barber shop; in fact, her father was a policeman! Yep! a Jewish policeman! And she had won a scholarship prize at Wisconsin!

> We'll raise a lot of little oh by gollies
> And we'll put them in the Follies . . .

Lil Klein wandered a few steps into the ballroom. Quickly she scanned the crowd, while she held her hand up languidly fluffing the hair over her ear. Sam Eisen had not come.

She put on a smile as the dumb cousin she had conscripted to take her to the dance approached from the men's room. . . . Well, at least he hadn't come with anyone else.

He might still come.

It was really disgraceful. Disgusting. Solly Meisel and his redhead were shimmying.

"I think somebody ought to speak to them," Thelma Ryskind whispered to Aline.

Rudy Stone felt responsible. Perhaps after the dance he would get Lou Margolis to say something to Sol.

He had heard that certain of the fellows were carrying flasks, although it had been decided at a meeting that this was to be a respectable affair. Couples were going out on the balcony and swallowing gin.

"Oh, let them drink." Mitch Wilner was scornfully liberal. "A little reverse peristalsis never hurt anybody."

Mort Abramson made a late entrance with Ev Goldberg. The girls took one look and nearly passed out in a body.

Evelyn was wearing a full-length evening gown, straight to the floor, just the sort they had seen pictured on the society pages with the headline, "Paris brings back long evening gowns."

It was a blue chiffon covered with sequins, and with a wide studded girdle low on her hips, centered in an ornamental buckle. Around her shoulders was a gorgeous scarf-like creation of white tulle.

—Ev Goldberg! Well, no wonder! Her father has all those dress shops, that must be a Paris model he bought to copy.

—I admit it's stunning but I don't think it's good taste to wear it to an affair like this!

—I don't like those long skirts and it's a lot of bunk, they won't ever come back.

—They're just trying to change the style so everybody'll have to buy new dresses.

—I could have worn my yellow moire, it's really stunning but I thought it was too—you know—for an affair like this.

—Oh, she's just a walking ad for the Evelyn Shoppes.

—I wouldn't wear a thing like that if you gave it to me.

"No wonder she wants to wear them long, she's knock-kneed," Aline said.

Happiness was in her like a tingle of two little silver bells in her heart, like the fluttering of Pavlowa's feathery toes, and an endless tip tip toeing butterfly dance in her heart. She and Joe came late, from seeing Pavlowa, and the purity, the virginity, the happiness of being and feeling pure and idealistic and knowing that such things could exist in the world, this emotion flooded Sylvia, and she was pleased with everything tonight. Why, because of the blue of her dress, and even Mort was behaving tonight, Mort had brought none of his flashy girls, but a nice girl, Ev Goldberg, whose father owned the Evelyn Shoppes, see how nicely Mort was behaving, oh, Joeboy darling! And this strange wonderful feeling of unaccountable happiness, of all her friends being so fine, of her brother being so handsome, and her sweetheart being so sure, this flooded Sylvia, and there was an idiotic song whose words would not leave her, going across all the other songs that were played, and across the rhythm of dancing——

> Sun shines east,
> Sun shines west,
> But you're the one
> That I love best . . . !

At the end-swirl of the dance, Joe cocked his head and looked carefully, critically, at her face, and grinned. "If you will forgive a stranger's impertinence, miss, you have a very beautiful head. Might I ask you to pose for me?"

"Thank you, kind sir," she said, dropping a curtsy. And at the moment she loved all, everybody, the world, even Alvin with his silly new mustache. "I bet it tickles when it kisses," she said, and of course Alvin said: "You'd be surprised." And turning to Joe, said: "May I?" (Kiss your girl?)

> Jada! Jada!
> Jada jada jin jin jon!

Alvin stuck his head forward and actually made a peck at Sylvia, she withdrew, laughing, and barely felt his mustache brush her cheek. And, as she laughed: "I guess I'll have to wait till Joe grows one," Joe Freedman got an exultant scare. It was so final. Sylvia was Joe's girl, Joe was Sylvia's. He remembered that little ring she had given him that night when the Chicago opened. He reached for his watch pocket, though of course the ring was in the other suit. But he knew it wasn't there either. He had let it go to the cleaner's, get lost. He had a strange impulse to run home and

look for that ring; it was an omen that everything so gay and good
and sure-seeing, here, could carelessly be thrown away.

Never mind; love is young, there will be plenty of mementos.

> . . . of you
> The whole night through . . .

5. Foxtrot. Yours Truly.
6. Foxtrot. Mort.
7. Waltz. Mitch Wilner.

Aline studied the dance-trades Rudy was making. The same
old crowd. "Oh, and Rudy," she relented, "give a dance to Harry
Perlin." Poor kid, he still had a crush on her.

> . . . who you're calling sweetheart
> Now that you call me friend . . .

Lil Klein liked to be seen in the company of Celia Moscowitz
because she believed they were contrasting types and sort of set
each other off. You had to admit that Celia looked very nice when
she fixed herself up. Not fat, but statuesque. That was the word,
statuesque. The low waistline was really a godsend to heavy girls
like Celia, Lil maintained, as it kept people from noticing they
had no waist.

They watched Rose dancing with Lou Margolis; her face was
rosy like a shining apple, she looked like she was on top of the
world.

"You know, poor Skinny, she really has a crush on Lou," Lil
volunteered. She laughed at the way Rose bent with her behind
stuck out so she wouldn't show taller than Lou. "Can you imagine! what chance has she got!"

"She hasn't got a chance in the world!" Celia said. Her voice
was firm, flat, and Lil was startled. Could Celia be after Lou herself? There was more to Celia than you thought.

> . . . I'll say she can . . .

You certainly couldn't call Lou a sheik, Celia Moscowitz
thought, and this made her unhappy. Her secret passion was the
sheik. Could it be with the other girls as it was with her? When
Valentino's swarthy, warm face and that hot lush mouth trembled

toward her from the screen, her body was all juices. "It's no use trying to resist!" his hot desert voice whipped her as he flung her onto a harem bed!

> . . . Jada jada jin jin jon. . . .

Now she danced with Chink Spingold. His black hair glistened, and his side-hair was shaved level with his ear-lobes, like the sheik's. When a fellow first danced with her, he began with fast and jumpy jiggling, but after a few steps she had him dancing pasted against her. Maybe it was something mean in her.

> Let me call you sweetheart,
> I'm in love with you . . .

"Don't tell me you guys don't take quant!" Mitch Wilner derided the premedic from Northwestern.

"We're supposed to be doctors, not chemists."

Mitch snorted.

"Everybody knows you Chicago medics can't even tell a case of measels without taking it to the lab," Schwartz countered hotly, looking to Rudy for aid. "All you guys ever learn is lab work. Northwestern turns out the best practitioners in the country."

"It's six of one and half a dozen of the other," Rudy said.

"You're crazy!" Mitch cried. "Northwestern is where they go when they can't make the grade at Rush."

"Ah, here you are!" Sylvia accused. "What's the matter, Mitch, are you trying to get out of your dance with me?" Listen to Mitch put it over that fellow! All her friends and Joe's friends were the smartest and nicest and wisest. They were a wonderful bunch.

"Hey, I got something more important to do than argue with you now!" Mitch gallantly told off the fellow from Northwestern. He grabbed Sylvia around the waist. "Shove off!" he said, and charged onto the floor.

She liked the way Mitch danced. He almost rushed you off your feet but he made you feel he knew just where he was going. Sometimes she loved dancing with Joey more than she could possibly ever love dancing with anyone, when they were in perfect accord, but sometimes it seemed to her he got confused, he would

change step at every turn, two-step, waltz, foxtrot, toddle, all to
the same music!

Skinny Heller was a scream. So good-natured! Instead of
taking it to heart that she was so tall and thin, she made fun of
herself! Back in the corner behind the potted palms she was
putting on her act. The way she stuck one finger alongside her
nose, and sang in the most comical Yiddish accent:

> "Papa has a bizness,
> Strictly second hend,
> Everything from toothpicks
> To a bebbe grend!"

She wiggled so the fringe around her knees swished comically:

> "I'm wearing
> Second-hend hets
> Second-hend cloes . . ."

She rolled her eyes dolefully à la Fanny Brice.

> I'm second-hend Rose
> Of Second Avenue!

And when she and Lou Margolis got together, were they a
pair! The fellows got hold of Lou's arms and tried to drag him
out to the middle of the floor but he shook loose, laughing.

"Hey, Lou, hey, Lou!" said Second-the-Motion. "Let's see an
imitation of Eddie Cantor imitating Al Jolson!" That was the
Sharpshooter's prize. He crouched down on his haunches, clapped
his hands like Al Jolson, rolled his eyes like Eddie Cantor, and
sang:

> "Maaaahmeh! Maaaahmeh!
> Sun shines ist, sun shines vest . . ."

There was a burst of applause. Practically the whole crowd
had collected at that end of the hall, trying to see over each
other's heads. Lou pretended he hadn't known anyone was watching, and hid his face in mortification. Lou Greene thought maybe
now there would be a call for the two Lous to do Gallagher and

Shean, but the orch took up the "Mammy" song, and Lou Margolis grabbed Rose Heller and they did the craziest imitation of a Bowery dance. Skinny's eyes were snapping and her cheeks were red, and did she look happy! And was she good-looking then!

Jada . . .

"Now," Harry Perlin whispered to the Polack, and off went the lights.

"Yay!" the yell rose from the floor. "Yay!" Like the kids on the street, Harry remembered with pleasure. "Yay!" When the lamplights bloomed.

> . . . In the winter, in the summer,
> Don't we have fun!

The couples danced in the dark, in the moonlight, with titters, with giggles, with shouts and smothered, laughing screams, then the spotlight went on, sweeping and weaving over the dancers. Harry felt good. It made him feel good to see everybody enjoying themselves, the Big Ten hop was a success; he had checked up on the money and they had at least broken even, due to the large last-minute turnout. It was swell!

> It's three o'clock in the morning
> We've danced the whole night through . . .

Sylvia, dancing with Mort, came moving down the spotlight swath. And as Sylvia, and then other girls, drifted across that white beam, X-rayed in silhouette, Joe felt a shock of their loveliness. It was the torso, the upward flow from the hips, whose form he seemed to notice for the first time. Woman, a vase, molding up from the hips! Seeing them dancing he wanted to place his hands against their sides, and feel the motion of their lines; the leg-movement flowing from the very center of the body.

> . . . with you!

The drumstick whanged on the cymbals. Announcement. Thelma Ryskind . . . persuaded to render the Moonlight Sonata. She took her place. Of course, she whispered to Rose, the piano was out of tune. . . .

"I'm so warm," Syl said, and curled her fingers with Joe's, leading him out the French window. The snow was just like the whiteness of her heart. It was snowing and not cold. Moist lazy windless snow, with flakes coming down large, floating. They walked out a few steps, their hips moving in unison. They stood watching the snow come down. It felt like tonight was the real New Year.

Thelma's music, dimmed through the doors, sounded beautiful.

"It's like the sound of the snowflakes falling," Sylvia said reverently.

The snow already sat on the branches of trees, and the fresh snow on the pavement showed two clean, curving tire-tracks. They felt all their life together would be so smooth and so clean and so beautiful.

They walked a little further in that joined walk, as if their bodies were one being. Around the corner they nearly stumbled over a couple huddled on a deep ledge, necking. The kissers came up for air. It was Sol and Estelle of course. They all laughed.

"Don't let us disturb you," said Joe, and he and Syl walked on. A moment later a snowball hit Joe in the back of the neck. He scooped up snow, and shot one back at Sol.

It hit Estelle. She shrieked, ran out, and began flinging snow, with that awkward, elbowy girl's way of throwing.

Before they knew it a whole crowd was outside having a snowfight. Harry Perlin was one of the first; this was something a fellow could do, stagging. He made a snowball on the run, and threw it at Sol; Runt Plotkin was on Sol's side; a snowball hit the window of a parked car, a fellow who had been necking in the car dashed out and joined in the war; Harry Perlin threw and threw, laughing in his funny high excited giggle; Mort Abramson joined him and Joe; and before you knew it there was a gang entrenched behind a row of bushes, shooting at the army behind the row of parked cars. The Bluebirds came out in force, and suddenly there was a flock of girls running in their spike-heeled dance slippers, running across the snow. Alvin was standing behind the French windows of the refectory, and he saw them poised,

and heard their mingled cries, titters, and screams like the pleasant tinkling of broken glass. He felt poetic seeing the young girls
in the snow, their twinkling birdlike legs, their skimpy silks
pressed against their outlines by the wind of their running, the
scalloped bottoms of their dresses, the billowing frosty tulle
against the snow, the red, green, mauve, and marigold fragments
of them, colors glowing by moonlight seen against the snow. And
the tender gawky attitudes of their figures, knobby elbows and
bumpy knees, the arch of their throats and the perch of their
heads as they poised momentarily scenting snowball danger,
then screaming ran! The girls ran scattering across No Man's
Land, shrieking and screaming with laughter. Estelle caught a
snowball in the neck and it slid down inside, and Sol had to reach
down a little, to wipe her, and they laughed and laughed. Harry
Perlin tried to lead a charge against the cars and got a big wet
soft snowball smack in the puss. Lil Klein stood there screaming:
"Give it to them, give it to them!" Rudy Stone put on his
coat before he went out but then he packed the balls hard and
shot them with deadly accuracy!

"Come on, gang!" Harry Perlin yelled again, and led a brave
charge, but when he and Sol Meisel and Joe and Mort got in the
middle of the arena everybody turned on them and began pep-
pering them from all angles.

"Yay! Yay!" Harry Perlin yelled as he sat down in the snow.
"Yay!" like the kids yelled on St. Louis Avenue.

"Well, that's enough, that's enough," Rudy was saying, helping him up and brushing him off, and the kids, all weak with
laughter, were stamping back into the building. The whole bunch
was there in the hallway stamping and dripping and laughing
and it was one of those bright grand moments when everybody
was friends.

The dancing went on. The going home started. Little snow-
fights popped and burst. Not a couple could stick their noses out
the door without getting a hail of snowballs.

> . . . But I know where
> The sun shines best . . . !

DAY OF ATONEMENT

by MYRON BRINIG

ROSH HASHANAH, THE JEWISH NEW YEAR, COMMENCED ON A SATUR-day, and would be followed on the very next Saturday by Yom Kippur, the Day of Atonement. These particular Saturdays happened to be pay days for the miners, and the coincidence made it particularly hard for the Jewish merchants of Silver Bow. Those who were sincere in their beliefs did not worry unduly about this coincidence. They were willing, even eager to sacrifice profits for the sake of their religion. Moses was such a one. Much as he loved his store and greatly as he looked forward to these golden pay days, he did not for a moment tolerate the thought of keeping his store open for business.

On the holy days it was Moses' custom to rise at six so that he might be in the synagogue an hour later. Rebecca, too, was up at that early hour and roused the children. Since the holidays occurred in the latter part of September, it was already cold in Montana. In Rumania, it had been pleasant to wake in the autumnal morning and walk through the rich red and gold countryside to the shul. Moses and Rebecca remembered the voices of the Rumanian congregation, a steady humming sound pierced by the rising supplications of the rabbi, a golden overtone in a full-bodied symphony. The contrast of Silver Bow was overwhelming and depressing, particularly on Rosh Hashanah. It did not matter so much on Yom Kippur, for that was the day of mourning, of deep grief for the sins committed during the past twelve months. The dark skies of Silver Bow and the penetrating winds that swept through the town were in keeping with the doleful nature of the day.

Cold as it was, no fire was started in any of the stoves; and whatever servant there happened to be in the house at the time was given the day off. It was not proper that servants should work on the holy days, no matter what their beliefs might be. Rebecca and Moses dressed in their cold bedchamber, and the children shivered in their own icy rooms. There was no hot coffee for breakfast, but Rebecca served cake and wine. Since Yom Kippur was a day of fasting, there was nothing to warm up congealed bodies, and the Singermanns formed a frozen, despondent group when they left their house to attend the services in the synagogue. They left a gloomy, cold house to emerge into a dim street harsh with smoke and sulphur. But it was comforting to reach the modest shul, dark and musty, warmed by the presence of many worshipers. The men with their hats worn low over their eyes, their shoulders draped by the inevitable prayer shawl, stood in many attitudes; some were bent low over the benches peering with a desperate concentration into the Hebrew prayer books; others stood with their eyes to the wall as though ashamed to show their faces agonized by grief and supplication; and still others, as if pursued by their daily temptations, strode up and down the narrow aisles, praying in their stride, beating their breasts rhythmically, on the heart, on the heart, on the heart. For it is from the heart that one must worship sincerely to Jehovah; it is as though the heart is a door to the soul, and one is beating upon that door, crying, "Open! Open! Open! I am without and lonely, and I would be in Thy presence, O Lord! *Adenoi Elohenu, Adenoi Echod!*"

On this Yom Kippur, Moses occupied a bench near the altar, and it was to this corner of the shul that he shepherded his flock, his wife and five children. Michael was still too young to appear in the synagogue, and Mary O'Brien had taken him to her home in Walkerville for the day. Last year Joseph had been here, praying by the side of his father; but now he was married and his wife was a Christian Scientist. There was a yawning gap where he should have stood, his slim shoulders draped by the prayershawl. There had been for Moses a kind of security in the knowledge of Joseph's presence in a shul, a warmth of kinship that cannot be far from God. But now he was gone—sold to the devil! "O Lord, have mercy upon my son and show him the right way!" Moses prayed, and his voice transformed the ugly wooden shack into an immortal place. He sang and all else seemed fugitive and dying; but his songs were one with the million nights that have passed over the earth since Abraham and David and Solomon. "This was my son, Joseph. Now I am bereft of him. Forgive Thou his many sins, O Lord! *Adenoi Elohenu, Adenoi Echod!* Hear, O Israel! The Lord our God, The Lord is One!"

At noon time, Moses went outside for a breath of air. He walked up and down the sidewalk in front of the synagogue, refreshing his body and lungs and feeling the wind in his eyes. Members of the congregation stood about in small groups holding earnest conversation with one another, seeking diversion and rest in gossip—aye, even on the Day of Atonement! When the afternoon prayers began, they would be able to renew their supplications to Jehovah with a more devout and strengthened ardor. After a minute, Moses became aware that they were casting furtive, uneasy glances in his direction. They would look at him and then resume talking with great heat and animation. He caught detached words . . . "His son, Joseph . . . Such a shame . . . the son keeps open his store on Yom Kippur . . . With my own eyes . . . disgrace . . . Only of money he thinks . . . Should I have such a son, I would hang my head . . . And we keep our stores closed that such a one . . ."

Moses knew that they were talking of his oldest son. He dared not meet their reproachful eyes, yet every word they spoke was a wound in his body. Usually the most courageous of men, he was moved now by a desire to flee from these critical eyes and hide away. He looked towards the door of the synagogue and saw David emerge, David so tall and strong, with grace in his walk and assurance in his manner. Moses felt suddenly free, and as he moved forward to meet his third son, he thought that Jehovah would not hold Joseph so much against him since there was David, so alive, so vivid in his young beauty.

But as David caught sight of his father, a frown appeared on his forehead, and his eyes blinked with troubled anger. For a moment, Moses was hurt by his son's expression; but it turned out that it was not with his father that David was angry. On the contrary, this was one of those rare occasions when David was thoroughly sympathetic with his father's attitude.

"Did you know that Joseph was keeping his store open today?" David whispered, drawing Moses to the edge of the walk. "Everybody's talking about it and cursing at us behind our backs. It's a shame!" David kicked at the rocks in the street.

"It was not like this before he married that woman," said Moses, throwing the blame on Daisy rather than on his favorite son. "She's to blame." And he added in Yiddish, "She should roll in the dust!"

"It ain't so much because I'm religious that I care," said David truthfully, and Moses looked moody at these words. "But how does it look for other people? Every Jewish store in the block closed for the holidays, and his open with the Gentiles."

"It is the woman," persisted Moses stubbornly, but he only half believed his own words. "She is to blame. She with her Christian Science! Do you think I don't know? I have seen her go into the church with the Christians. But why do I talk? He is no more a son of mine. Let her give him flesh of the swine to eat."

The worshipers returned into the synagogue. The rabbi's voice that had been droning on and on during the interlude, in a kind of passive monotone, was once more raised to its high pitch of intense supplication. Its sharpness, its vehemence of expression stabbed the quietness of the street and recalled the men and women to their various places within. "It is beneath me to talk from such a son," said Moses and returned within the shul, leaving David to stand alone on the sidewalk.

David stood there in front of the synagogue staring at the cheap colored glass windows parallel with his eyes. A weak, timid-appearing sun shot its gleams through the dark, smoky clouds for a short space, and the answering reflections of the glass were imprisoned in David's eyes. He became, thus, for the slightest interval, a very striking young man, a crusader striding out of the muddled cheapness of his background. For that moment he was all beauty, all young manhood attempting to free itself from the grasping tendons of a materialistic octopus. But David's thoughts were less concerned with beauty than with ideas of right and wrong; and even his ideas of right and wrong were by no means straightened out in his mind. He only knew that it was a sin to transact commerce on Yom Kippur. Joseph was therefore sinning. David did not bother to argue the question to himself. For all he cared, religion might be useless and out of date. Indeed, he had entertained a suspicion of this sort for some time. But futile or worthy as his religion might be, it was his religion, and no member of his family had ever scorned it as Joseph was doing today.

Since Joseph had opened his own store, he had dug a chasm between himself and his younger brothers, a chasm filled with bitterness. David acknowledged that his oldest brother had worked hard; he acknowledged, too, a certain initiative and hustle in Joseph that the younger members of the family did not possess. But these worthier qualities of Joseph's were overshadowed by the indubitable fact that he had seized, by stealth, what he had no right to have. He had built up a new business on the money that he and Daisy had taken from the original Singermann store. Joseph was a hard worker and Daisy a clever manager, but that did not alter the truth of the situation.

"It makes me sore!" said David to himself, and without quite realizing it, started to walk away from the synagogue towards the business part of town. He was not clear in his mind about what he wanted to do, but he was filled with that soreness, that blind anger against Joseph and Daisy. As he neared East Park Street, his thoughts became less amenable to discipline. "It's a shame!" he kept repeating to himself. "That guy thinks he can get away with anything!"

So intensely was David wrapped up with his angered thoughts that he started with some surprise when he found himself in front of his brother's store. Doubts began to enter his mind and he hesitated. Like his younger brothers, David had always held Joseph in a certain awe. The oldest son had always been a dictator to his brothers; he had always sneered in a superior way at any idea Louis or David had set in motion, as though no one his junior could possibly say or do anything that would bear the scrutiny of an intelligent human being. Since his marriage to Daisy, he had exhibited even less patience where the rest of the family was concerned. David was fully aware of this attitude on

Joseph's part, and it tended to create within him a certain despondent feeling of inferiority. So now, as he stood in front of Joseph's store, he wondered what he had better do. All his hatred and jealousy had ceased to be effective weapons. He must be sure of himself before he entered within to do battle with Joseph. And now, he felt sure of nothing. He even wondered whether he had the right to interfere in his oldest brother's business. The fact that they were brothers meant very little as they grew older. Each man for himself . . . that was it. If Joseph chose to look out for himself, who could blame him?

David turned his eyes to the opposite side of the street and regarded his father's store with the sign, Closed acc't Holidays, hanging behind the door. How deserted the place looked, how cold! And here, on the other side of the street, everything was light and business. Joseph's was the only store open on the block, and he was profiting at the expense of his father and younger brothers. All these customers thronging the aisles of Joseph's store, their pockets jingling with money, their fingers eagerly caressing the merchandise! And on the Day of Atonement, the day that Singermanns for generations past had set aside for the worship of the one God, the true God!

It was this thought, concerned with the mysterious Deity, that set David's fears at rest. He cast off his inferiority with one stride and passed into the crowded aisles of Joseph's store. There, in the center of the floor, seated on a chair that was like a throne, was Daisy, pressing the keys of the cash register and calling out instructions to the clerks who scurried like ants beneath her. Like a queen she commanded all; with one hand she reached for money and counted change; with the other she delved absently into a bag of peanuts, cracking each shell between her strong, pointed teeth. A sudden realization of her power overcame David as he halted in the aisle looking up at her. He knew, without stopping to formulate any logical train of thought in his mind, that it was this handsome, formidable woman who had ordered Joseph to keep his store open on a Jewish holiday. And with that thought came a succeeding one, painfully obvious to him, that it would be worse than useless to argue with Joseph who was dominated by this stubborn, crafty woman.

As David continued to look up at her, almost drugged by her power, she caught sight of him. For a moment she was taken aback by his abrupt materialization out of a crowd of milling shoppers; but she was quick to regain her composure, perceiving, almost instantly, David's motive for coming into the store. She waved at her brother-in-law gaily. "Hello, Dave! How's tricks?" At the same time there was an interrogative glint in her hard blue eyes, as if she were saying: Out with it! You might as well tell me why you've come.

"Where's Joe?" asked David in a voice that was just this side of rudeness. And as he asked the question, he began edging away from the chair upon which Daisy was enthroned, his eyes darting in many directions.

"He's in the rear waiting on a customer," was Daisy's almost mechanical response. "Is it something important you wanted to see him about, dear?" She had a habit of calling her brothers-in-law "dear" thus instantly placing them on the defensive. The term caused them to feel ridiculously young, mere children, and served to fortify Daisy's self-esteem.

David did not answer his sister-in-law's last question. He had caught a momentary glimpse of Joseph in the rear of the store; for an instant their eyes met, and the older brother's face had turned a trifle pale. Joseph quickly lowered his gaze and pretended an almost fierce interest in the customer he was waiting upon. Like his wife, he knew why David had come, and the realization threw him into one of his peculiar, spasmodic fits of action. He talked rapidly to his customer, shifting about nervously on his feet. He was in the midst of selling a suit of clothes, and his agile hands were in bewildering movement, patting the back of the coat, running along the man's collar, pulling at the sleeves. "It fits you perfect—just perfect," Joseph said with a deliberate, intense concentration. "You don't have to take my word for it. Just take a look for yourself, here in the glass." And as the customer turned to the mirror, Joseph followed him, petting, cajoling, assuming the slightly cringing attitude of a clever salesman who wants to flatter his prospective victim. Yet all the while, out of one corner of his eyes, Joseph was aware of his brother's approach, the approach of a handsome young animal filled with a fury of anger. He was aware, too, of Daisy leaning far out of her swivel-chair, watching David's progress with a nervous alarm.

David spoke instantly and quickly, lest his words take fright before they were uttered and remain unsaid. "You—you damn fool! What d'ya mean keeping your store open like this on a Jewish holiday? Don't you know it's Yom Kippur? You're a fine one, you are!" David possessed a husky, resonant voice. There was strength in his lungs that his words were audible all over the store.

Joseph went even whiter and stretched out an impatient arm as if to shove his younger brother away. "Where do you think you are? . . . Who do you think you're talking to?" He made a movement as though to strike David, and then hesitated and turned to his customer who was looking at the brothers with wide, startled eyes.

It was David who closed the gap. He stood over Joseph like a great bear, and his eyes were blazing fire. He had now completely lost control of his temper, and Joseph was no longer a brother and not even an acquaintance. He was merely an exasperating worm who had somehow got in his path and who must somehow be shown his place. "A fine one you are! And all that papa has done for you, too! I'd be ashamed to look a decent man in the face . . . Every other Jew in town is closed up, and here you are . . . shoving in money so that your wife can get fat . . . and eat more ham . . . afraid you'll lose a little business!"

They stood facing one another, almost touching, one a strong, handsome animal, the other like a worried, petulant gnat. Joseph's anger was bottled up, tensely, tightly, and drew all the color of his face within him until he was seething with a poison of emotions. "Get out of here!" he whispered furiously. "What right have you got to come in here anyway? You've got nothing to do with me. I'll throw you out! I'll throw you out like the dog you are!"

The customer who was buying the suit stepped aside and looked on. He had forgotten that he was worried about the length of the sleeves. That, in itself, was something of an event in his life. He was a poor man and it was not often that he bought a new suit. For weeks his wife had been pestering him. "You look a perfect fright in that old suit of yours. It's about time you bought a new outfit. I saw something in the window of The Hub . . . Now don't come home tonight and tell me you forgot all about it. I'm sick and tired . . ." He had left his wife feeling shabby and out of sorts. Now he was in The Hub about to purchase a new suit, a rare event, and the sleeves had been rather short. But he could not think of sleeves as he looked at Joseph and David.

"Why don't you throw me out then?" asked David. He did not wait for an answer and brought the palm of his hand against Joseph's face. It was a sharp, painful blow, and when he withdrew his hand, he could see where he had left a dark red imprint on his brother's face. The finger prints fascinated him. He could not move his eyes from the dark red marks with the intensely white spaces in between. He even forgot that he had struck Joseph. There seemed neither rhyme nor reason to it all. There was only that imprint, somehow horrible and shameful.

For a moment, Joseph stared wildly at his brother. Tiny crystals appeared in the corners of his eyes, but they were tears of astonishment rather than of grief. Suddenly, he lost control of his tightly packed passions. It was as though the cork that had been bottling up the poison had given way to a sharp, explosive pressure and blown off, loosing the angry fumes within. He jumped at David, a snarling caricature of himself, and the two brothers became intricately mad, aiming a tempest of blows at one another, most of which failed in their aim. Joseph's impact forced David against a movable clothing rack; the rack swayed from side to side and finally fell to the floor and the two young men fell on top of it, becoming involved in sleeves and trousers. They struggled fiercely in this maze while customers and clerks surrounded them, shouting, imploring, fascinated at the unexpected show. Then, a woman pushed her way through the gaping spectators. It was Daisy, white and desperate. A coil of her hair had come loose and straggled down her neck to her shoulder, so that she looked like an easy woman from down on Galena Street. "Pull them apart!" she screamed to one of the clerks. "Don't stand there lookin' at 'em. What do you think we're paying you for?" The clerk looked at her helplessly, as if saying, Well, I know what you're paying me for, but it's not for this. As he hesitated, Daisy bent over and with all her strength clutched at David's shoulders. Her entrance into the tangle was the signal for the clerk to do likewise; while she held firmly to David, the clerk pinned Joseph's arms behind him and jerked him to his feet. The two brothers subsided almost as abruptly as they had begun. David looked frantically about for his hat that had been knocked off his head during the battle. It was crushed out of shape and covered with dust. He stood creasing it nervously for perhaps a minute, and then started on his way to the outer door.

He was nearing his objective when he felt some one clutching at his sleeve. He turned about, and it seemed as though Daisy's eyes were boring through him, blue daggers, sharp and pointed, twisting in his sickened consciousness. "You hit him," she gasped. "You struck your own brother, and he's older than you. I'll always hold this against you. Barbarian! Don't think I'll ever forget it. There was no reason . . . I could have the police on you. . . . I could send you to the penitentiary . . . as God is my witness. . . ." And always he felt the eyes, like blue needles, stabbing him through and through.

He shook off her grasp, impatiently, yet he was full of sadness. He could not understand why, all of a sudden, he should be so unutterably sorry, so full of loathing for himself, for everyone. "You're to blame!" he cried out, and his eyes were brimming over with tears. "If it hadn't been for you there'd be no trouble. But it's because you changed him. Since he's known you. . . ."

"I can never forgive you for this," she went on breathlessly, as though she feared that her strength would leave her before all her words were said. "It's like you was hitting me. You're like a criminal. But wait! You'll come to a bad end. You'll be in a bad fix some day and we'll—spit on you! Coming around here—the idea . . . before all our customers . . . Do you think I'll ever forget this? Some things burn in me. I'm a sensitive woman. If it wasn't that God's truth was in me I'd . . . But wait . . . you'll be punished. . . ."

"Aw, let me go!" He shook off her grasp and walked on, but she continued to follow him, over the threshold, to the sidewalk, clinging to him while passers-by looked over their shoulders. Many of them nodded to her, for by this time she was well known in the town. "Joe Singermann's wife . . . she ain't nobody's fool . . ." Many of them stopped, but the look in her eyes bade them keep a respectful distance. "Go tell your father that I never want to look at him again. Every day I was in his hell of a store he made me suffer . . . insulting me . . . and now that God has provided us with our own business, he sends you to pester us. But nothin' can harm us because God is our strength. . . ."

"Let me go!" said David gruffly, and walked away from her, but she stood looking after him for a long time. He could feel her eyes stabbing through his back until he turned the corner. And even when he knew that she could no longer see him, he felt her presence like a plague in his body.

"Get back to your customers," Joseph ordered his clerks, and flicked the dust off his trousers with his hands. His necktie had come undone and he drew it tight under his collar. He smoothed his hair and wiped the dust and perspiration off his face. "Where's Daisy? Tell her to get back to the cash register. Where does she think she is, standing like that out on the sidewalk? Call her back there, you—I mean you. I'm not paying you to look at me. . . ." He turned to the customer who had been trying on the suit. "That's brothers for you," and he forced a weak, wretched smile. "That guy was my brother . . . Would you believe it? . . . I want you to excuse me, friend. How's the fit?" And he began pressing his agile, nervous hands down the back of the coat, patting the collar, the shoulders. "You couldn't get a better-looking suit made to order." Already he had forgotten David. Once more he was intensely concentrated in the suit, the customer, the necessity of making a sale. "Turn around. See how it lays in the back?"

The customer was embarrassed; he tried to interest himself in the suit, but all the time he kept thinking of the two brothers, one like a great, enraged animal, the other like a gnat, restless, spasmodic. "Kind of bad tempered, that brother of yours, ain't he? Hurt you? He's bigger'n you. But you put up a great battle. How much is the suit? . . . Yaa, I'll take it. It's a good thing

your wife separated the both o' you. Plucky woman, Mrs. Singermann . . . How are you, Mrs. Singermann? Thirty-five dollars.
Yaa. My wife kept pesterin' me to get a suit, an' now I got one,
an' I hope she's satisfied . . . You said it! They always want you
to be dolled up like a million dollars. Say! That brother-in-law o'
yours, he ain't to be trifled with . . . Hit your husband a nasty
one. I just stood there. I'm neutral. Ha! Ha! Naw, I wasn't a bit
inconvenienced, Mrs. Singermann. Just forget about it. Them
boys they're just like the old man. I used to do all my buyin'
across the street until Joe opened this place. Always liked Joe
to wait on me. He treats me square. But I like the old man. He's
a proper old devil. The boys is just like him. Once they get mad!
. . . Thanks, Mrs. Singermann. I will come in again, thanks.
You got my whole pay roll, now. Ha! Some fight that was. . . ."

David strode along back to the synagogue. It was growing
dark now. The smelter smokestack south of the town was lifting
its plume of fire into the sky, as though the devil were lying in
there on his back breathing defiance to the heavens. There was
a hard, vicious beauty about it, unconscious and unpremeditated.
David lifted his eyes to this burning splendor, but its beauty was
a blankness in his mind. He had that sadness in him, that deep
loathing of himself and of everyone. What a fight that had been!
What ever made him do it? What was the use of it all? He should
never have gone to the store. If Joseph wanted to keep open on
Yom Kippur, if he were sinning, why he'd be punished, that's all.
Sinning! thought David bitterly. What did sinning have to do
with it? They were getting the money while all the other Jewish
stores were closed tighter than drums. They were too damn
smart. Well, he'd got one on the nose just the same. Maybe it'll
teach him a lesson. "I'll never speak to you again." Well, Mrs.
Daisy Singermann, I should worry whether you do or whether
you don't.

David's thoughts ran on: That woman! She's the cause of it
all. If only she'd be decent and let somebody else have a chance
. . . the greedy snake . . . Aw, I guess I shouldn't have hit him.
The way my hand looked on his face . . . He's not so strong.
What did she mean when she said that some day I'd be in a fix?

What's she pokin' her nose . . . aw, I shouldn't have hit him. But what the hell? What right has he to keep his store open on Yom Kippur when it is the law to fast and pray?

It was dark when he reached the synagogue and he could see the dim light within reflected through the colored glass. There were a hundred or more voices raised in that piercing agonizing song so full of blood and tears. They were singing Kol Nidre. David stood out there in the darkness and a peace came over him, a quietness. If that piercing, ecstatic song, broken by deep sobs, significant pauses, could go on forever! But the song ends, thought David. The song ends and prayers are forgotten, and you struggle blindly and work yourself to the bone . . . And at night you seek diversion in those dives, those cheap cribs. Where is Kol Nidre then? Where are the thoughts of Moses, Abraham, and Solomon?

And David turned into the synagogue. And the candlelight was soft and kindly to his eyes.

PART TWO

Old World Pomegranates

THE SLAYING OF THE WOLF

by ZALMAN SCHNEOUR

AFTER THEY HAD LEFT KOPUST THE WOOD BECAME MORE DENSE, and the night was black. Sender's coach, packed with goods, glided along the road between two green walls of pine loaded with snow. Sender's horses, all three of them, sensed that they had done the greater part of the journey, and they trotted along happily, especially Shmarovoz, the glutton, who was harnessed in the shafts between Djirka, Sender's mare, and his young favorite, Shmendrik. Shmarovoz could scent his warm stable ten miles off and the manger full of oats, with no chaff in it. And he ecstatically whisked his tail over his white legs and brown dapples. And did all he could to get home as quickly as possible. Noah Pandre, who had got to know some of the ways of Sender's horses and to speak to them as Sender did, touched Shmarovoz with the butt of his whip on his behind, and said to Sender:

"Look what a hurry he is in! Can't wait any longer for his feed!"

Sender took a pinch of snuff and did not answer. He was a little annoyed that Noah had not seemed to be much affected by the story of the death of his father's driver, and of his father's heroism, and his brain-wave in dealing with the bear. Pandre had listened very closely, and very respectfully, but he had not gone into raptures about it. Indeed, he had said, this butcher boy, that he wished that he had come across those robbers and he would have dealt with them!

He is like a block, Sender thought to himself, with a glance at Pandre's broad shoulders, and his bent head. Everything about him was hard and firm, as if cast of bronze. He couldn't give up being a butcher boy!

The trees drew back on one side of the road, and an empty field stretched along this side of it. It grew darker still, and more gloomy. There wasn't the snow now that had clung to the branches of this side of the road before, and had given off a little light. There was no sound in the gloom except that of the three horses galloping like the devil. They moved along like three short waves, one up, the other down. And twelve hooves beat in rhythm. They drummed a queer little hoof tune.

Sender's coach turned, and a cold wind suddenly blew from behind, from the frozen Dnieper. The horses pricked up their ears, and breathed harder through their big nostrils.

It's a good thing, Sender mused, that one doesn't hear anything about wolves in these parts nowadays, or else this would be a rotten wind now, blowing behind us. It would keep off all scent of the wolves from the horses.

But he seemed to have taken it into his head that evening to frighten Pandre, to move that imperturbable butcher boy out of his stolid calm. And he forgot that only a moment ago he had been swearing at Noah for "calling up" robbers by challenging them to a fight, and he launched into a new tale.

"Listen, Pandre, did you know Miron, the woodman? You were only a tot at the time, but you ought to have heard of him. He was a bad-tempered fellow; he wouldn't let a Jewish child pick one single blackberry in the forest. I see that you do remember him! Of course, you would! What Jewish child could resist going into the forest on a Saturday to pick blackberries, instead of sitting down to read the Ethics of the Fathers? Miron had been appointed by the lord of the manor as the keeper of the forest, to stop the peasants from felling timber, and to prevent Jews taking away foliage to roof their tabernacles. He had a cottage built for him in the forest. It must have been about five miles from here, before you get to Shklov. Did I say a cottage? Catch the lord of the manor building a cottage for the woodman! He was a miserly dog, who wouldn't give away a stick. It was only a shed, half sunk in the ground, and there was a tin box with the bottom knocked out, to serve as a chimney. That was the sort of palace that he built for Miron. And he gave him an old blunderbuss that made more noise than did actual damage. 'Here you are!' he said. 'And if a peasant comes along to fell a tree, shoot him down on the spot! I'll answer for it!'

"But that Miron was a beast! He couldn't bear the sight of a Jew! Everybody knows that Jews don't fell trees, and don't steal timber. It isn't a Jewish habit. Jews haven't got choppers and saws and sledges to carry away the timber on, but Miron always tried to pick a quarrel with Jews. If Jews travelled past on their way from market he would ambush himself behind the trees along the road, and fire up in the air. Just to frighten them! Just to see the horses bolt with fright! If Jewish children came into the wood to pick blackberries, Miron would suddenly appear with his pug-nose and his blunderbuss, out of nowhere, and start chasing them. At first he shouted: 'I'll get you! I'll get you!' And then, when they had outdistanced him, he fired up in the air, and then doubled up with laughing, at the way he had scared them. Children used to come home scared to death, with their poor bottoms all wet.

"Once he played a trick like that on Rabbi Itche. Did you happen to know him? He was the assistant to the Rabbi of Kopust. You don't know what that means, do you, Pandre? The Rabbi's assistant repeats by heart the teachings of the Rabbi. You see, the Rabbi expounds Hasidic lore, and the assistant memorizes it. Word for word, as if he were reading it out of a book. He wouldn't miss a syllable! It needs a marvellous memory! You see, the Rabbi is a frail old man, and he can't be everywhere. So the assistant travels about, visits all the little towns and villages, and repeats the teachings of the Kopust Rabbi. Do you think that our Rabbi goes to Kopust every couple of days to bring back a new exposition of Hasidic teaching? The fares alone would eat up the few roubles a week that he gets in salary from us. Today, the assistant is Rabbi Baruch. At that time it was Rabbi Itche. Now Itche, peace to his memory, was coming from Kopust to Shklov, to see our late Rabbi, peace to his memory. It was summer time, and it was beginning to get dark. Rabbi Itche wouldn't miss the twilight prayer, so he asked the coachman to stop for a bit, and he got down from the coach, rubbed his hands on the damp grass, and went into the wood, away from the road, and stood up against a tree, to say his prayers. It was very quiet. Rabbi Itche swayed backwards and forwards, and so did the top of the tree. And then suddenly, bang, bang, bang!

"That was the sort of thing that Miron would be up to! He had trailed Rabbi Itche to the tree, and when he saw that he was most rapt in his prayers, he had discharged his blunderbuss in the air. The coachman found Rabbi Itche lying on the ground in a dead faint, with his face buried in a heap of pine cones, and a big bump on his head, that he had got in falling. The coachman thought he was dead. He had a job to bring him round!

"They say that when Rabbi Itche came to, and found out what had happened, he put a curse on Miron. He prophesied that he would be devoured by wolves, and nothing would be left of him, only his boots, to tell the tale.

"A couple of months later, that same winter, just before Christmas, when the peasants were travelling backwards and forwards to church, and Jews, too, went on their customary pilgrimage to the Rabbi, to sit at his table and sing Hasidic songs, Miron became more savage than ever. He had heard that the Jews had crucified Christ, and he also knew that the Jews would be coming past on their sledges on their way to Kopust, to be with their Rabbi on Christmas night. That made him mad. And he resolved that this time he would account for a Jew or two. He began by pouring a lot of spirit down his throat to warm up, and then he loaded his blunderbuss with shot. He didn't want bullets. He only wanted to wound, not to kill. The blunderbuss was found afterwards, so we know. It was lying next to his jack boots.

"Miron came out of his shed, carrying his blunderbuss over his shoulder, and made his way among the snow-laden trees in the direction of the road. There would surely be a Jewish coach coming along soon, and then he would pay them for what they had done to Christ. As he walked along, he caught sight of a little green flame among the trees. Then there were two little flames. There, he thought to himself, with his fuddled brain, there comes a Jewish sledge with a lantern, two lanterns, three lanterns. Look at them, what a lot of green lanterns they've got! Aren't they feeling happy about it! Killed our Christ, and feeling happy about it! I'll pay them!

"Talking to himself in that way, he crept along, with his

blunderbuss slung over his shoulder. But the green lights went on growing in number. There were a great many green lights, and they spread out all round him. Wherever he looked, the green lights burned in front of him. Presently, he heard a stealthy tread in the snow and a snarl. That didn't sound like Jews! Miron took to his heels, cold shivers running down his back. That sobered him! But he didn't shoot Mr. Wolf and Mrs. Wolf and the little wolves were right on top of him now. He wanted to run, but he was in the thickest part of the forest, and the wolves were all round him. He hit out with the butt of his blunderbuss, but it only caught against a tree.

"The first to approach him was Mrs. Wolf. If you meet with wolves, God forbid, on the road, you have to deal first with the mother wolf. She leads the pack, and makes the kill. The males follow her. Plenty of them, with green lights for eyes. 'Ha! What's that?' Sender suddenly cried 'Look Pandre! What's that over there? Look! Hear, O Israel!' "

Two green lights had suddenly appeared in among the pine trees, on the edge of the field. And behind them were two smaller green lights. Before Noah could move the horses had already scented the wolves, and snorting with terror, had stopped dead. It was too late to run. The wolves had used the wind to cover their scent, and had suddenly cut off the road. Only Shmendrik, the youngest horse, was tearing at the reins, tugging and pulling to get away. Djirka and Shmarovoz had jumped one step back, and then stopped dead, with their heads down, looking at their front legs, and they stood there lost in thought. Only the mare was quivering, every inch of her. Djirka, the mare, had suddenly remembered what her mother had taught her to do in such a trouble. And she began to paw the ground with her heavy hooves. They kept coming down on the hard road, thud! thud! Shmarovoz took the lead from her, and did the same, and Shmendrik followed suit. All three spread out in the shafts, fanlike, with Shmarovoz in the middle, in order to extend the front, and their hooves moved like shears. If a wolf jumped at their throats, he got a hoof on top of his head as he jumped.

A she-wolf, as big as a calf, was suddenly seen at the side

of them, in the light of the gleaming snow. She crept up, almost on her belly, like a cat following a bird. Her head was between her paws, and the glinting eyes glared at the horses. The horses kept their eyes fixed on her, and she kept her eyes fixed on theirs. Behind her came two young wolves, being taught by their mother to hunt. It was the usual wolfish strategy, to frighten the horses to death, to stare fixedly at their eyes, and so hypnotize them, to deprive them of the will to resist.

It all happened in less than a minute, from the time that Sender had first noticed the wolves, and Noah had got a bit bewildered. In that one minute the horses had felt that there was no master to take care of them, so they had tried to defend themselves. Their own inherited horse sense had taught them how. But the next minute, Pandre had pulled himself together. He bent down, and got out the heavy iron wedge that lay under the hay in the coach, used to steady the sledge on a slippery slope, and also to help in rolling heavy bales out of the sledge. He held the wedge in his right hand, like a Cossack his lance, and he tugged at the reins with his left hand. At the same time he stood up, one foot planted on the box-seat and the other on a shaft. Now let them come, the she-wolf and her sons!

Mrs. Wolf did not wait for the invitation. She crept nearer and nearer, still keeping her head between her paws, and, lifting up the green fires of her eyes, she let out a terrifying howl, which grew louder as she lifted her head. And the fire in her eyes, and her howling, seemed to come out of the snow-decked earth. Behind her followed her sons, doing everything just as mother did. The performance was repeated several times in succession, howling and then crawling nearer, crawling nearer and howling. "Waa-ow! Waa-ow!" The lupine cry spread across the field and wood. The sound was dismal and cruel, as if orphaned beasts were complaining to these two men on the box-seat: "Do you think that we want to kill your horses? But we are famished! Waa-ow! Waa-ow!"

A wave of horror ran down Pandre's spine. And that same horror must have communicated itself to his horses, conveyed to them along the reins. Because their hides began to quiver, and a moaning came from their distended nostrils. Pandre felt that there was not a moment to lose. He tugged at the reins with his left hand, holding the iron wedge tight in his right, and he whistled sharply through his lips, and in that way roused the horses out of their stupor.

The horses immediately felt the hand of a man and a protector, and all three of them, as if they had talked it over, suddenly pulled the coach, and neighing, with their ears flat, galloped off like the wind, straight at the wolves.

Sender came round as if from the dead, and started shouting: "Atu! Atu!" The word is a kind of charm against wolves. Pandre caught up the cry, and standing up on the box-seat, lunged out with his iron wedge, and cried again: "Atu! Atu! Devil take you!"

The sudden shouting and the galloping of the horses and the coach coming straight at them, forced the wolves back, and the sledge ran past them. But they soon realized that their supper with the tasty horse-sweat was giving them the slip, and they all three took up the pursuit. The she-wolf on one side, and the two young wolves on the other.

The she-wolf was stronger and more determined, so she got ahead of the horses, and sprang at them. Another minute, and it seemed that they would trample her down. But she twisted herself out of the way like a snake, almost from under the hooves and tried to hurl herself at the throat of Djirka, the mare.

Sender felt everything spinning round. It all got mixed up in his mind, the howling of the wolves, the terrified neighing of the horses, the creaking of the coach, the beating of the hooves. He suddenly saw near him two wolfish muzzles with bared fangs. "Hear, O Israel!" he muttered with dry lips. In the midst of it all he suddenly saw Pandre, his driver, standing up on the seat, aim his iron wedge and immediately after throw up both his arms, as if they were wings. He seemed to fly off. A terrible cry rose from under the sledge. And the horses galloped on, more wildly than before. Sender was afraid that they would break their necks, speeding the way they did. Shmendrik pulled to the left, and Djirka pulled every now and again to the right, and Shmarovoz in the middle, did not know what to do. Suddenly, everything went black. Sender could no longer see the white road. The coach jolted, and stopped still. Sender turned to look back.

He could hardly steady himself by holding on with both hands to the box-seat. Lumps of snow fell down on his head from the trees. So he sat there, wedged in as if under a roof. He looked round. The horses had run the coach right in between the pine trees, uphill, and had stopped dead. They were panting like punctured bagpipes. And there wasn't a wolf in sight. Nor was Pandre.

Sender began to grope along the box-seat, like a dazed man. A cold sweat broke out under his fleece-lined hat. "God Almighty! What is happening?"

Sender caught up the reins lying loose, that only a moment ago had been held in Pandre's strong hands. Now they were hanging down from the box, dragging in the snow. He pulled this way and that way, but the coach would not budge. The horses had wedged it between the trees and they were up to their necks in a mound of snow. And not a sign of Pandre.

Sender faced round, and with a prayer in his voice, as if he were in synagogue on the solemn days of intercession, he cried: "Noah! Noah!" An echo answered from the forest, mocking him out of the darkness, "No-ah!"

"God have mercy!" Sender mumbled, his lips gone dead. "They have devoured him! I spoke in an evil hour; talked about wolves, so the wolves came."

The steam rose from the horses' hides. Djirka's mouth, which was wedged between two trunks, dribbled thick froth. She turned one eye upon her master, rolling the white appealingly, like a hard-boiled egg: "Please, Sender, I'm feeling the cold! Wrap me up!"

But Sender had other things to think about now. With bitterness in his heart he thought of the encounter with the bear, about which he had told Pandre. And of how his father's horses had carried his coach into a narrow path in the forest. That, too, had come to pass. Here is your path, he thought to himself. And you'll have to spend the night here.

"Noah! Noah!" he called desperately into the night.

"No-ah!" the echo mimicked him, softening his rough voice as if to say: "That's the way to shout, not like you do, coarse fellow that you are!"

But immediately after the echo, Sender heard a faint voice far off in the distance: "S-e-end-er!"

A thrill of joy passed through Sender's every limb. "That's Noah! He's alive!"

Slowly, lumberingly, Sender climbed down somehow with all his fur coats from the sledge, left his horses to look after themselves, and ran down the road, shouting as he ran, with every ounce of his strength:

"Noah! Noah!"

"Se-ender!" he heard Pandre's voice clearly now, coming from the forest.

"Eh? What's that?" Sender said to himself, listening intently. He could have sworn that there was a note of triumph in Pandre's voice. Not at all like a man who has been devoured by wolves.

Early next morning the whole town was astir. In the market-place, outside the coachmen's guild, there lay on the muddy snow a great, grey beast, with its yellow belly up. The fangs were bared and bloodstained. The paws were clenched and stiff, and the bushy tail was spread out. Through the mutilated head was stuck a heavy iron wedge, showing how Pandre had killed it. Besides, there's no point in taking chances with wolves. How was one to know that it wasn't going to get up suddenly? So there was the heavy iron wedge to keep it down.

Noah Pandre himself, the hero of the day, was not in sight. He stayed modestly in the coachmen's guild, at the bar, having drinks with his fellow-drivers. His place was taken by Sender Pardon, who stood, with his whip under his arm, in the midst of the crowd and told, slowly and deliberately, what had happened to them during the night in the Kopust forest, and what a terribly strong and brave fellow his driver, Noah Pandre, was. Who could have believed it! Flying along with the coach, keeping a firm hand on the maddened horses, he had settled the hash of the wolves as well. With one hand, while he was standing up, he had lunged out at the she-wolf with his iron wedge, and had pinned her to the ground. It was true that the force of the blow had carried him off his feet, so that he flew off the coach. And where do you think he landed? With his head right on the wolf's belly! What do you think of that! If it had been anyone else, she would have finished him off with her claws. But Pandre jumped up like lightning, and kicked her in the belly with his boots. He smashed her ribs! The younger wolves turned tail and fled.

"When we found each other again in the forest after an hour's shouting, he came up to me, this same Pandre, all flushed and excited, with his iron wedge slung over his shoulder; and on the point of it, hanging down behind him was the she-wolf herself, so that he looked like Zalman, the fisherman, walking about with a lot of fish strung up in a row, dangling down his back. She was still moving her paws when I found them, and her blood was still running down on to Pandre's fur. When the horses smelt the blood of the dead wolf, they wanted to rush off again with the coach. We had a job to get the three horses out into the road again, and then we threw the dead wolf at their feet. Here you are! Look for yourselves! She's dead! Shmendrik lifted up his hoof and brought it down on her head. What do you think of that?" Sender finished up his tale. "If he gets a dead wolf, even a young colt, like Shmendrik, can play the hero!"

Uncle Shama, the furrier, bought the skin. And when Pandre got his few roubles for it, he stood a drink to all the coachmen in the guild, and won their hearts. From that moment he was one of themselves. They held him in respect. And Jewish servant girls gazed after him through the windows in every street.

But the schoolboys were even more proud of him than the coachmen and the servant girls. They had always looked up to Pandre, because of his strength, even in the days when he was a butcher's boy. They always thought of him as another Samson, who would one day rise up and deliver all the Jews of Shklov. Here was the proof! He was Samson himself. And the wolf was the lion that Samson had met in the path, and rent. And the honey that Samson took from the carcass of the lion, when he went off to the Philistine woman at Timnath? Of course, the honey was the cart-grease which was always on Pandre's hands. Queer honey! Blackish brown! And hard to wash off. But you don't ask any questions when you deal with a Samson!

ELIJAH THE PROPHET

by IRVING FINEMAN

A SATURDAY NIGHT, JUST AFTER EVENING PRAYERS. HIGH IN THE
clear and frosty sky hangs a young crescent moon. In the street of
the synagogue, white with snow, the Jews stand in groups with
moonlight on their bearded faces and say over and over, "Peace
be to you!" "Peace be to you!" "And to you peace!" "David, King
of Israel, David, the Jewish King lives and flourishes!" "May it
be a good omen for us and for all Israel!" "Amen!" "Amen!"
One little man fervently pours out his spirit in a louder voice, his
eyes brightly fixed on the moon. With three little leaps in the
air he cries, "Just as I spring toward you and cannot reach you,
so shall our enemies vainly try to touch us with malice and
evil;" and another, standing by, hastily adds, "And may I have
no more toothaches." It is the benediction of the moon. At the
end they wish each other a good week and a good month; the
groups of long black-clad figures dissolve in the moonlit street,
they move off in pairs, crunching the snow under foot, stroking
their beards and talking with little white plumes rising from
their lips on the frosty air.

On the way home I ask my father if the moon hears what
one says to it. "God hears," answers my father.

"But why do they say those things to the moon—about King
David? And why does one say, as to a stranger, 'Peace be to you,'
though these are all Jews of our own town. And why. . . ."

"Now," says my father, "we are going home to havdallah, to
celebrate the departure of the Sabbath. Later, when Reb Shmuel
comes, everything will be explained to you."

On the mantelpiece stood the oil lamp with its shining
round-bellied chimney, then a novelty in our town. In the hanging

candelabrum the three half-penny candles burned with a sub-
dued and dreamy remembrance of passing holiness in their tiny
flames. The table was still covered with the white Sabbath cover,
but one corner of the cloth had been pushed aside and the bare
brown wood with its substantial week-day air looked as if it had
come back from a long and distant journey, bringing with it
those homely week-day gifts, of hope, of willing work and joyful
gain. On the uncovered corner stood a small carafe of brandy, a
silver beaker, a filigree silver spice box, and a plaited wax taper.

"A good week," said my father, "and a good month." And
my mother coming a step toward him with a candle in her hand
answered, "A bright week and a blessed month may we all have."
My father lit the lamp and remarked on the rare and beautiful
moon we had this time; not the tiniest bit of cloud in all the
heavens. "May it be just such a month, O Father in heaven!"

We were then six children at home; my oldest sister Dinah,
almost seventeen, was already betrothed. Then came Rachel,
Naomi and Deborah; then I and my little brother Benjamin,
six and three years old. We all stood about my father, watching
him prepare for the benediction.

When he filled the silver beaker with pungent brandy he
poured it more than brimful so that a little stream flowed down
over the side. That was for prosperity in the new week. The
lighted taper my mother gave to Rachel saying, "Hold it high,
Rachel, and you will get a tall bridegroom like Dinah's." The
six tiny lights from its six strands united in a broad yellow flame
that shone in Rachel's brown eyes. The silver spice box, six-sided
and mounted on a silver spindle, my mother herself held.

Raising the cup on one outstretched palm, my father, en-
circled by his family, faced the taper and the spice box and cried
out, "Behold! God is my salvation; him will I trust; I have no
fear . . .

"With the Jews of old was light and joy, gladness and honor.
So be it with us. The cup of salvation will I raise, and upon the
name Eternal will I call.

"Blessed art thou, O Eternal! our God, King of the universe,
Creator of the fruit of the vine." He sipped from the beaker and
set it down. He took the spice box from my mother's hand, and

opened its tiny silver door whence issued a strange mingling of
odors, like the breath of a far-away and mystic land. He held it
to his nostrils and said, "Blessed art thou, O Eternal! our God,
King of the universe, Creator of all manner of pleasant spices."
Then he raised his hands to the taper, with palms upward and
fingers slightly bent, and regarding his finger-tips as if examining
them by the light he said, "Blessed art thou, O Eternal! our God,
King of the universe, Creator of the radiance of fire.

"Blessed art thou, O Eternal! our God, King of the universe,
who distinguishes between the sacred and profane, between light
and darkness, between Israel and other nations, between the
Sabbath and the six days of labor . . ." His voice trailed off in a
faint, as if confidential murmur, and with that we knew the Sabbath was at an end, the new week begun.

We children used then to dip our fingers in the brandy
which had overflowed on to the table, and write out the names
of things for which we wished. Then my mother ignited them
with the taper and we watched our wishes go up in fiery words
which burned down with a blue flame leaving only faint traces of
moisture on the unvarnished wood.

But I was full of curiosity, impatient to learn the reasons
for this or that part of those rites which had so clearly an earnest
significance for my father. Why, I asked him, was the plaited taper
lit when so many lights burned in the house? And why did one
scrutinize the fingerprints when saying the blessing for fire? . . .
Then my father, pleased with my eagerness to learn, pointed out
with a gravity that made me feel my years that the taper was
plaited of six thin tapers representing the six days of the week
which, when they were consumed, gave off a radiance that was
the holy Sabbath, and this in turn gave light and renewed life to
the whole of the following week. If one lived honestly according
to God's commandments and did good deeds all of the week one
was rewarded with true holiness on the Sabbath, with a spiritual
joy in life, with freedom from week-day worry and barter, with
pleasure and peace. And of these the cup of wine and the fragrant
spices were the symbols. And lastly, since it is not permitted to
make any fire on the Sabbath, its end was signified by the lighting
of fire over which a blessing was said, and in the course of this

one availed oneself of the light, meanwhile praying God that the wherewithal for life in the week to come might be honestly earned with our own ten fingers and that we might not, because of misfortune, have to resort to the aid or the charity of others.

My sisters had taken off and folded the Sabbath tablecloth, and laid an oilcloth cover in its place. Naomi and Deborah brought the samovar, set it on the table and lighted it. The two older girls, Dinah and Rachel, went to empty the wooden slop bucket by the door, which got quite full and heavy on the Sabbath. They took hold of its ears and carried it out into the yard between them, my mother following with a lighted candle. All three wore thick woolen shawls over their heads so that only their white faces were visible. I stood in the doorway watching, shivering in the cold that came in from the moonlit yard. The sky rose like a dome of luminous silver in which the young moon hung high over the low black houses. Far away the shadowy edge of the heavens rested on the dark wall of the forest and there stars twinkled. In the middle of the yard the girls set down their burden and bent over ready to tip it up. The moon swam about in the water. My mother, shading her candle from the wind, called out three times, "Stand back! We are going to pour!" This was a warning to those spirits still fleeing back after the Sabbath lest one get wet and do some mischief in anger. After the third time the girls up-ended the bucket and the water poured out in a curving silver cascade.

My mother told how one black Saturday night big Samson, the porter, having been sent with a lamb to the slaughterer, was taking a short cut through a back yard when he came upon two women emptying their bucket. At the third cry, "Stand back! We are going to pour!" he answered from the darkness, "Pour, I am standing by." The women fled in terror and he went on enjoying his joke. But when he returned with the carcass on his shoulder he found the place in an uproar; the rabbi had been called and the women were imploring him to do something to lay the restless spirit. Then Samson confessed.

My father meanwhile set about arranging his goods for Sunday's business, since shops were permitted to sell for an hour or two to the farmers who came on their way home from church.

Ours was not really a shop, but in a barnlike wing connected with the kitchen my father kept the grains in which he traded. There besides were salt and sugar, oil, cement, clay and other things for the convenience of the farmers and the servants from the princely estates roundabout who came to buy his grain, for he was well known in the countryside. A reserve stock was kept in a store-house in the yard.

My father bade me put on my coat and come with him to the store-house to hold the lantern while he chopped up huge cakes of salt, and hauled down bags of sugar. It was at the beginning of the seven weeks of Lent, in which the peasants ate no meat or fat and used much oil for frying. In the storehouse we had a fifty-gallon barrel of oil, out of which my father tapped a five-gallon cask to take into the house for sale on the morrow.

It was freezing cold. In the storehouse I stood shivering with the lantern in my hand, turning it so that long shafts of light and shadow circled like the spokes of a gigantic wheel over heaped-up boxes, barrels and bags, while the oil ran thick and yellow in a solid twisted stream from the spigot of the large barrel into the funnel of the small one. We loaded a sled with the various things and my father dragged them across the frozen yard to the house, where everything was arranged in its proper place. The little cask of oil, full to its top bunghole, which was covered with the down-turned funnel, was set on a stand with a copper basin under the spigot to catch the drippings. Nearby, in the middle of the store, stood the pot-bellied iron stove. This too was a novelty in our district, and on the morrow the peasants would come stomping in from church, still smelling of the barn and the dung-heap, to cluster round its radiant warmth. Already a wood fire crackled inside it and shone through its isinglass window.

All this work done, we washed, and sat round the kitchen table whose oilcloth cover glistened in the lamp light. The brass samovar, shining warmly, bubbled and steamed. Pickled herrings and the remains of a large twisted loaf were served out, and we began the little weekly feast of melava malka, the farewell to the Queen—which is the Sabbath; a custom dating back to King David. For it is told in midrash that when advanced in years David prayed God to disclose to him the day of his death; but

God refused. Then David begged to be told on what day of the week he would die, and God answered it would be the seventh day. Then David kept himself so occupied with the holy study of Torah on the Sabbath that when his time came the Angel of Death could not approach to take him. And each Sabbath after sundown, when the King saw that he had been spared for another week of life, he sat down to a feast celebrating the departure of the Sabbath.

When we had eaten, my father sang an old song of thanksgiving; but at the last verse——

> "And this shall be a month of blessedness,
> A time such as our prophet promised us.
> Glad voices shall throughout our house be heard—
> The voice of joy, of song,
> The voices of the bridegroom and the bride . . ."

he broke off with a sigh and turned to my mother. "The voices of the bridegroom and the bride," he repeated. "You know, my love, I have been wondering if we shall ever come to that! It lies, I must say, like a burden on my head. In the mid-week of Passover the father of Dinah's betrothed will come about the dowry; and I haven't more than half of it. Then besides where are the expenses of the wedding itself? I should dislike very much to have to bargain with him, to try and tear a bit off the promised amount. It is such a good match; it would be a pity if it fell through. And we mustn't forget the others growing up. Rachel not yet fifteen (may no evil befall her) is already taller than our little bride. May the Lord find a way to help us."

My mother looked impatient. "But what sort of spirit is this with which to end the Sabbath and begin a new week! We are really not so badly off; and God will help. Don't worry. It is still eight weeks to Passover." She smiled indulgent of his fretfulness.

"I don't worry," my father hastened to say, "may I be preserved from all worry; but of marrying off daughters, it is said, one may speak even on the Sabbath." Then turning to us, "But let us call upon Elijah;" he began a loud chant:

> "Elijah the prophet!
> Elijah the Tishbite!

Elijah! Elijah! Elijah of Gilead!
Soon, very soon will he come,
Bringing Messiah, the Son of David.
Elijah, the man who saw twelve generations.
By his lordly presence and fine long beard,
By his broad leather belt he was known.
Elijah, Elijah!
Whose word filled the widow's jar with meal
And her cruse with oil.
He made the false gods laughable,
And the sinful to repent and cry;
    God is one God!
Elijah, Elijah! The man who rode up on fiery steeds,
And was destined never to know
The bitterness of death and burial.
Elijah, Elijah!
Happy is he who has seen your face in a dream.
Fortunate is he, and he shall have peace.
Elijah, Elijah! . . ."

It was so earnest, so fervent, that it seemed to me Elijah must surely be there in the house listening to my father.

My mother had gone into the store-room to get some sugar from the bin. Now she stood in the door looking at us with beaming but secretive eyes. "Come," she said to my father, "come, you will see something." My father rose and followed her into the store-room. We children, filled with curiosity, asked if we might come too. My mother said we might if we promised to look without asking questions. She led us to the cask of oil. The only light was the flickering of fire from the door of the stove; but we all saw how the oil had risen above the bung on top and was running down the side in a steady drip that was filling the copper basin underneath. My father stood still and put his finger to his lips as a sign to us of silence in the presence of a miracle. And with his hand on Dinah's head he murmured, "Father in heaven, —this is for the sake of the bridegroom and the bride."

He opened the spigot a bit to let the overflow run into the basin, my mother set a screen around the barrel, and we went back to the kitchen. We were admonished to tell no one how Elijah the prophet had blessed us with a gift of oil: it might disturb the miracle. Also we were not to keep count of how much we drew from the big barrel, and we were always to add oil to the little one before it ran dry: nor were we to keep track of the actual quantity sold from the cask; for it is said in the Gemara that a holy blessing can rest only on what is concealed from the eye. We sat about the kitchen table, and sang again, "Elijah the prophet, Elijah the Tishbite!" convinced that for us was happening the same miracle recounted in Kings of the widow of Zarephath whose cruse of oil did not run dry because of Elijah.

Reb Shmuel, my teacher, used to come Saturday night to collect his stipend. It was remarkable to see what the day of rest and a clean Sabbath shirt did for him. He was another man; and when he came in that night saying, "Good week! Good week!" he added, cheerily rubbing his frost-bitten hands, "There is something in the air of this house, the sweet odor of sanctity, as if Elijah the prophet himself had been here."

And my mother answered with a guileless face, "Yes, Reb Shmuel, on Saturday night Elijah is to be found in every Jewish house." She set some of her good things before him and he ate with gusto. Then my father asked him to be so good as to answer some of my questions.

"As to the benediction of the moon," said Reb Shmuel, "You must know that we Jews reckon our months by the new moon; because in many ways we resemble the moon: Like the moon the Jew has been the enlightening star in dark places before the bright sun of civilization had yet risen." Reb Shmuel was taking the opportunity to impress my parents. "Like the moon the Jew tries ever to destroy darkness; and, like the moon, after the Jew has waned and seemingly died out of existence he is born again waxing great and shining anew in the world. And this will continue until the prophecy of Isaiah will have come to pass; 'then the earth shall be full of the knowledge of the Lord as the waters cover the sea.' Then the moon will shine equally with the sun, and the Jew will be acclaimed for the great service he has performed in the world of men.

"And now," continued Reb Shmuel, "why one says 'David King of Israel lives and flourishes,' and 'Peace be to you!' as to a stranger; that is because in the olden days when we Jews were still in the land of Israel, it was the custom of the Sanhedrin to proclaim the beginning of the month only after two witnesses came and declared they had seen the new moon. And when clouds obscured the sky over Jerusalem, they had naturally to rely on the reports of men who came in from places within the days' journey. But there were then, as now, sects which hated our religion and did their best to undermine it and disturb the Jews. When the moon was not visible in Jerusalem they would send in false witnesses to declare that they had seen the new moon not in the proper time, in order to confound the Sanhedrin. For this reason a system of passwords was invented: secret words agreed on by the Sanhedrin were made known only to the rabbis in distant places, who gave them over to their appointed messengers sent to report the new moon, in Jerusalem. Once the sign was, 'David King of Israel lives and flourishes!' and when the true witnesses appeared before the Sanhedrin and pronounced this password they were greeted with 'Peace be to you! A good omen shall this be to us and to all Israel, Amen.' And so today at the blessing of the moon we repeat these words as a remembrance of those ancient days of glory in Israel." With that Reb Shmuel, having fortified himself the while with several drinks of my father's best brandy, took his pay and departed.

Then my father brought out the sack into which the proceeds of Friday's market had been hastily gathered at the moment when, the eve of the Sabbath impending, Berrel, the sexton, came down the street crying, "To the synagogue! To the synagogue!" and my father pushed the last bargaining peasant from his store, barred the door, washed, and arrayed himself in his Sabbath coat of broadcloth. Now he poured the coins and papers out in a heap on the center of the table. There were usually some hundred roubles or so, and each child was given a certain coin to collect, little Benjamin the groschens, I the twos, Deborah the threes, Naomi the sixes and so on. And earnestly we labored, each one sorting out his own stacks of coin; with my mother watchful to smooth out the little squabbles that rose when one over-zealous worker encroached on another's field. At the end my father counted the stacks, reckoned the roubles and distributed amongst us the more weather-beaten coppers and the odd coins left over above the last rouble. We felt ourselves veritable partners in his struggle to provide for the household.

The next day we began selling oil from the cask with the full conviction that the blessing of Elijah still rested upon it. My father held strictly to his resolution not to keep track of how much came out of it; he kept replenishing it from the barrel in the storehouse so that the little barrel was constantly almost full, and more than once it began to overflow of its own accord. The cold spell held all through Lent. We had a prosperous trade until Easter not only in oil but in all our goods; and when the father of Dinah's betrothed came during the Passover week, Dinah's dowry was ready, as well as what was needed for the wedding. And what is more, Dinah's prospective father-in-law brought with him a friend from his town who had a son, reported to be a splendid young man, and my second sister Rachel finding favor in the father's sight, a second betrothal was arranged.

Naturally a feast was spread to celebrate all this good fortune, and at grace after the meal when he came to the words, "May the Allmerciful send unto us Elijah, the prophet of blessed memory, and may he proclaim the good tidings of salvation and solace," my father, greatly exalted in spirit and with gratitude in his eyes, cried, "Blessed is the people who have such a prophet as our Elijah and fortunate indeed is the Jew to whom he reveals himself." Just then my father was called into the store; a farmer, a stranger to him, a tall spare man with a thick leather belt around his middle, stood there asking for salt. And pointing to the barrel the man said, "It is after Lent and oil is no longer being bought; why then do you still keep your barrel standing there?" After the stranger had gone my father saw that the cask was empty. When he told us about it my mother said it was surely Elijah himself; the leather girdle proved it. He had come to end his blessed mission.

For many years the empty oil cask remained there in the store for a memento, and often my father recounted the miracle of Elijah the prophet.

THE DUTY TO LIVE

by SHOLEM ASCH

ON THE WAY FROM SHOCHLIN TO GOMBYN IN THE OLD POLAND, BE-
tween the thick woods and the dark pools that are to be found on
both sides of the road, there marched two high-booted Germans
driving a long line of children with their whips as though they
were driving a flock of geese. The children cried, and some of
them were bleating "Mama," like lambs bleating out a long
Maaa. Others were no longer calling "Mama"; they trudged along,
sobbing. The Germans paid no attention to their weeping, but
when a child unintentionally—or perhaps intentionally—got
separated from the flock, or when a child tried to sit down on
a stone by the edge of the road, or instinctively looked for protection toward the tall dark pine trees whose shimmering arms
reached out from the woods as though inviting the children to
hide among them, then a burning stroke of the long leather whip
would flash over the child's head and cut his skin, while a brutal
white-haired hunting dog would sink its teeth into the child's leg.
Sometimes the child ceased to feel the sharp teeth of the hound.
It simply remained lying on the road. And then the German
guard would whip the dog away from the dead body. But when
the children still had some life left in them, they would limp
back screaming into the ranks.

After a time the crying of the children diminished. The calls
of "Mama" became softer and at last were lost. The children were
weary after their long march in the heat of the day. They were
hungry and thirsty, and their little eyes were sticky with sleepi-
ness. Their little feet became raw under their cotton stockings
and blistered from the stony road. They wanted only to lie down,
even here on the road, even if the whip screamed over their

heads. But an unknown fear—the fear of death in which the instinct to live is rooted—gave the children strength to bear the hardships of the endless day. The instinct to live, which is ingrown in every living being, in every germ of matter, was stronger than their desire to drop and rest. Therefore, the older children carried the younger. They helped those who crawled and those who fell behind. And they struggled on under the lash of the two whips that the high-booted German guards cracked over their heads.

The flock of children was gathered together from the Jewish population of the town of Shochlin. There the Germans had dragged them out of Jewish homes, sought them out in their hiding places, torn them from the arms of mothers, and even snatched them out of cradles. In order to get the parents to send along the children's clothing, the Germans had declared they were taking the children for a summer vacation in the country, "where they would get better nourishment." The mothers knew that their children were being dragged away to be slaughtered or to be burned, to the same fate that had befallen the children of other towns—of Lovitz and of Kutno. Still, out of the need to cling to a last straw of hope, they forced themselves not to disbelieve in the Germans completely, and they dressed their children in their holiday clothes, put their best coats on them, and packed up their last bit of food for them. They gave their children their toys to carry along—for what use would the toys be without the children? The mothers fainted, falling like flies in the doorways. Then they would recover and run after the children, with their eyes bulging and their hair wild, looking half insane. They would run after them until they were out of the city. They were not allowed to go farther.

The fathers had long since gone, carried off by the Germans, to slave labor or to death. And now the mothers stood, held back by the bayonets against their breasts, as they watched the Germans driving away their children. And they screamed after them, "Channeleh, take care of Shlomoleh!" "Mosheleh, guard Rocheleh, as the eyes in your head!" until the children were lost to sight, covered in a cloud of dust that rose after them. Thus they were marched away into the woods. Some of the mothers went mad. Others cursed God for having permitted this to come to pass. And after that, some went and tied stones around their necks and threw themselves into the river.

Among the grief-mad mothers who watched the Germans driving off their children on the road to Gombyn, from which they would be led to the river Vistula and never more to be seen, was Zelda, the pushcart woman. Her menfolk—her husband and her grown son—had been taken off in the first wave, just after the Germans had come into the town. And now all she had left had been taken. Her twelve-year-old girl Iteleh and two-year-old Shlomoleh, the son of her old age, were in the flock being driven away by the Germans. Zelda did not tear her hair, nor did she curse. She did not scream like the others when she saw the Germans driving away the children. She only shouted into the group of children, "Iteleh, Iteleh, do you hear me?"

"Yes, Mother." She recognized her daughter's voice amongst the children's cries.

"Do you remember what I told you?"

"Yes, Mama."

"Then do it."

"I'll do it," she heard her daughter's voice.

Then Zelda drew her head scarf over her marriage wig down to her eyes. And so she went back into the town.

Iteleh trudged along in the group, carrying her two-year-old brother Shlomoleh. This was not too difficult for her. She had been used to carrying children in her arms from the time she was five years old. When her mother would get up in the morning and go to the market to buy goods, she would leave the household in Iteleh's hands. At first Iteleh had raised her brother Moshe Aaron. She had raised him with a bottle and a nipple. But Moshe Aaron had died young. He had caught the whooping cough; the poor thing had suffered in her arms for two nights and then died. At the same time her mother had been pregnant with this little brother, Shlomo. And so Iteleh soon had Shlomo on her hands. When her mother had weaned him, she gave the baby over to Iteleh, and Iteleh raised him with a bottle and a nipple until the Germans came.

Now she carried him on one arm, while on the other arm

she carried the little pack that her mother had given her. In the pack there was a bit of bread and a little honey. There was Shlomoleh's bottle of water mixed with a little milk that the mother had obtained—God only knows how—and there was a rubber nipple.

For though little Shlomoleh was already two years old and could speak a few words—even though he had already reached the stage of asking "why?" "why?" "why?"—he nevertheless had the infantile habit of not being able to go to sleep without his bottle or at least a nipple in his mouth. It is true that the mothers of the poor nurse their children longer at their breasts than do mothers of the rich. As though to give their children a memory of childhood pleasure to carry along into the wearisome struggles that lie before them in life, the mothers protract the nursing of their children. This becomes a kind of instinctive compensation for all the lacks and hardship that the child of poverty has to endure in his infancy.

And now as Iteleh marched along, with the weight of the child on her frail arms, she kept in mind the bottle that was in her little sack. She walked carefully so that it would not spill.

Her mother had given her one instruction, just before she had been taken away from the house, one thing she must always remember, must keep in mind every moment. And as she walked among the children and looked into the dark shadowy woods that stood on both sides of the road and kept growing darker as the evening approached, even now she thought of her mother's injunction.

For when the Germans had surrounded the town and began to break into the homes and to take away the children, Zelda had not lost her senses. She had neither screamed nor shouted; she had not torn her hair like the others. She had simply called her daughter Iteleh out of her hiding place in the cold cellar.

"Iteleh," she had said to her daughter, "they will find you there. They will take you away, you and your little brother, just as they take the other Jewish children. Now listen to me. Listen to me with all your mind. You're grown up already. You understand things. You know what the Germans do with Jewish children."

"Yes, Mother, I know." Iteleh nodded her head, scarcely moving her lips.

"Iteleh, do you know what duty means?"

"Yes, Mother, Father taught it to me. It is our duty to repeat Modeh Ani, the holy prayer."

"Yes, to repeat Modeh Ani, and to go to the synagogue on the Day of Atonement and on New Year's Day, to listen to the blowing of the ram's horn, to light the Sabbath candles, to honor your father and mother, all this God told us to do. And all that God tells us to do is good and becomes a duty. Now, do you know what God tells us to do today? Today, God tells the Jews that they must live. To do everything, to overturn worlds, but only to remain alive. Do you understand me, Iteleh? You and your brother are being led to your death. They are slaughtering Jewish children. They are killing all the Jews."

"Yes, Mama," Iteleh nodded her head.

"Do whatever you can. Everything and anything is permitted —only to save your life. There are no other duties. There is no more Sabbath; there are no more holidays; there is no more blessing of the candles. Only one duty remains—to stay alive. God wants the Jews to survive. Iteleh, I am putting your brother into your hands. He is the only male left to us. Preserve his life; be a mother to him."

And the words "preserve his life; be a mother to him" now rang in Iteleh's ears. Ceaselessly, they demanded that she do something. That she do something now, even here, to save her brother's life. She kept looking about, seeking a hole, a shadow, a little house in the woods, a stream, any place where one might hide. But she was sensible enough not to risk a false step. She knew very well that a single false step might cost her and her brother their lives, and therefore she was careful that all might not be lost.

The Germans had two dogs, one on each side. If a child strayed from the road, the hound immediately rushed after it, barking. And yet Iteleh knew she had to manage something here in the woods before they came to the station by the river Vistula. The woods were still in the neighborhood of her town. They belonged to the owner of the manor of Korovitz. Behind the woods there were scattered cottages. She knew a few of the peasants who lived in these cottages, for she had helped her mother carry her bolts of cloth to sell among the peasants. There was one named Kaminsky in whose place her father used to spend the night when he had to stop over in the village. In another little cottage there lived the woman Yadwiga, who used to leave her children in her mother's house when she came to town for the fair. And she knew one or two other peasants from whom her father used to buy animal skins. And at the edge of the wood on the other side there were the large ponds of Korovitz, where fish were caught. The Jews of the town had always bought their catch from the fishermen, carrying it into the town to be sold for the Sabbath. Perhaps there she would be able to find a corner where she could hide overnight. And then tomorrow she would see what to do. She would go and knock on the doors of the peasants.

A little farther beyond the woods on the way to Shochlin, there stood the big church of the "Black Sisters." That was the Jewish name for the nuns of the Sacred Heart, who were always dressed in black. The nuns often came riding into town with their own horse and wagon, and they bought supplies in the Jewish stores. Sometimes they would buy cloth at her mother's stall—linen and woolens and cloth from Lodz. People said that the nuns were good to Jewish children. They took them into the church and hid them. It was also safer among the nuns, because the Germans were hesitant about forcing their way into a church. But it was said that they converted Jewish children. She would not let them convert her little brother. No, not in any circumstances. No, she would not permit it. She would not even go into the cloister. It would be better to hide in the woods or to try to crawl under a haystack. Then she could try to approach a peasant. Somehow she would know what to do. If she could only get into the woods! She must get away in the woods before they reached the open road to Gombyn.

And thus Iteleh marched on, carrying her little brother and carefully holding the sack as well as the few bits of clothing that her mother had put under her arm. She kept on making plans, scarcely noticing that the woods were thinning out and that the fading reddish rays of the evening sun could now be seen between the sparse trees.

"Oh, Mother! We're coming to the end of the woods!" Iteleh cried out to herself in fright as she suddenly noticed that there were fewer trees. She glanced at her little brother. He had fallen asleep in her arms with his finger in his mouth and the murmur "Mama, Mama" trembling on his lips. For he had not ceased calling out the word, together with all the other children, the entire length of the way. "It's a good thing Shlomoleh has fallen asleep," Iteleh thought, "now it must happen before we come to the last trees. Now—now—but how can I do it, while the two hounds are on the watch?"

She could feel their sniffling wet nostrils behind her; she could hear their breathing. "But it must be done, it must be done! God, God, make it happen!"

And as she was saying this to herself, a convoy of wagons filled with German soldiers approached from the opposite direction. The wagons raised so much dust on the dry country road that everything was covered in a cloud of sand and filth. The two Germans hurriedly drove the children to a side of the road, using their whips freely. They drove them into the ditches so as to make room for the convoy. The dogs ran furiously along the entire length of the convoy, barking violently and keeping the children in line. And in this Iteleh saw a sign from God. It was God's will that the Jews should survive.

"Children! Follow me into the woods!" she shouted, running pellmell, with all her remaining strength, into the forest. The children ran after her. She heard the dogs barking behind her; she heard the Germans shouting; she heard revolver shots; she did not turn around. She ran back the way they had come, so as to reach the thicker woods. And to avoid leaving a trace behind herself, she was careful not to drop anything. With one arm she pressed the awakened terrified infant to her breast. With the other hand she clutched her little sack. She zigzagged, ran from tree to tree, hid in the heavy shadows of the trees, until she came into a thick cluster of brambles. The brambles stuck into her bare feet, but she felt no pain. She hid among the bushes, sitting down for a moment to catch her breath. She kept one hand over the baby's mouth so that he might not give her away with his crying, which had now begun in full force. With the other hand she got out the little bottle of water and milk that her mother had given her. And she forced the bottle into the baby's mouth to quiet him. The child sought and found aid and comfort in the nourishment. He nuzzled his face into his sister's breast while he clutched the bottle with both his hands, sighing from time to time. He found peace as he suckled.

As soon as the child became quiet, Iteleh crawled out on all fours from under the bush. It seemed to her that she was too close to the road. She could hear the dogs howling as they rooted around the trees, rounding up the fleeing children. Once when it seemed to her that she heard the shouting of the Germans directly behind her, she crawled out on all fours and looked around to make sure that no one was on her trail. Then she took the child in her arms and the sack along with him and started running with all her strength toward the pond. The night was coming down into the woods, weaving its darkness from tree to tree, and shielding her beneath its curtain. But when she emerged from among the trees, at the edge of the pond, she saw the full moon shining in the sky. It was a night late in September when the reddish moon glitters like a great open eye that sees everything. Nothing is hidden from it. Iteleh became terrified of the naked emptiness in which she found herself. The pond lay open and broad, guarded by the surrounding trees, and the moon hung above, its full shining light uncovering everything. She was afraid to remain by the pond. It seemed to her that the moonlight pointed her out and gave away her hiding place. And it still seemed to her that she heard barking and the cries of the children.

Iteleh turned back into the forest and sought a dry bit of ground where she might rest. But scarcely had she sat down when her fright brought her to her feet again. She still seemed to hear the Germans coming with their hounds. She started deeper into the woods. Her knees now began to buckle beneath her. Her bare feet stumbled over roots. The child became heavier and heavier on her arms. Frightened and weary, she began to shiver with anxiety. Her arms fell asleep. Her feet seemed to be broken.

She wanted to sit down and rest, but, if she rested a moment, it seemed to her that the Germans were coming and so she would start up and walk and walk and walk.

At last she saw a light shining between the trees. She was at first frightened by it, and yet it gave her hope. She slipped between the trees, coming closer to the light, until she saw that it came from a peasant's hut. With a beating heart she crept to the fence, but as she felt for the lock she was frightened by the barking of a dog in the yard. She hid behind the fence and waited. The dog would not be quiet. He barked and barked. Finally the door of the hut was opened. She saw someone coming out of the house. The light inside was extinguished. A shadow approached the fence.

"You'd better go away from here. The Germans were here looking for Jewish children. They've surrounded the whole woods with bloodhounds."

"Please have pity. Let me in. I'll hide in the stable. God will reward you."

"What's that on your arm?"

"A baby. My little brother."

"The child will give you away. He will start crying and be the death of all of us. Go away from here. The Germans are on the trail."

"Please, sir, help us." Iteleh stretched out her hand.

"Without the child I might have let you in. But as it is, you'd better get away. They'll be on your trail."

"But where can I go?"

"Drop the child and save yourself. Run to the nunnery. It's a mile and a half from here on the other side of the pond. They'll let you in."

"Drop the child? He's my little brother. My mother trusted him to me."

"Run away, little Jew. Here's a piece of bread."

And the shadow threw a piece of bread over the fence to her.

Iteleh left the bread lying there and went off with the baby. She stumbled farther among the trees, running from one tree to another. Her legs grew weaker and weaker. Her arms were breaking under Shlomoleh's weight. But the worst thing was that the child had been awakened by the dog's barking. He began to wail at the top of his voice, "Mama, Mama."

She sat down under the nearest tree and tried to quiet the child. The bottle had fallen out of his hands while she was running. She searched in her bag and found a nipple, which she tried to press into his mouth. The child sucked for a moment and then spat out the rubber nipple and began to howl.

Iteleh tried to cover his mouth with her hand, but this made him cry even louder. Iteleh's hair began to stand on end. Sweating with fear she couldn't think what to do. "Now I am lost," she thought, remembering the peasant's words. "The child will give you away." It seemed to her that the Germans were lying in wait with their hounds behind the trees, and the baby's crying was leading them to her. She could already hear the running of the dogs and their howling before the wind. She had to quiet the child. She had to. "Shlomo, I beg you, be quiet, be quiet. Shlomoleh," she kept repeating, although she knew her words could have no effect. Desperately, she tried to think of some way to hush the baby. Suddenly a thought came to her. She remembered what her mother used to do at times when Shlomoleh began to cry and would not let himself be stilled by any means whatever. Neither the bottle nor the nipple was of any use. Iteleh tore open her coat and took out her round little breast which had just begun to take form, like an unripe apple on a tree. And she put her breast into the baby's mouth.

"There, now, be still!" she repeated her mother's words. And the child was quiet. Surprised by the warmth that engulfed his little face, he nuzzled against her warm body and found the motherly comfort that quiets and relaxes all wailing children.

With his face nuzzled in her breast, the baby fell into a restful sleep. But not only the child was quieted. Without knowing how it came about, Iteleh herself felt a merciful peace settling down upon her. All at once the fearful thoughts and horrible imaginings were gone. No one was pursuing her any more. She no longer heard the dogs barking, and there was no more baby's crying. All around her everything was still, except for the hooting of the owls, invisible among the branches and leaves. They might have been creatures out of a strange world of fantasy. Yet even the hooting of the owls faded to a cradle song, and Iteleh slipped down until her head rested on the dewy grass. And still holding her little brother warm and close against her breast she fell asleep, untroubled and unafraid.

When she awoke from sleep, her fright returned. It was already full day. And here she sat with her little brother by the road. She had not noticed that she had instinctively followed the direction that the peasant had showed her during the night, around the pond toward Gombyn. All the danger of her position came over her. At any moment the Germans might pass by—a soldier, or a policeman—any German might come along and catch her. She had not the heart to return into the woods. It seemed to her that the woods was a trap surrounded by Germans, while their bloodhounds sneaked amongst the trees.

On the road before her was the nunnery. She had often seen it when riding with her mother to the market at Gombyn. The church was surrounded by a wall, and two large crosses stood out among the green trees on the other side of the high wall. She knew that if she took only a few steps out of the woods toward the road, she would see the crosses. And she tried to decide whether to go toward the crosses or back into the woods.

In the woods were the Germans and their bloodhounds, while under the crosses she might find safety for herself and her brother. But with the crosses came conversion. She would have to give up being a Jew and become a Gentile. And her little brother also would no longer be a Jew. No, she would not go toward the crosses, she would rather go into the woods. She would never become a Christian, and little Shlomo would never become a Christian. . . . But in the woods there were the German beasts. . . .

And in the meantime she sat there, with Shlomoleh in her arms. He was still asleep. His little face looked worn out, and he groaned with babyish groans. The Germans would take Shlomoleh and throw him into a fire. They would roast him in their ovens. But the nuns would take him and convert him. What would be better to do? And then she remembered what her mother had told her.

"Iteleh, you must live, and see that Shlomoleh lives. Your greatest duty is to live."

Yes, she wanted to live, and she wanted her little brother to live. They had to live. So many Jewish children were dying. Everyone was killing them. And someone had to remain alive. But she would not become converted. She would somehow manage that they should remain Jews. They would never, never become Christians. She remembered the prayer that her mother had taught her to say every morning. Oh, Lord, our Gracious King, bless and protect my little head. And as though these words had been a last straw to grasp, she kept repeating over and over, *"Oh, Lord, our Gracious King, bless and protect my little head."* She would repeat this prayer every morning; she would repeat it with her brother. She would teach him this prayer, and through it, they would remain Jews. She looked at Shlomoleh. The child's eyes were now wide open, and he stared around him in wonder.

"Shlomoleh, Shlomoleh, repeat after me." The child stared at her and made a face as though he were about to cry.

"No, don't cry, just repeat after me, say Lord, Lord, Lord."

"Lord," the child repeated.

"Bless, Bless, Bless, say Bless."

"Bliss, blass, bliss, bee."

"Bless."

"Bless."

Armed with the prayer that the child had repeated after her, she got up from the ground, took Shlomoleh in her arms, and left the woods, for the road. She could see the two crosses from afar surmounting the tall green wall that ringed the church. The crosses no longer stabbed her eyes as before.

When Iteleh with her little brother in her arms was brought before the Sister Superior, Iteleh made her declaration.

"Our mama told us to save our lives. She said that it was a command of God that we should live. We escaped into the woods and we came here because people told us that you were kind and that you hid Jewish children so as to save their lives. But we are afraid of you because of one thing."

The aged gray Sister Superior studied the little mother with the child in her hands, saw her bare little feet torn and battered by brambles and stones, her hair undone and tumbling wildly over her frail back. She saw how the child stood quivering like a little green branch. The pallid maidenly face of the Sister Superior contracted into innumerable wrinkles. Her clear blue eyes became clouded under the gaze of the little mother who had fought her way through the woods and saved her baby brother from the German beasts. She took Iteleh by the hand, drew her closer to herself, and asked with tenderness, "Why are you afraid of us?"

"We are afraid that you might make us become Catholics. People say that you force Jewish children to become Catholics."

"We don't force anyone to become Catholics," the Sister Superior said. "Whoever doesn't want to, doesn't have to become a Catholic. But why are you afraid to become a Catholic? All of us here are Catholics, and you see we don't murder little children, instead, we save them."

"It's because we are Jews and want to remain Jews."

"That is very good of you, my child. You can remain a Jew, and your little brother can remain a Jew. No one will force you to do anything."

"Yes!" Iteleh cried out joyously. "And we can stay here with you? And you won't hand us over to the Germans, even if we remain Jews?"

"You can stay here with us. No one will betray you to the Germans, and you can remain Jews."

"Oh, that is wonderful!" the little girl cried happily. "But I would like to ask the Lady Superior one more thing."

"What is it, my child?"

"Every morning and every evening, I and my brother want to say the Jewish prayer. May we?"

"Of course you may, my child. It will please us for you and your brother to say the Jewish prayer every day. Does he know the Jewish ritual, young as he is?"

"I am teaching him. I began to teach him this morning in the woods when I was hiding from the Germans. He says every word after me. Would the Lady Superior like to hear how he says it? Shlomoleh, repeat after me, Lord."

"Lord."

"Bless."

"Bliss, Belis, Bess."

"Bless, Bless, Bless."

"Ba, Ba, Bess."

"Did you hear him, Lady? Did you hear how he says it after me? Oh, how happy my mother will be!"

"Come, Sister! Come here and behold the power of ancient Israel. Their God throws their children at the feet of the dogs, and from the very jaws of the beast their children praise the God of Israel," said the aged Sister Superior.

And the cloud over her clear blue eyes was dissolved in tears.

SHYLOCK, THE ORIGINAL ANCESTOR

by ALEXANDER GRANACH

WHEN THE WAR WAS OVER, I BOUGHT A TICKET IN VIENNA AND returned to Berlin.

In the station I threw my arms around a pillar and kissed it, holding it in a long embrace. A fat Berlin beer-wagon driver looked down at me over his horses and said: "Man, it's girls you should kiss, not stones!"

"I promised myself that in 1914 when I went off!"

"Well, then, you must keep your word," he growled amiably.

In 1914! It was 1919 now!

I was soon in my old Café des Westens, found friends, went around auditioning, and soon had an offer from the Schauspielhaus in Munich. Hermine Koerner, the great actress, was organizing a company of her own there, and engaged me as a leading character actor. We opened with Schiller's *Intrigue and Love*—I played Wurm. Earned eight hundred marks a month. On our first bi-monthly payday, I had four hundred marks in my pocket, four hundred marks earned on the stage!

I went to a restaurant and bought myself caviar and champagne, just as I had read in novels. Now I had a room of my own again, new friends, and every two weeks I played a different classic or modern leading part.

One day there was great excitement at the theater: the parts for *The Merchant of Venice* were assigned, and I was given Shylock! Four older character actors were fighting for the role. But I had Shylock in my contract, I had him under my belt, I had him in my heart, I had him at my fingertips! I trembled with excitement, I could not sleep. A dream, a longing of years, was to be fulfilled. The day of the first rehearsal came. I was shaking inside like an earthquake.

The director was a young, flaxen-haired, stupid man, a Herr Nebeltau from Bremen, the son of a rich father. He financed the company and was business manager. Before rehearsal he took me aside and said to me, word for word: "You understand, with this play we want to take a poke at the Jews!"

"Why?" said I, angrily.

"Why not?" and he looked at me suspiciously. "You aren't by any chance——"

"Yes, yes, yes, I am a Jew," I shouted in his face, so that he stumbled back and almost fell into the orchestra pit.

The four old character actors who were trying to get the part, one with a monocle, one in white gloves, suddenly woke up and laughed provocatively, delighted at the explosion. I hurried away, and the first rehearsal blew up.

Hermine Koerner, the artistic director of the theater, had me come to the office at once, and Herr Nebeltau was also present. She was a great actress; I honored her, and my heart always thumped when I was in her presence. She knew it, and now she said, smiling and full of charm:

"Well, it was wonderful, the way you thought that up— of course you only made a scene for the sake of the superstition."

"Of course, Hermine," Herr Nebeltau bore her out.

"I do just the same thing before an important part, don't I, Otto?"

"Just exactly," Herr Nebeltau agreed, and they both laughed.

"When I like a part very much, there has to be a row at the first reading rehearsal and the first dress rehearsal."

"Yes, yes, reading and dress rehearsal," confirmed Herr Nebeltau, laughing, and I laughed too without knowing what for.

"And of course what Herr Nebeltau said earlier today was said only as a joke, wasn't it, Otto?" she now asked the flaxen-blond directly.

"Yes, of course, Hermine," he agreed.

"How could you think such a thing of him!" she turned to me. "He is far too intelligent for that. So, children, shake hands, and tomorrow rehearsals will begin again. And I shall be present myself!"

And so it came to pass.

At seventeen, I lay on the ground and became acquainted with Shylock in Karl Emil Franzos' novel. I lay there and wept over the injustice that was meted out to him. I was determined to put my whole life into gaining the ability one day to fling that injustice into the world's face. I was now twenty-nine, and again I lay on the ground, with the fulfillment of my task just before me.

For twelve years I had been absorbed in Shylock, and still I could not wholly understand him. I compared him with my father, I compared him with my beloved Hebrew teacher, but could find no great resemblance.

The play itself I had often read and seen, and it was always two plays: First, there is that gay, careless circle around the rich Antonio, whose heavily laden ships sail all the seas. There is the wild Gratiano, who chatters gaily and goes on audacious adventures. There is the elegant coxcomb Bassanio, who is set on marrying the richest girl in Belmont and borrows money any and everywhere to put up a fine front and swindle a marriage. There is the singing and dancing Lorenzo, who steals the girl along with her father's money. To the strains of sensuous and seductive music and under and eternally blue sky, there are balls and masquerades, all at the expense of Antonio, the rich man, the melancholic youth who is so glad to be amused by these boon companions. Later Portia's world comes in too, but it is still the same.

On the other side lives the Jew Shylock, in a narrow ghetto alley. He is a foreigner in the city, there are laws against him, he wears a yellow patch, the symbol that he has not the same rights before the law as others. He lives alone, with no festivities, no society, no great expenditure; he lives his creed, his business, and for his little, delicate daughter Jessica, whom he loves more than all else, because she is all that is left to him of his beloved wife, his Lea. He loved her very much, his Lea, for since her death many, many years have passed and he has not married again. He lives with the memory of his beloved and the thought of his child.

Then, one day, the other world appears at his house, the world that despises him, spits on him, persecutes him. They come and want to borrow money from him! Instead of saying yes or no, he says both. He is pleased that his enemies need him, and he proposes a weighty, jesting contract: that, if his enemy, who only last Wednesday spat in his face, who had spurned him from his doorstep like a strange dog—that if this enemy cannot pay back the specified sum he wishes to borrow at the specified time and the specified place—a jest—he will then have the right to cut a pound of flesh from his body, in whatever spot he may please! An utterly insane bond! An audacious, impudent bond! A grotesque bond, which can only be taken as a devilish joke.

So at least we understand the poet's intention. The play is a comedy, a merry game of love. The fun is in the fact that at first obstacles are put in the lovers' way—first they are threatened with great perils, first their life is made bitter and sour, in order that they may overcome the perils, the obstacles, by the sweat of their brows, so that, at the end, the song of love may sound even more sweetly, even more intimately, even more happily. Then everything becomes like a midsummer night's dream! Then everything is as you like it!

Therefore, in this gay game, in this comedy of Venice, a black figure is needed, to frighten the lovers, to threaten them, so that the denouement in Act V, beginning with the poetic "The moon shines bright: in such a night as this . . ." may be resolved in the giving of the rings and a happy going to bed! Yes, Shylock was only a black obstacle, planned by the poet, a black fool, a wicked fellow, to be made a goat of at last.

But, but, but . . . and here the world stops in wonder! If that was the plan, how does it happen that Shylock's defense becomes an accusation?

"If you prick us, do we not bleed? if you tickle us, do we not laugh? if you poison us, do we not die? and if you wrong us, shall we not revenge?"

The answer must be a perfectly simple one. God and Shakespeare did not create beings of paper, they gave them flesh and blood. Even if the poet did not know Shylock and did not like him, the justice of his genius took the part of his black obstacle and, out of its prodigal and endless wealth, gave Shylock human greatness and spiritual strength and a great loneliness—things that turn Antonio's gay, singing, sponging, money-borrowing, girl-stealing, marriage-contriving circle into petty idlers and sneak thieves.

I now know how Shylock, by the whim of his creator, entered that circle. But I must also know what happens to him after the curtain goes down, when the play is over. What does our Shylock do when, swindled out of his rights by the trick of not shedding one drop of blood, when, a broken man, he leaves the courtroom, when he whispers his last words; "Send the deed after me, and I will sign it"? Will he sign it? Can he? Perhaps he can sign away all his property. But can a Shylock also sign a deed by which he renounces his faith and accepts another? Would my father have done that? Would my Hebrew teacher have done that? No, no, no! They would rather have died a thousand deaths. Neither a believer nor a man of character can change his faith, his point of view. When a man is sixty years old, like Shylock, his view of life does not change. It remains the same until his life comes to an end. To that he clings, to that he holds, or he dies of emptiness and loneliness. Never can a Shylock change his faith, the man who sobbed out in the courtroom:

> *"Nay, take my life and all; pardon not that:*
> *You take my house when you do take the prop*

That doth sustain my house; you take my life
When you do take the means whereby I live."

For that, he is first mocked, and then the "noble" people divide
his property among them before his face; and for that "mercy" he
is to forsake his old faith besides, his only traditional and moral
strength. No, no, no! *That* my Shylock will not do! A man of his
intelligence and strength fights to the last breath with every
weapon—especially with craft. I see it like this:

When Shylock, a broken man, leaves the unjust court of
justice, it is already evening. He walks slowly at first. But when
he sees that no one is following him, he hurries, rouses his friend
Tubal and the other fellow believers who live with him in the
ghetto, and complains to them of the new danger which threatens
them. For, though they live in the ghetto, though they were persecuted and oppressed, the All-Highest was not touched. And since
Shylock owned no houses and land, only easily transportable
goods, money and jewels, he puts it all in his bag and charters a
boat that same night and runs away, and he makes a successful
escape.

Then one day he arrives in Holland, in the rich city of Am-
sterdam, which is already full of refugees from the Spanish In-
quisition. There he decides to wander still farther, into the East!
He wanders for a long time and travels through the lands of the
Hungarians and the Rumanians, the Poles and the Russians. He
wanders through those countries until one day in East Galicia, in
the Ukraine, he finds a wise old wonder rabbi, the wisest in the
country round. To him he goes to bemoan his sorrow and to ask
for counsel.

The lean old man is tall and ancient, he has a long yellow-
white beard, and bushy brown shadow his knowing eyes. And his
fame has spread far over the earth, and it is unbecoming to talk
of his age—the thought of the years he has lived makes men
tremble.

He sits there in his high ancestral chair, like an incarnation
of human dignity. He smiles at our Shylock hospitably. The old
man's goodness and understanding trust unlock Shylock's tongue
and his heart, and he begins to tell his story. He tells of his

father's house, his youth, his schooling, his wanderings, until he had met Lea. How he loved her, his Lea, and how she had given him Jessica and died, and how he had lived with her memory, embodied in his daughter, and how then his own child had betrayed him, and how in his old age he had to take up the wanderer's staff again. He tells everything: he talks for many days and many nights, until his heart grows warm and light. Meanwhile the sage encourages him with questions and hears him attentively.

And when he has finished speaking, friendly comprehension and trust smile at him from the old man's face, and the old man speaks softly and warmly: "It is well, my son, that you have come to us, for after such sorry experiences a man must change his habitation, because that changes his luck as well. It is well that you have come to us. Here we live among a friendly people, and here we may not only engage in business, we can follow trades too and till the soil. And that does us good, and we live according to our old laws. Had you asked a wise man in the lands from which you have come he would likewise have advised you to come here, for it is written 'Meshaneh makom, meshaneh mazal—Change your dwelling and you change your fortune.' Now," the old man sighs with a smile, "the Eternal be praised—you are here!"

And Shylock feels wholly eased, but he is embarrassed by gratitude, and the old man goes on: "And now I wish to give you some advice: that is, you must marry again, you are still vigorous, and I know that the Lord will bless you with children."

"Rabbi," Shylock almost stutters, "I wanted to ask your counsel about that very thing."

"Yes, my son, take a daughter of the people, a healthy girl, a tradesman's child," and both men now smile understandingly, and Shylock rises and takes his leave respectfully, a thankful and redeemed man.

Then Shylock married a daughter of a carpenter there in the Ukraine, and the Lord made his marriage fruitful and blessed it with children. The children grew up on that black and juicy earth and tilled it, and they sowed and harvested and saw the four seasons come and go and heard no more that light, seductive music under the eternally blue skies of the South. Their Hebrew melodies were mingled with the long-drawn-out, melancholy songs of the Slavs, and they grew up, the children, broad-shouldered, industrious, and inquisitive. . . .

Then many, many generations went by, and one or another of their descendants would often feel a longing for the West again and would set forth on his wanderings. There they chose new professions; many became actors and found their original ancestor, Shylock, in Shakespeare again. They had heard the story of his sorrows from their parents and grandparents and recognized him in their kindred hearts. And they acted that ancestor tragically and one-sidedly, fortified by the genius of Shakespeare, which had given a black, negative figure so much strength, so much life, such a sense of justice, such human dignity. They acted him against the evil society that spits on him and persecutes him, and for the positive qualities that his Creator had bestowed on him.

And thus he must be acted, until all artificial distinctions fall from us, and man recognizes his brother in his fellow man and loves him, his neighbor, as himself, and does not do to him what he would not want done to himself.

With these feelings I played the part I had longed to play, Shylock, and my tremulous dream was fulfilled. It was not yet as I wanted it to be—but with the years it will grow better.

A NAP, PRAYERS, AND STRAWBERRIES

by MENDELE MOCHER SEFORIM

HARDLY DOES PRECIOUS SUMMER INVADE THE WORLD AND THE radiant sun make human beings feel that they have been born anew and rejoice at God's wonderful creation, when the saddest season begins for the really pious Jew. There are numerous days of fasting and days of mourning throughout the summer right up to the late autumn, harbinger of mud and cold winds. However, for me, Mendele the Bookseller, summer is a busy season. I work hard and do a brisk trade, supplying the children of Israel in the villages and hamlets with whatever they need for their fasting and lamentations, that is to say, prayer books of every size and quality. In a word, pious Jews spend the summer praying, fasting and mourning while I pursue my business. But I am running on.

It was the early morning of a day of fasting, the seventeenth day of the month of Tammuz when Nebuchadnezzar captured ancient Jerusalem. I was seated on the box of my wagon, whip in hand, decked out in my prayershawl and phylacteries, as is the custom of a pious Jew. My eyes were closed; for I did not want to look at the joyous world while reciting my prayers. However, nature, as they call it, just to spite me was at that moment a vision of beauty and I felt as if some mysterious power was driving me to open my eyes and express my admiration.

A fierce struggle was going on inside of me. Two powers were waging war and my mind was the battlefield. The good spirit was urging, "For shame, you must not!" But the evil spirit, the tempter, kept whispering in my ear, "Listen to me. Don't be a fool. Enjoy the world!"

The tempter, by use of force, pried open one of my eyes which I was trying to keep closed. Dear me, what a beautiful panorama I beheld. Fields overflowing with blooming buckwheat, white as driven snow, intermingled with golden rows of wheat and tall dark green sunflowers. An exquisite green valley nestled between forests of nut trees; below, a crystal-clear stream runs its course, sparkling with the rays of the sun like molten gold. In the distant pastures the sheep and the cows are no more than white, black and speckled points. "Take care!" the good spirit cautioned and pricked my morals with a quotation from *The Sayings of the Fathers:* "A Jew must never interrupt his prayers. If he ever interrupts his prayers to exclaim, 'How beautiful is this tree or how lovely is that field!' he is guilty of a serious sin." But the tempter intensified his efforts to lead me astray. Under my nose he wafted the intoxicating smell of new-mown hay and the perfume of sweet flowers. A warm breeze caressed my face, played in my hair, and murmured in my ear, "Look, you silly Jew, enjoy the great beautiful world!" I struggled to resist the temptation. I prayed hard and at the same time invented insults against nature and her creatures. "After all, what are they?" I asked mentally. "Merely dead matter, dead leaves! Bodies without life or soul!" Then I concentrated on my morning prayers, swaying my body vigorously back and forth, to chase away evil thoughts. I finished a prayer with the words, "He who returns their souls to the dead bodies." But what was I saying? I was ashamed of the thoughts that flooded my brain. As though to excuse myself before the Creator, the Master of the Universe, I pretended that the insult was intended, not for His creatures, but for my own horse. Lashing him with my whip, I yelled, "Hurry up, you stiff."

But even that idea didn't help too much. I felt disturbed that on a day like this such thought should invade my mind against my will. Then I recalled that it was a fast-day, the day of commemoration of a great calamity that had befallen Israel. On the seventeenth of Tammuz, King Nebuchadnezzar of Babylon had captured Jerusalem and sacked it. The memory saddened me so I intoned the penetential prayers, the Selichoth, raising my voice to heaven and all the while choking with sobs.

Now when a Jew has said his prayers, and especially the Selichoth, he believes that he has fulfilled a great religious obligation; he feels quite contented like a child after a whipping. So I sat on my wagon-box, lighthearted and stroking my beard, as if saying: Father in Heaven, I have done my duty and now it is time for You to do something and show me Your mercy and justice. "Giddiyap," I said to the mare, mentally asking forgiveness for the epithet "stiff" I had just bestowed upon it. My Jonah gets down on its forelegs, touches the ground with its head and groans as though saying,

"My honored master, what about the feedbag?"

"Clever," I thought, "very, very clever," and I gave it the sign to get up on its legs.

My mind was again caught up in bitter memories. I imagined that I saw that python Nebuchadnezzar with his hordes; was watching a fierce battle; saw his beasts plundering, burning, destroying the Temple and the homes. I saw Jews burdened with packs, valiant and courageous, shouting for help and—fleeing for their lives. I, too, grabbed a pack and tried to run; and suddenly I was on the ground, lying stretched out like a casualty.

What had happened? During my prayers—may God forgive me—I must have fallen asleep. I looked at my wagon-box. It was in the middle of a mud puddle which, in the lingo of wagoners, is called an "inkpot." The rear wheels were entangled with the axle of another wagon, and my poor mare, with one leg outside the shaft, was standing there in distress, wrapped in the reins, panting like a goose. From the other side of a strange wagon, I heard someone cursing in Yiddish, punctuated by coughing and gasping. Angry, I ran over there. I found the wagoner lying under his wagon, entangled in his prayershawl and phylacteries, his whip knotted with the straps of the phylacteries, trying to extricate himself. I yell, "What the devil!" He yells, "What do you mean?" I curse him and his father; he curses me and my father, throwing one in for my mother too. I shout, "How dare you fall asleep during prayers?" He replies, "How dare you snore during prayers?" I whip his mare. He whips mine. The two mares get up on their forelegs while their masters are on the ready for a battle, like two fighting-cocks, and are about to pull each other by the earlocks. But we stand still, waiting for each other to make the first move.

That must have been a sight for the gods: two heroes arrayed in prayershawls and phylacteries, boiling with anger, eager to slap each other's ears in an open field, as if it had been in the synagogue. As we stood still for a moment, raising our eyes for the first time to measure the enemy, both of us made the same motion. We jumped aside at the same time, shouting, "Well, well, Alter!"— "Well, well, Mendele!"

Alter Yaknahaz is a stumpy, fat fellow. His face sprouts soiled, yellow hair—plenty for beard, earlocks, moustache, both for himself and a couple of others. From this ocean of hair emerges, like an island, a flat, fleshy nose which generally suffers from a chronic cold. However, a change comes about during the Passover season when the weather thaws and the ice in the river breaks up. Then the owner of the nose begins to work on it with both hands. He gives a concert, blowing upon his instrument like a master. The nose emits sounds like those that shrill from a ram's-horn and resound throughout the town of Parasiteville, bringing the people to a halt on the streets and causing them to stand agape. On such occasions snuff is offered generously to the nose, and the owner is showered with congratulations. There must be some reason for the noses in our little towns to strike up their concerts at that season; but to go into the reasons would make too long a digression.

Old Alter, an acquaintance of mine of long-standing, is a bookseller from Parasiteville. He is a selfish fellow, not too bright, not too talkative, always sulking as though angry with the world; but at heart he's not a bad man. We greeted each other warmly, and then, as is our habit, began to make conversation in a round-about way.

"Where are you going?" I asked Alter.

"And where may you be going?" replies Alter, answering my question with another question.

"I'm going straight to the devil."

"And where is Mendele going?" he asked.

"Where I usually go at this season of the year."

"I understand." said Alter. "You are going to Foolstown, where I'm going too." There was an undertone of annoyance in his remark, as though I were planning to do him out of business.

"And where have you come from?"

"From where do you think?" answered Alter. "From your fine fair of Yarmelinetz, a plague on it."

While Alter was cussing out the fair, we were suddenly confronted with a gang of wagoners, cursing and wanting to know why the road was blocked. Seeing us in our prayershawls and phylacteries, they became more insulting. "Look at the gentlemen!" they shouted coarsely. "Hurry up, Yids, make way for your betters!"

We quickly moved our wagons. A couple of the roughs had the decency to help us and we soon had the wagons out of the inkpot. If they hadn't put their shoulders to the wheels, we might still be there. We shouted and gave advice and went through the motions of pushing, but those fellows had the brawn and got the job done. As soon as the road was clear, they laughed at us and mocked us—two Jews dressed like priests and serving their Creator even with whips in our hands. A few of them, holding up their coattails like a sow's ear, blurted out epithets too coarse to repeat.

Alter was unconcerned about their behavior or their insults. "Piffle," he said, shrugging his shoulders. "Nobody gives a hoot about them. Why should we be ashamed?" But I felt otherwise. Their mockery pierced my heart. "Why, Master of the Universe?" I cried, "why?" and I recited an impassioned prayer to God, pleading with Him to have mercy upon His people, and to remember His faithful followers, including me, Mendel the son of Gnendel.

Without further ado we climbed into our wagons and moved on. I was driving in front, and Alter directly behind me. His wagon had a box-cover made of tattered mats, it ran on four rickety wheels of different sizes and held together with pieces of rope, which groaned and screeched as they turned. This excuse for a wagon was pulled by an ancient, tall, lean mare.

Well, I had just finished my afternoon prayers when another struggle began with the tempter. He was urging me on, whispering in my ear, "Come, Mendele, have a slug of brandy, give yourself a pickup." But I fought back, "No, no, no, it is the seventeenth of Tammuz, a day of fasting. How dare I drink?"

"Tut, tut," he answered, "What have you got to do with Nebuchadnezzar? Jews have suffered greater catastrophes since then and they're still alive. Don't be a fool. You are tired and weak. Forget the fasting." I passed my hand over my face as if to drive off a nuisance of a fly, and meanwhile I stole a glance under the box where I kept a suitcase with a bottle of brandy, honey-cakes, Spanish onions and other delicacies. My mouth was watering, my stomach was groaning. "For pity's sake," it was pleading, "a drop of brandy!"

I turned my head away in order to drive off these evil thoughts. The sky was deep blue, without a trace of a cloud. The sun was hot, and there wasn't the feeblest breeze. The cornstalks in the fields and the trees in the forest stood motionless, as though chained. The cows were lying in the pastures, chewing the cud or bellowing because of the heat. By the side of a shrivelled-up willow tree, split in half by lightning stood some horses, with their

heads jostling each other so as to find a bit of shade, their tails
wagging to chase off the flies. A magpie is perched high up on the
twig of a tall tree, looking from the distance as though covered by
a prayershawl with a blue border; it appears to be stretching up
and bending low, making movements as if engaged in prayer. It
is hot, it is still, it is truly beautiful. God's creatures are enjoying
a rest!

But the scorching sun brought beads of perspiration to my
face, and I was sweating like a bear. You can imagine how I
longed for some refreshment. My throat was parched; I was burning for a drink. Again the tempter began his whisperings, tempting me by reciting all the most appetizing Jewish dishes.

I was ravenous, while the tempter continued to read the
menu. Then, all of a sudden,—don't ask me how it happened—I
found the suitcase in my hand.

"Go on, you fool," the tempter was talking out of my own
mouth, "just enough to give you strength." My hand moved as
though on its own, I opened the suitcase, seized the bottle and
looked around like a thief afraid of being caught in the act. Suddenly my eye met that of my horse. He had turned his head towards me and he had a look of shame and disappointment. He
seemed to say, "Master, take a look at me! My hind leg is swollen,
patched up in rags. One eye is running and my throat is parched.
May lightning hit me if I remember the taste of oats! Yet here I
am dragging this wagon without refusing my duty or throwing off
my yoke." The bottle fell from my hand into the suitcase.
Ashamed, I returned it to its place. Sighing from the bottom of
my heart, I exclaimed. "It is the horse from whom man should
take an example and learn virtue."

So I felt a better man, almost refreshed and strong. I now
began to think of business, happily humming a melody from
the book of *Lamentations*. Suddenly, I saw a peasant woman
standing before me, extremely attractive, offering to sell me a
pot full of fresh strawberries—my favorite fruit. Someone else
in my place would have imagined that she was not a real woman,
but the devil in disguise, coming to tempt me again. But I was
not such a fool. I took a close look at her. There was no question
about it, she was a real woman. She begged me to buy the straw-

berries for a trifling sum. As she held the pot up to my nose, the fragrance penetrated my nostrils. My mouth watered. I felt a dizziness come over me.

I feared that I would not be able to resist the temptation any longer. What should I do? Only something desperate would save me. I girded my loins, flew into a rage and jumped down from my wagon. It is strange that I did not break my neck for I was like a man running away from a fire. I shouted, "Alter, Alter." My idea was to have Alter near me and have him act as guardian of my piety.

Alter was lying under the hood of his wagon, face downwards; his shirt was open, his face red as a beet, sweat running down it. I felt sorry for him.

"What's up, eh?" he asked in a voice that sounded like that of a cow. "What's wrong?"

I looked about. The woman with the strawberries had apparently been scared to death and ran away. I had to make some excuse for waking Alter.

"What time do you think it is now?"

"What time?" says Alter, still only half-awake, "What time?" How should I know? Surely some time before the first stars will appear. Well, it can't be helped. My, it's hot!"

"A pleasant heat, eh?" I said, walking alongside of Alter's wagon. "You're perspiring, Alter. I think it's time to pasture our horses who are dragging their legs. A little farther on, where the wood runs toward the high road, I see a good place."

We reached the spot a few minutes later. There were beautiful meadows, a running stream and fine woods. We unharnessed our lions and let them pasture at will while we stretched ourselves under a tree.

THE SILVER CANDLESTICK

by ALBERTO GERCHUNOFF

THE ADOBE HUT LAY STEEPED IN LIGHT, THE PLACID LIGHT OF A clear autumn morning. The little window cut in the thick, cracked mud wall framed the Argentine pampas stretching far in the distance, far beyond the low knoll on which stood the yellowing stalks of giant thistles and a solitary tree, with scanty upraised branches. A little nearer still the rough-coated cow, a bit of rope around her neck, stood tenderly licking the back of her calf.

It was the Sabbath. The little Jewish settlement was wrapped in deep silence, only broken now and then by the voice of a woman as she softly hummed an old song.

When his wife came into the one room of the hut, Guedali had already put on the white tunic and, deep in his early prayers, hardly noted her presence. He signed to her, with tight closed lips and a backward movement of his head, not to interrupt him. The woman glanced about the room for the threshold and slipped out silently. Guedali heard, half consciously, that she said to the daughter outside the doorway, "I could not ask him; he had begun the prayers."

Guedali was devout. He was not considered to be among the best educated of the colony nor did he distinguish himself in the discussions at the synagogue about obscure points of the ancient books and their commentaries. He was of gentle spirit, with a low sad voice; in his large eyes, shaded by thick graying brows, there glowed a soft timid light like a lifeless flame.

His face turned toward the East, his tall thin body seemed longer in the tunic which fell in even folds to the floor. Suddenly, he felt the presence of someone at the window. Without stopping his chant, he slowly turned his head to see, thinking it might be the neighbor's son who had been away to Buenos Aires for military service and came back making fun of what he called old-fashioned religion. It was not the neighbor's son, but a stranger. He was reaching his hand for the candlestick—the silver candlestick, the family heirloom, the one thing in this rough hut of an immigrant colony that stood witness to their former position. Tall and gleaming, the polished cups of its seven curved arms reflected the light as if they still held the sacred candles. Guedali did not interrupt his prayers. Looking severely at the stranger, he interposed between the sacred words the warning,

"No, no, it is the Sabbath—it is the Sabbath."

He could say only so much without profaning his devotions. The stranger took the candlestick, and Guedali went on with the service, moving his shoulders to the chanted rhythm of the verses. Reciting the benedictions, he continued in a muffled tone until the last prayer was done. Drawing a deep breath, he raised his face, the light striking full on his rugged forehead and the long thin beard that had begun to grow gray.

He folded his tunic with minute care, laying it away in a box, and when his wife came in he announced quietly.

"The candlestick has been stolen."

He took a bit of white bread from the table and began to eat, as he always did after prayer. The woman gave a cry of indignation,

"And you, weren't you here—you dolt?"

Earnestly, as one who proved having done his whole duty, he replied,

"I reminded him it was the Sabbath."

THE CALF

by MORDECAI ZEEB FEIERBERG

IT WAS SUMMER, AND I WASN'T QUITE NINE YET.

The sun from its high dwelling-place gazed with fiery eyes into the dark heder. As if to embarrass our teacher it directed a mocking shaft of light to his soiled shirt and irritated him by entangling its bright beams in his pointed beard. Mischievously, it also focused its golden rays on the mud and filth of the gutter in the "Holiness Street," which was also the "Synagogue Street," the "Teachers' Street," the "Ritual Slaughterers' Street," and the marketplace.

With all the magic it could command the sun beckoned to us laughingly, "Silly boys, why do you sit there all locked up with that fool of a Rabbi?"

And indeed, how dear, how precious those sunbeams capering and skipping about so lovingly and charmingly outside the window! How lovely and gay out of doors! So nice to play there! How pretty the vapor rising from the gutter, and how gay the children romping there, rolling in the dirt, making mud pies and drying them in the sun! But teacher is hardhearted and cruel; he knows no rest. He sits and studies! Sits and repeats! Beads of perspiration drop on the Talmud. His shirt is soaked and sticks to his body; his hands are heavy, his head aches and his voice is hoarse; but teacher goes on, studies and repeats. . . .

But soon he, too, tires. Now he stops, reproaches us a little and warns us to go to synagogue to say the evening prayers. We stampede from the classroom into the street, and as we get outside we see a herd of cattle and other animals coming toward us. The dignified bulls stroll at the head of the procession, composed and full of self-importance, like rabbis and illustrious

townsmen on their way with "common folk" to some sacred celebration—a reception for a bridegroom, a circumcision ceremony,
or a funeral. After them come the cows and the calves, the goats
and kids, the pigs, and the ponies. The dust rises to the heavens.
We mingle with the procession—one rides a bull, and the other
a goat. The third throws dirt at the animals and scares them to
let them know that he is a "man," a member of the breed that
rules the whole wide world with its might and daring. And there
is our cow, walking alongside the herdsman who is carrying a
charming little calf on his shoulders.

I understood the "secret" immediately, for my mother had
told me more than once that our cow was "pregnant." I was therefore in seventh heaven, and gazed longingly at the herdsman who
was carrying the lovely calf straight to my father's house. I wanted
so to run after him, fall all over the calf and shower it with loving
kisses. But what could I do? What about the Rabbi? And the
evening prayers? And what would my mother say when she saw
her "big boy," who was already studying Talmud, wasting his
time so.

So, against my will, I had to go to the synagogue and pray.
As soon as services were over, I rushed home to welcome the calf.
When I got home my brothers and sisters greeted me with the
news of the birth of the calf. "If you could see, Hofni," they all
cried excitedly, "how lovely this calf is, and if you could only see
his high brow, his wide nostrils, his long tongue, and his full
red lips. If you could only see. . . ."

I couldn't wait for them to finish and ran breathlessly to the
barn. I knelt in front of the calf, felt all his limbs one after the
other, and then took him in my arms and carried him to the
kitchen to look at him by the candlelight. There I salted a few
pieces of bread and put them on his tongue. He ate them hungrily
and watched me with a look of appreciation. At that moment I
knew that the calf had taken a liking to me, and that he considered me worth associating with. I felt that he had chosen me
over the rest of the children, my brothers and sisters, and that his
adoring look would follow me, and me only, wherever I went.
I was overcome by a strong feeling of love mingled with pride

for this beautiful calf, and with all my heart vowed to love and cherish him, and to return him love for love.

"Well," my mother told my father when he got home in the evening, "we have a 'new blessed event.' The cow has given birth to a calf. We'll slaughter it next week and have roast for the Sabbath, the way you like it."

"Is that true, mama? Are you really going to kill this adorable calf?" I asked full of trepidation.

"You're still young, son! You're still young and foolish. If you spoke like that in front of other people they'd laugh at you."

When I went back to the kitchen to visit my precious, my darling calf, and saw his eyes looking at me as though begging for mercy, I began to cry. In an outpour of love I caressed him while my warm tears dropped on his neck. I kissed him and cried and cried.

That night, I recall, many thoughts went through my mind.

It was then that I first felt as if some chick had hatched in my brain and was pecking at it with its sharp beak. I could almost hear it saying, "Hofni! What did this calf come into the world for? To be slaughtered? Why should it be slaughtered? Why should this nice calf be killed? And if it did come into this world just to be slaughtered, why is it so pretty? It could have been born as a chunk of meat wrapped in some skin, and finish. Why does my mother want to kill it? What right has she to kill this pretty calf?"

That night I promised eighteen pennies to the charity fund of "Rabbi Meir, the Miracle Worker" if my mother changed her mind about the calf, and fell asleep.

In my dream I saw the calf bound, with the slaughterer standing near him holding a knife. He puts the knife to him. The calf writhes, the blood spurts. . . .

When I got up in the morning, I ran directly to the barn. To my great relief, I saw the beloved calf lying peacefully down, very much alive. His mother was licking his back with her tongue and curling his short hair in rows.

The next evening as I returned home I saw the cook talking with my mother—discussing, among other things, buying the calf's hide from her. I kept silent because my mother had already told me the day before that I was a fool. But I was in a turmoil and my heart thumped.

"Am I really a fool?" I asked myself. "But why? Who says that it is forbidden to pity this lovely calf? My mother? But she had told me time and time again that it is a mitzva to be kind to living creatures, and that it is wrong to be cruel to them! Not be cruel—and slaughter?! Be kind—and slaughter?! My mother said so! But who says she is right? But can my mother be wrong? Can mothers be mistaken? Oh God, my mother and the little calf are both in your hands. Why did you breathe life into the calf, and why did you give my mother the desire to kill him? Oh God, this calf, whom you have created with all his limbs and sinews, whom you have given the strength to live on this earth for many years—why should he be slaughtered? God, you certainly know which calf is going to be killed and which isn't. Then why did you create calves that are due to be killed, and why did you give them the desire to live and bring forth offspring on this earth? And if you have really created them to live, how is it that your wish is not kept by others? And what about my little brother who died eight days after he was born? My mother said at the time that before he was even formed in her, it was already written in the Heavenly Book that it would be so-and-so. Then why was he born a human being in all its glory? What were his legs for if he didn't walk on them? What were his hands for if he didn't use them? And his mouth? And his lips? And what would he have been if the wet-nurse hadn't strangled him? And where did the nurse sin if the 'Angel of Death' killed him? . . . Mama said the 'Angel of Death' had killed the boy, but if the nurse strangled him, why did the angel also have to kill? Is it possible that a person, even a child, dies without the 'Angel of Death'?"

"Mama, can anybody die without the 'Angel of Death'?"

"Are you crazy, Hofni?" mother exclaimed, ashamed, in front of the slaughterer, of my blunt question. "Why do you have to know that? Do you know the whole Talmud already that all that's left for you to know is how people die?"

Minute followed minute and day followed day. It was already the second day, the third, the fourth, and the fifth . . . The calf was to be slaughtered on the eighth day. What could I do?

Meanwhile the calf grew from day to day, pranced about on his long, spindly legs. Whenever he saw me he would run toward me, dancing and skipping while I—I greeted him with a silent sigh and wept and laughed at the same time.

The dread eighth day finally arrived.

The sun rose, higher and higher and now it was setting in the west. I saw the horrible moment approaching.

I knew that the calf would not be slaughtered. It couldn't possibly be slaughtered. It just couldn't . . . And yet my heart was beating fast. I knew that Heaven would come down to help him . . . The angels would come to his rescue . . . The knife would break, or his neck would turn to marble . . . Some miracle would have to occur. The calf was so lovely, and I had promised so much to the Rabbi Meir fund. I had kept on promising for hours and hours.

And yet, who knows. . . .

My eyes were full of tears. Thoughts rushed in and out of my mind. It was difficult to explain, even the Rabbi wouldn't be able to. No! I will not ask the Rabbi. He too, like my mother, will laugh at me and call me a fool.

And the calf was slain. . . .

THE PRODIGAL SON

by ISRAEL ZANGWILL

THE NEW YEAR DAWNED UPON THE LONDON GHETTO, HERALDED BY a month of special prayer and the long-sustained note of the ram's horn. It was in the midst of the Ten Days of Repentance which find their awful climax in the Day of Atonement that a strange letter for Hannah came to startle the breakfast table at Reb Shemuel's. Hannah read it with growing pallor and distress.

"What is the matter, my dear?" asked the Reb, anxiously.

"Oh, father," she cried, "read this! Bad news of Levi."

A spasm of pain contorted the old man's furrowed countenance.

"Don't mention his name!" he said harshly. "He is dead."

"He may be by now!" Hannah exclaimed agitatedly. "You were right, Esther. He did join a stock company, and now he is laid up with typhoid in the hospital in Stockbridge. One of his friends writes to tell us. He must have caught it in one of those unsanitary dressing-rooms we were reading about."

Esther trembled all over. The scene in the garret when the fatal telegram came announcing Benjamin's illness had never faded from her mind. She had an instant conviction that it was all over with poor Levi.

"My poor lamb!" cried the Rebbetzin, the coffee-cup dropping from her hand.

"Simcha," said Reb Shemuel sternly, "calm yourself; we have no son to lose. God has taken him from us. The Lord giveth and the Lord taketh. Blessed be His name."

Hannah rose. Her face was white and resolute. She moved towards the door.

"Where are you going?" inquired her father.

"I am going to my room to put on my hat and coat," replied Hannah quietly.

"Where are you going?" repeated Reb Shemuel.

"To Stockbridge. Mother, you and I must go at once."

The Reb sprang to his feet. His brow was dark; his eyes gleamed with anger and pain.

"Sit down and finish your breakfast," he said.

"How can I eat? Levi is dying," said Hannah, in low firm tones. "Will you come, mother, or must I go alone?"

The Rebbetzin began to wring her hands and weep. Esther stole gently to Hannah's side and pressed the poor girl's hand. "You and I will go," her clasp said.

"Hannah!" said Reb Shemuel. "What madness is this? Do

you think your mother will obey you rather than her husband?"

"Levi is dying. It is our duty to go to him." Hannah's face was rigid. But there was exaltation rather than defiance in the eyes.

"It is not the duty of women," said the father harshly. "I will go to Stockbridge. If he dies I will see that he is buried among his own people." He reseated himself at the table, pushing aside his scarcely touched meal, and began saying grace. Dominated by his will and by old habit, the three trembling women stood in reverential silence.

"The Lord will give strength to His people; the Lord will bless His people with peace," concluded the old man in unfaltering accents. He rose from the table and strode to the door, stern and erect. "You will remain here, Hannah, and you, Simcha," he said. In the passage his shoulders relaxed their stiffness so that the long snow-white beard drooped upon his breast. The women looked at one another.

"Mother," said Hannah, breaking the silence, "are you going to stay here while Levi is dying in a strange town?"

"Father wills it," she said, sobbing. "Levi is a sinner. Your father will not see him; he will not go to him until he is dead."

"Oh yes, surely he will," said Esther. "But be comforted. Levi is young and strong. Let us hope he will pull through."

"No, no!" moaned the mother. "He will die, and my husband will only read the psalms at his death-bed. He will not forgive him."

"Let *me* go. I will give him your messages," said Esther.

"No, no," interrupted Hannah. "You are not of the family. Why should you risk infection for our sakes?"

"Go, Hannah, but secretly," the Rebbetzin said to Hannah in a wailing whisper. "Tell Levi that I—oh, my poor child, my poor son!" Sobs overpowered her speech.

"No, mother," said Hannah quietly, "you and I shall go. I will tell father that we are accompanying him."

She left the room. The Reb was changing his coat when Hannah knocked on the door and called "Father."

"Do not speak to me, Hannah," he answered roughly. "It is useless." Then, as if repentant, he threw open the door and passed his great trembling hand over her hair. "You are a good daughter," he said tenderly. "Forget that you have had a brother."

"But how can I forget? Why should I forget? What has he done?"

"He has profaned God. He has lived like a heathen; now he dies like a heathen. His blasphemy was a byword in the congregation and has given me gray hair."

"Yes, father, I know," said Hannah more gently. "But he is not all to blame!"

"You mean that I am not guiltless; that I should have kept him at my side?" said the Reb, his voice faltering a little.

"No, father, not that! Levi could not always be a baby. He had to walk alone one day."

"Yes, and did I not teach him to walk alone? Did I not teach him the Law day and night?" he asked eagerly.

"Yes, but he is not all to blame," she repeated. "Your teaching did not reach his soul; he is of another generation; the air is different; he lived in conditions for which the Law does not provide."

"Hannah!" Reb Shemuel's accents became harsh and chiding again. "What are you saying? The Law of Moses is eternal; it will never be changed. Levi knew the divine commandments, but he followed the desire of his own heart and his own eyes. God has punished him; he will die, for it is ordained that whosoever is stubborn and disobedient shall surely be cut off from his people. But you, Hannah," he started caressing her hair again, "are a good daughter. You have nothing in common with Levi. Think of him as one who died in boyhood. O God! Why did You not take him then?" He turned away, stifling a sob.

"Father," she put her hand on his shoulder, "we will go with you to Stockbridge—I and mother."

He faced her again, stern and rigid.

"Stop your entreaties. I will go alone."

"No, we will all go."

"Hannah," he said, his voice tremulous with pain, "do you, too, disregard your father's wish?"

"Yes," she cried, and there was no answering tremor in her voice. "Now you know. Levi and I are brother and sister."

"You will go even though I forbid it?" he cried in acrid accents, still mingled in surprise.

"Yes: I wish I had taken the journey you would have forbidden ten years ago!"

"What journey? You are talking madness."

"I talk truth. You have forgotten David Brandon; I have not. Ten years ago I was ready to leave with him, to marry him, in defiance of the Law and you."

A new pallor spread over his face, already ashen. He trembled and almost fell backwards.

"But you did not?" he whispered hoarsely.

"I did not; but I don't know why," she said sullenly, "or you would not have seen me again. It may have been my respect for our religion, although you did not dream of what was in my mind. But your religion will not keep me from this trip."

The Reb had hidden his face in his hands. His lips were moving: was it in grateful prayer, in self-reproach, or merely in nervous trembling? Hannah never knew. Presently his arms dropped, great tears rolled down towards the white beard. When he spoke, his tones were hushed as with awe.

"This man—tell me, my daughter, do you love him still?"

She shrugged her shoulders with a gesture of despair.

"What does it matter? My life is but a shadow."

The Reb took her to his breast, though she remained stony to his touch, and laid his wet face against her burning cheeks.

"My poor Hannah! I thought God had sent you peace ten years ago; that He has rewarded you for obedience to His law."

She drew her face away from his.

"It was not His law; it was a miserable juggling with texts. You alone interpreted the law thus. No one knew of the affair."

He could not argue; the breast against which he held her was shaken by a tempest of grief, which swept away all except human remorse, human love.

"My daughter," he sobbed. "I have ruined your life!" After an agonized pause, he said, "Tell me, Hannah, is nothing I can do to atone to you?"

"Only one thing, father," she articulated chokingly, "forgive Levi."

There was a moment of solemn silence. Then the Reb said,
"Tell your mother to put on her things and take what she
needs for the journey. Perhaps we shall be away for days. Perhaps
God will hear my prayer, and he will yet be restored to us."

A new peace fell upon Hannah's soul. "My sacrifice was not
in vain, after all," she thought, with a throb of happiness that
was almost exultation.

But Levi never came back. The news of his death arrived on
the eve of Yom Kippur, in a letter to Esther who had been left
in charge of the house.

"He died quietly at the end," Hannah wrote, "happy in the
knowledge of father's forgiveness . . . He borrowed father's
phylacteries. When he had them on and the prayershawl round
him, he grew easier and began murmuring the death-bed prayers
with father . . . Your name was often on his lips. I was glad to
learn he thought so much of you. 'Be sure to give Esther my
love' he said almost with his last breath, 'and ask her to forgive
me.' He looks calm now. They have closed his eyes. The beard
he shocked father so by shaving off, sprouted scrubbily during
his illness. On the dead face it seems a mockery, like the prayershawl and phylacteries that have not been removed."

A phrase vibrated in Esther's ears: "If only the boys could
see me!"

ON A SEDER NIGHT

by HEINRICH HEINE

IN THE TOWN OF BACHARACH ON THE BANKS OF THE RHINE, RABBI
Abraham sat in his spacious room, surrounded by relatives, disciples and guests, to celebrate the Passover seder on the first night
of the great festival. The room was brilliantly illuminated. Over

the table was spread a gaily embroidered tablecloth whose golden fringes touched the floor; the large silver plate glittered with the traditionally arranged symbolic food as did the tall goblets filled to the brim with red wine and embossed with pictures of sacred themes. The men sat in their black mantles and black, broad-rimmed hats and wore white-linen ruffs around their necks; the women were attired in dresses of Lombardy silks and wore on their heads glittering gold and pearl ornaments. The silver Sabbath lamp brightened the happy faces of parents and children. On a high chair, leaning against purple velvet cushions reclined Rabbi Abraham, who read and chanted the Hebrew text of the Haggadah as the mixed assembly joined in or responded as the ceremony required. The Rabbi also wore the traditional mantle of sedate black, enhanced by a gold-embroidered, white-silk prayershawl. His nobly formed but somewhat severe features looked milder than usual, and his lips smiled out of a dark-brown beard as though they would like to relate something pleasant; his eyes shone with a mixed expression of happy remembrances and strange foreboding.

Beautiful Sarah, who sat on a high velvet cushion like her husband, wore, as the hostess, no jewelry: only white linen covered her slender figure and gentle features. Every now and then she glanced at her husband, but she followed the Haggadah which lay before her, an exquisite volume bound in gold and velvet— an heirloom with old wine spots on the parchment that had come down from her grandfather. It was illuminated with many bright hand-painted pictures which had delighted her as a child at the seder evenings and which portrayed many Biblical stories: Abraham smashing with a hammer his father Terach's idols; Moses slaying the Egyptian taskmaster, Pharaoh, on his throne in misery because of the plague of frogs; the Egyptians drowning in the Red Sea; the children of Israel standing open-mouthed at Mount Sinai; pious King David playing his harp; and finally, Jerusalem, with its towers and battlements glistening in the splendor of the sun.

The second cup of wine had been filled. The guests were becoming more cheerful. The Rabbi took a mazzah, gaily raised it up, and read from the Haggadah:

"Behold, this is the food which our ancestors ate in Egypt! Let everyone who is hungry come and enjoy it! Let everyone who is sad come and enjoy our Passover feast! This year we celebrate here, but next year in the land of Israel. This year we are still in bondage, but next year may we celebrate in freedom!"

At this moment the door opened and two tall pale men wrapped in broad capes entered.

"Peace be with you!" they said. "We are brethren on a journey and would like to join you at the seder."

"Peace be with you!" replied the Rabbi, warmly. "Please take seats near me."

The strangers sat down at the table and the Rabbi continued reading. While the others joined in the responses, the Rabbi from time to time murmured a word of affection to Sarah. Alluding to an old belief that on Passover the father of the family is regarded as a king, he whispered,

"May you be full of joy, my Queen!"

"But the prince is not here," she answered.

She meant that a son, as a passage in the Haggadah requires, must ask his father the meaning of the festival. The Rabbi did not answer. He pointed to a picture on the open page of the Haggadah, which showed three angels appearing before Abraham to announce that he would have a son by his wife Sarah. Stirred by feminine curiosity, Sarah is listening intently to these revelations behind the entrance of the tent. The intimate allusions brought a deep blush to the cheeks of the beautiful woman. She lowered her eyes and then looked gratefully at her husband who went on chanting the wonderful story of how Rabbi Joshua, Rabbi Eliezer, Rabbi Azaria, Rabbi Akiba and Rabbi Tarphon sat up all night at Benè Brak conversing about the Exodus from Egypt. They continued until their disciples came to tell them that it was daybreak and that morning prayers were already being recited in the synagogue.

As Sarah listened reverently to her husband's chanting, she saw his face become suddenly transformed. His cheeks and lips became deathly pale and his eyes looked like balls of ice. But after a fleeting instant his face returned to its usual serenity and cheer, his lips and cheeks became red again, and his eyes sparkled with joy; indeed, he appeared to be in the grip of a mood of reckless gaiety, a mood quite strange to his nature. Sarah shivered with fear, less from the passing despair that she had seen in her husband's face than from the frantic merriment that now possessed him. He comically shifted his hat from ear to ear, pulled his beard and curled it rakishly, and sang the text of the Haggadah like a tavern ditty. When he came to the passage enumerating the Ten Plagues, where the index-finger is usually dipped in the wine-goblet and drops of wine shaken off on the floor, he instead sprinkled the young girls near him with red wine. At first there was lamenting over spoiled dresses which was quickly followed by gay laughter. Sarah became more and more fearful at the convulsive merriment that gripped her husband. Oppressed by a strange fear, she stared at the guests drinking wine, nibbling sponge-cakes, gossiping, singing aloud—all happy and merry.

Then came the time to serve supper. They all arose from the table for the ceremonial washing of hands. Sarah brought in an enormous silver basin richly adorned with gold figures, which was given to each guest in turn. As she held it before the Rabbi, he gave her a meaningful look and quietly slipped out of the room. Sarah followed him. Outside, he grasped her hand and hurriedly led her through the dark lanes of Bacharach beyond the city gate to the highway that leads along the Rhine to Bingen.

It was one of those warm and starry spring nights which fill a person with awe. Lovely Sarah carried the silver basin in her right hand while the Rabbi held her left and she felt his hands were ice-cold and his body trembled. But she followed him silently. They stopped at a cliff which arches out over the bank of the Rhine.

The rabbi stood still, moved his lips without being able to utter a word, and after a while exclaimed,

"Do you see the Angel of Death? Down there he hovers over Bacharach. But we have escaped his sword, praise God!"

In a voice still trembling with terror, he told her that while he was happily reciting the Haggadah he happened to look under the table and saw at his feet the blood-stained corpse of a child.

"Then I knew," the Rabbi went on, "that the two guests were not of our people but were godless men who brought the dead child into our house in order to accuse us of a ritual murder and to instigate a massacre of our community. Had I betrayed what I discovered I should have brought destruction to all of us. God be thanked! Do not be afraid, dear Sarah. Our relations and friends will be safe; it was only my blood for which they thirsted. They will be satisfied now with my gold and silver.

"Come, we will go to another land, and leave this evil behind us. Come, the God of our fathers will not forsake us!"

THE DEAD CITRON

by SHOLEM ALEICHEM

WHENEVER YOU SEE THE NAME LEIBEL IN THIS STORY, IT REFERS TO me.

I am short and fat and soft as down. But if you look at my body closely, you'd find that I am not as chubby as I appear. I am really rather scrawny, but I wear thicklined trousers, thicklined underwear and a thicklined coat. My mother, you see, wants to keep me warm. She's afraid I might catch pneumonia, God forbid, so she wraps me in wool padding from head to foot. She thinks that it's alright to wrap a boy in wool but it's wrong to use wool for stuffing balls. However, I have my own ideas. I pulled the wool out of my coat and trousers and distributed it to all the boys until she caught me. She slapped me and pinched me and whacked me. But Leibel went on doing as he pleased—handing out wool to his pals.

My face is red, my cheeks are blue, and my nose is always running.

"What a nose!" shouts my mother. "If he had no nose, he'd be all right. He'd have nothing to freeze in the winter."

I often try to picture myself without a nose. If people had no noses, what would they look like?

But I was going to tell you the story of the dead citron and I have digressed. So I'd better get back to my story.

My father, Moshe-Yankel, has been a clerk in an insurance firm for many years. He is paid five and a half roubles a week. But he is expecting an increase. He says that if he gets more wages this year, please God, he will buy a citron. But my mother, Basse-Beila, thinks he is daydreaming. She says that the military barracks will crumble before father is given more pay.

One day, just before the New Year, Leibel overheard the following conversation between his father and mother.

"Even if the world turns upside down," he said, "I must have a citron this year!"

"The world will not turn upside down," she replied, "and you'll have no citron."

"That's what you say. Suppose I tell you, though, that I've already been promised something with which to buy a citron?"

"That belongs in a joke book. In the month named after the town of Kremenitz a miracle happened—a bear died in the forest. So what? If I don't believe it, I won't be a great unbeliever."

"Believe it or not, I'm telling you that for this Feast of Tabernacles we will have a citron of our own."

"Amen! I hope it's true. From your mouth into God's ears."

"Amen, amen," repeated Leibel to himself. He pictured his father entering the synagogue, like one of the rich men, with his own citron and his own palm-branch. When the men walked around the Ark with their citrons and their palms, Moshe-Yankel, though only a clerk, would follow them with his palm and his citron. The idea made Leibel very happy.

When he was in heder that day, he told everyone that this year his father would have his own citron and palm. But nobody believed him.

"What do you say to his father?" asked the young rascals of one another. "A beggar like that wants a citron of his own. He must think it's a lemon or a crab-apple!"

Those are the remarks the boys made. They pushed Leibel around and gave him a few good whacks and punches. Leibel began to believe that his father was a beggar. So you can imagine his surprise when he came home and found Reb Hensel sitting at the table, in his Napoleonic hat, facing his father. In front of them stood a box full of citrons whose fragrance filled the room.

Reb Hensel's hat was the kind worn in the time of Napoleon the Great. Over there in France these hats had been long out of fashion. But in our village there was still one to be found—only one, and it belonged to Reb Hensel. The hat was long and narrow. It had a slit and a button in front, and two tassels hung from the back. I always wanted these tassels. If the hat had gotten into my hands for two minutes—only two—the tassels would have been mine.

Reb Hensel spread out his delightful stock. He picked up a citron with his two fingers and passed it to father to examine.

"Take this citron, Reb Moshe-Yankel. You'll enjoy it."

"Is it a good one?" asked my father, checking the citron from every angle as one might examine a diamond. His hands trembled with joy.

"The best," replied Reb Hensel and the tassels of his hat shook with his laughter.

Moshe-Yankel played with the citron. He smelled it, and could not take his eyes off it. He called his wife and with a happy smile he displayed the citron as though it were a priceless gem or an only, dear child. Basse-Beila came close and put out her hand slowly to take the citron, but she did not get it.

"Be careful of touching it. Just smell it."

Mother was satisfied with a sniff. I couldn't get even a sniff. I wasn't allowed to get near or even look at it.

"Look," said she, "He's here, too. If he gets near the citron he'll bite the stem off it."

"God forbid!" cried my father.

"God preserve us!" echoed Reb Hensel, and his tassels shook again. He gave father some wool in which he could nest the citron. The fine fragrance spread to every corner of the house. The citron was wrapped up as if it were a precious gem. It was placed in a beautiful round, carved and decorated sugar box. The sugar was emptied out and the citron was nestled in, like a beloved guest.

"Welcome art thou, Reb citron. Into the box—into the box!"

The box was carefully closed and tenderly placed in the glass cupboard. The door was closed over it and—goodbye!

I heard my mother whisper to my father, "I'm afraid the heathen"—that was meant for me—"will get at the citron and bite off its stem." She took me by the hand and hustled me away from the cupboard.

Like a cat that has smelt butter and jumps down from a shelf for it, straightens her back, walks round and round rubbing herself against everything, looks into everyone's eyes and licks herself, so did Leibel, poor boy, go round and round the cupboard. He gazed through the glass door, smiled at the citron box until his mother saw him. She remarked to his father that the young scoundrel wanted to get his hands on the citron and bite off its stem.

"To school, you scamp! Make yourself invisible!"

Leibel bent his head, lowered his eyes, and went off to school.

What his mother said about biting off the stem of the citron burned itself into Leibel's heart and ate into his bones like deadly poison. The top of the citron buried itself in his brain. It did not leave his thoughts for a moment. He dreamed of it at night. It worried him and almost dragged him by the hand.

"Don't you recognize me, foolish boy? It's I—the citron stem."

Leibel turned over on the other side, groaned and fell asleep. It worried him again.

"Get up, fool. Go and open the cupboard, take out the citron and bite me off. You'll enjoy yourself."

Leibel got up in the morning, washed himself and began to recite his prayers. He ate his breakfast and started to leave for school. On the way he passed the cupboard and stopped to look at the citron box. He imagined the box was winking at him. "Over here, over here, little boy," he seemed to hear. Leibel walked out of the house quickly.

Early one morning Leibel found himself alone in the house. His father had left for work, his mother had gone to the market.

The servant was busy in the kitchen. Leibel again looked inside the glass cupboard and saw the box. It seemed to be beckoning to him. "Over here, over here, little boy." Leibel opened the glass door softly, took out the beautiful box, and raised the lid. Before he had time to pick up the citron, the fragrance filled his nostrils —a pungent, heavenly fragrance. Before he had time to turn around, the citron was in his hand and the top of it close to his eyes.

"Do you want to enjoy yourself? Do you want to know the taste of Paradise? Take hold and bite me off. Don't be afraid, little fool. No one will know. No one will see you. No bird will snitch on you."

You want to know what happened? You want to know whether I bit the top off the citron or held myself back from doing it? I should like to know what you would have done in my place—if you had been told ten times not to dare bite off the top of the citron. Would you not have wanted to know what it tasted like? Would you not also have thought of a plan—to bite it off and stick it on again with spittle? You may believe me or not—that is your own affair—but I do not myself know how it happened. Almost before the citron was in my hands, the top of it was between my teeth.

The day before the festival, father came home a little earlier from his office to untie the palm branch. He had put it away in a corner, warning Leibel not to go near it. But it was a useless warning. Leibel had his own troubles. The top of the citron haunted him. Why had he wanted to bite it off? What good had it done to taste it when it was as bitter as gall? It was for nothing he had spoiled the citron and made it unfit for use in the synagogue. That the citron could not now be used, Leibel knew very well. Why had he spoiled this beautiful creation, bitten off its head, and taken away its life? Why? Why? He dreamt of the citron that night. It haunted him and asked, "Why have you done this thing to me? Why did you bite off my head? Now I am useless— useless." Leibel turned over on the other side, groaned and fell asleep again. But the citron plagued him, "Murderer, what did you have against me? What had my head done to you?"

The first day of the Feast of Tabernacles arrived. After a frosty night, the sun rose and covered the earth with delayed warmth, like that of a stepmother. That morning Moshe-Yankel got up earlier than usual and practiced by heart the festival prayers, reciting them to a beautiful festival melody. That day also Basse-Beila was very busy cooking the fish and the other special dishes. That day also Zalman the carpenter came to our tabernacle to make a blessing over the citron and palm before anyone else so that he might be able to enjoy the festival.

"Zalman wants the palm and the citron," mother told father.

"Open the cupboard and take out the box—but carefully," said my father.

He himself stood on a chair, took the palm from the top shelf and brought it out to Zalman.

"Here," he said, "make a blessing. But be careful, in heaven's name, be careful!"

Our neighbor Zalman was a giant of a man—may no evil eye harm him! Each finger of his two huge hands could knock down three such Leibels as I. His hands were always sticky and his nails red from glue. When he drew one of these nails across a plank, there was a mark that might have been made by a sharp iron.

In honor of the festival, Zalman had put on a clean shirt and a new coat. He has scrubbed his hands with pumice-stone, but had not succeeded in making them clean. They were still sticky and the nails were still red with glue. Into these hands fell the dainty citron. There was good reason for Moshe-Yankel to get excited when Zalman gave the citron a good squeeze and the palm a good shake.

"Be careful, be careful," he cried. "Now turn the citron head downwards, and make the blessing. Carefully, carefully. For heaven's sake, be careful!"

Suddenly Moshe-Yankel threw himself forward and shouted "Ooh!" The cry brought his wife running into the tabernacle.

"What is it, Moshe-Yankel? For God's sake, what is it?"

"Fumbling ninny! Dope!" he shouted at the carpenter and looked as though he were ready to kill him. "How could you be such a fumbling fool? Is a citron an ax? a bore? You have cut my throat without a knife. You've spoiled my citron. Here is the stem here, look! Fumbling ninny! Dope!"

We were all paralyzed. At this moment Zalman resembled a corpse. He could not understand how this misfortune had happened. How had the stem broken off the citron? Surely he had held it lightly, with the tips of his fingers? It was dreadful—a misfortune.

Basse-Beila was pale as death. She wrung her hands and moaned.

"When a man is unlucky, he may as well dig a grave and bury himself alive."

And Leibel? Leibel didn't know whether he ought to dance with joy because God had performed a miracle for him, or whether he should cry for his father's agony and his mother's tears, or whether he should kiss Zalman's thick hands with their sticky fingers and red nails because he was his good angel. Leibel looked at his father's face, his mother's tears, the carpenter's hands and at the citron that lay on the table, yellow as wax, without a head, without a spark of life, a dead thing.

"A dead citron," said my father in a broken voice.

"A dead citron," repeated my mother, gushing tears.

"A dead citron," echoed the carpenter, looking at his hands. He seemed to be saying to himself, "There's a pair of hands for you! May they wither!"

"A dead citron," said Leibel, in a joyful voice. But he caught himself, fearing that the tone of his exclamation might proclaim that he, Leibel, was the killer, the murderer of the citron.

THE TREE OF LIBERTY

by CECIL ROTH

IN THE SEMI-DARKNESS, MARCO-MORDECAI ABOAF WATCHED HIS elder brother, Leone-Judah, huddle on his clothes and stumble out of the room after perfunctory ablutions. He heard the footsteps clang away up the Ghetto Vecchio in the direction of the Spanish synagogue, the *scuola spagnuola*. For Leone-Judah, in the first flush of adolescent religiosity, belonged to the society of Mourners for Zion, who gathered together, an hour or more before dawn, to recite dirges for the loss of Jerusalem. One day, Marco-Mordecai promised himself, he also would become a member of that pious society and have the privilege of joining in their eerie rites, sitting barefoot on the floor of the synagogue, in complete darkness save for the flickerings of the perpetual lamp. . . . The macabre thought lulled him again to sleep.

He awoke with a start. It was almost broad daylight, now. At the next house, he heard the long drawn-out cry of the beadle summoning the "Watchers for the Morning" to their special service: *"Shomerim laBoker! Shomerim laBoker!"* The footsteps next stopped outside his own house. He heard the beadle's staff beat on the door, once and twice, and waited with bated breath, for it was only when a death had occurred overnight that two knocks were given. The third came, accompanied by a wheezy cough and the hoarse cry. Marco-Mordecai breathed again. His father, in the adjoining room, climbed heavily out of bed. Within a few minutes, the ghetto was filled with the sound of footsteps hurrying synagoguewards, and cries of *Buon Giorno*, with comments upon the weather, echoed at increasingly frequent intervals across the narrow street.

Marco-Mordecai stayed in bed a little longer, for a boy of

twelve was not expected to put in too early an appearance at service. The sun was already penetrating the rare interstices between the houses, promising a day of blazing July heat, before he reached the baroque *scuola,* which Longhena had built a century and a half before.

Within the building, there was an air of suppressed excitement. The *cantarino* seemed to be gabbling over the prayers more rapidly than usual. There was a continual undercurrent of conversation. Some even of the most pious interrupted their devotions to exchange words with their neighbors. The climax was reached when Isaac Grego, in the height of fashion from his powdered hair down to his silver shoe-buckles, and actually wearing a sword at his side, bustled into the building with a self-important air and strode up to the rabbi's seat. A whispered conversation took place between the two in front of the Holy Ark itself. Grego bustled out, looking even more self-important than before. The white-haired rabbi, Abraham Jonah, who had been imported from Spalato thirteen years before to administer to the community, took off his prayershawl and his phylacteries with unaccustomed haste.

"After service today," he announced, "there will be no *Limmud.*"

The congregation broke up in unaccustomed confusion. To suspend the daily course of study, regarded as being on an equal footing with the daily course of the prayers, was an almost unprecedented event. Marco-Mordecai was however becoming daily more and more accustomed to such phenomena. In the course of the last few months, a whole succession of them had taken place. Venice had not seemed the same city. The narrow *calli* were filled with soldiers, lounging at every corner and occupying half the seats in the wine-shops. Great ships of war had been anchored in the lagoon, as though prepared to fire at the slightest pretext on the Piazza S. Marco. There had been suspiciously inexhaustible conversations throughout the ghetto, which ceased suddenly as soon as any stranger approached.

Marco had caught talk of the French, and of a French general with an Italian name, Bonaparte (*Helek Tob,* or the Good Portion, his father once called him). One day in March, the silverware had been sent to the Mint from all the seven synagogues, in order to assist in carrying on the war. On the next Saturday, service had seemed very strange, without the perpetual lamp in front of the Ark or the jingling bells which were placed above the Scrolls of the Law. But the sacrifice had been useless. Before long, news had come through that Padua had fallen. The reverberations of the cannon could now be heard across the lagoon. "Tonight we are not safe even in our beds," the Doge was reported to have said. The gossips repeated this from mouth to mouth, with increased forebodings.

Indeed, they had some reason. During the course of the next week, a force of five hundred Slavonian mercenaries were billeted in the ghetto to maintain order. There were a couple of them in the Aboaf household—wild looking fellows with long moustachios and curved sabres, who played dice interminably on the doorstep and could not say a sentence without *Per Dio Santo!* as a prefix. Everybody treated them with the utmost deference, and the community provided them with a few casks of the best wine; but all the same, there was a general fear that they would sack the whole place at the first chance. Fortunately, Rabbi Abraham Jonah was well-versed in the Holy Kabala. He had written a number of special amulets, and affixed one on each of the ghetto gates. So long as they remained there, the place was safe; and it was noteworthy that the Slavonians deported themselves from that moment like so many lambs.

Even this had not sufficed to check the terrifying activity of General Bonaparte. The next Saturday but one, when the time for reciting the prayer for the Doge and the Signoria arrived, the *cantarino* had gone over to consult the rabbi, and then had solemnly called down the divine benediction, according to a new formula, upon the Provisional Government of this exalted city. The rule of the Doge had come to an end, after so many centuries of pomp and glory, and Venice was now governed by a Revolutionary Council. A couple of days after, the French troops entered the city. They were to be seen everywhere, lolling luxuriously in the gondolas and ogling the girls. A number of them, Jews, had come to the ghetto, where admiring groups would surround them and listen to their tales of recent exploits and accounts of how freedom had been brought to their co-religionists in a dozen cities of the *terra ferma*. That was happening in Venice, too. Moses Luzzatto, Vita Vivante, and Isaac Grego had been elected members of the new municipality. One day, Marco-Mordecai's father came home bearing a musket, with a tricolor badge in his hat. He had enrolled himself in the new Civic Guard.

The revolutionary spirit penetrated the Ghetto, too. The day before—it was Sunday, July 9th—a fresh election had been held for new Deputies of the Jewish Nation, as they were now to be called, under the auspices of the Committee of Public Safety itself. For the first time, every adult had been allowed to vote, excepting strangers and of course paupers. A detachment of French troops had been placed on duty at the Spanish synagogue, to maintain order. Their presence had not indeed been necessary. The proceedings had been orderly, though highly enthusiastic. At the close, Marco-Mordecai had heard tumultuous cheers for "Fraternity, Democracy, and the Italian Nation."

That night, at supper, his mother had mentioned the *Signor Rabbino*. His father had interrupted her with twinkling eyes.

"There are no *signori* now, my dear," he said. "We are all equal. We must speak of the Citizen Rabbi in the future."

"In that case, anyone is our equal—the beadle, for example," said Leone-Judah, doubtfully; for he was proud of the position which the family had enjoyed in the community for the past two hundred years, and of their ultimate descent from Grandees of Spain.

"By all means," rejoined his father. "They called him *Cittadino Nonzolo* at the meeting just now."

That had been yesterday. Since then, excitement had been steadily growing. When they came out of synagogue that morning, a semi-festive air reigned in the street, although it was the eve of the Fast of Tammuz, anniversary of the breach of the walls of Jerusalem and of manifold other disasters in the history of the race. Half the shops were closed, and excited groups were gathered at every corner. There was no activity save in the Ghetto Nuovo, where the three pawnbroking establishments which the Jews were forced to maintain as the price of their toleration in Venice were open, and already surrounded (for times were hard) by eager clients.

After breakfast, Marco ran off to school, picking up one or two of his friends on the way. The red-headed *rubbi* chased them off with unwonted cordiality.

"No teaching today, you rascals," he said. "We all have better things to do."

Marco-Mordecai preferred not to return home, fearing that he might be set to occupy his leisure with private study or household chores. He spent the forenoon with his friends on the Fondamenta della Pescaria, playing a hazardous game of football among the barges and watching the gondolas as they passed backwards and forwards along the Canareggio canal, with their loads of laughing French officers.

Towards noon, there was an unwonted flow of people under the low archway which led back into the ghetto. They followed. Mealtime was approaching, but they were too excited to give it much thought. Marco-Mordecai, as he passed his home, ran in and begged a hunk of bread and onion which he munched as he ran—though with slight misgivings since he had not recited the prescribed grace.

In the Ghetto Nuovo, the only open space which the Jewish quarter could boast, there had been set up a tall pole gaudily decorated. It was the Tree of Liberty, Marco-Modecai heard someone say. The workmen were putting the finishing touches on it. Around it, there had gathered a vast crowd of Jews and Gentiles, all with tricolor cockades in their hats, talking excitedly together and clapping one another on the back with needless and unaccustomed geniality. Among the crowd there were even several priests, who seemed to be setting the example in fraternization. Marco-Mordecai recognized the curates of the neighboring parishes of SS. Ermagora e Fortunato and of S. Geremia, who in the past had been anything but notorious for friendly feelings towards the Jews. That was all over now. A new era dawned.

The work on the Tree of Liberty was finished. A number of young Jews and Gentiles, linking hands, began to dance around it in a circle. Everybody laughed. An old ragged-bearded Jew disappeared into his house and returned bearing a couple of flasks of wine, which he offered to drink to all and sundry. A burly gondolier seized him in his arms, and kissed him on the cheeks. Marco-Mordecai caught a glimpse of his own father, arm-in-arm with a young priest fresh from the Seminary.

There was distant sound of drums and fifes approaching up the Ghetto Nuovo. The boys made a simultaneous dash to see what was happening. It was a detachment of the newly-enrolled Civic Guard, under the command of Cittadino Ferrari. They marched, with military precision, to the Ghetto Nuovo, where they formed a hollow square round the Tree of Liberty. The French soldiers in the crowd eyed their movements superciliously.

Suddenly a cry arose from the crowd. *"Le Porte! Le Porte!"* A couple of days before, the Committee of Public Safety had given instructions for the removal of the gates of the Ghetto, which had hitherto been kept closed from sunset to sunrise, as well as on the major solemnities of the Christian year, converting the Jewish quarter into something in the nature of a prison. It was today that this order was to be executed, though in the general excitement the main reason for the proceedings was almost in danger of being overlooked. There was a general surge of the mob headed by a blacksmith brandishing a hammer, towards the Rio di S. Girolamo, where the nearest of the three entrances was situated. Another detachment rushed down the Ghetto Vecchio, and another to the Ghetto Nuovissimo. Marco could not get near enough to the front to see what was happening. He could hear, however, above the shouting of the mob, the sickening thud of hammers and axes against the woodwork. Suddenly, there was a crash, followed by a yell of triumph. The crowd surged back, dragging the gate behind them, into the middle of the square where, in a delirium of excitement, it was hacked into small fragments. The same was done to the other gates as they were added to the pile. Somebody produced a steel and flint. Before many minutes were passed, the symbols of centuries of degradation were being destroyed in a roaring bonfire.

In the crowd there was an old rabbi wearing, through sheer conservatism, the red hat formerly prescribed for all Jews by law, as their badge of shame. A member of the Civic Guard snatched it from his head, and threw it into the flames.

"We are all equal now," he called, jovially. "Away with these shameful relics of the past!"

His words evoked a general huzza. Another Civic Guard, seeing the look of discomfort on the old man's face, clapped his own hat, with its enormous tricolor cockade, upon his head.

"Take this, Citizen Rabbi," he said. "This is the right head-gear for a good republican, in the first year of Italian Liberty."

The guffaw which followed his jest was drowned in a shout of triumph, as the flames suddenly leapt upwards. Somebody began to dance the Carmagnola. Everyone followed his example. Within a few moments, Jews and Christians, men and women, soldiers and civilians, were capering deliriously round the flames.

There was a call for silence. Marco-Mordecai saw Raphael Vivante, a member of one of the most prominent Jewish families and an active member of the Civic Guard, climb painfully on the parapet of one of the three wells from which the inhabitants of the Ghetto Nuovo drew their water. He began to speak impressively, accentuating every phrase with a gesture:

"Brothers! At length, there has arrived that happy day, in which prejudice and superstition have been cast down, and the insults from which we have unjustly suffered for so long are avenged!"

A burst of applause followed. The orator resumed:

"The light of philosophy has shone forth from the happy shores of France to this country, where an arid aristocracy aggravated our woes and our ignominious chains."

The applause this time merged into a general hum of conversation which did not completely die away; and the uproar of the mob, combined with the crackling of the flames, prevented Marco-Mordecai from hearing any more of the speech consecutively. Nothing daunted, the cultured Isaac Grego, the foremost among the Jewish members of the new municipality, and who had recently been elected head of the communal organization, next mounted the improvised platform. Little could be heard of what he had to say, excepting that the shameful word Ghetto was henceforth to be banished from the Italian language, and that what had formerly been the Jewish quarter was henceforth to be known by the auspicious name of *Contrada della Riunione.* He was succeeded in turn by the Abbate Staddita, a Dalmatian priest, whose enthusiasm for the Revolutionary cause was notorious. His speech was listened to with the silent respect due to his cloth; for no Christian ecclesiastic had ever before honored the Jews of Venice with a friendly address. He had little to say, however, excepting to thank the Jewish community for its generous gift of three hundred ducats to the Christian poor of the neighboring parishes.

The crowd was by now beginning to thin out. Marco-Mordecai discovered with a start that the time for evening service was approaching. His father, he knew, was not likely to excuse his attendance even on so memorable an occasion; and, reluctantly, he made his way towards the Spanish synagogue. As he approached, he saw a number of non-Jews filing in, automatically fingering their hats, which they were unaccustomed to leave on their heads in a place of worship. The building was uncomfortably crowded, but Marco-Mordecai was just able to squeeze in. To his surprise, he found that there was to be no service. Those who had just gone in were the members of the Society for Public Instruction, whose main function was the propagation of republican doctrine; and the object of their attendance was to hear a patriotic harangue from Citizen Massa, who was to celebrate before a mixed audience the dawn of equality between Jew and Gentile.

Twilight was drawing on before the meeting was concluded. The distinguished guests were subsequently entertained to a splendid repast in the Vivante household. Marco-Mordecai's father, as one of the more prominent members of the community, was among the notables invited to meet them. Late into the night, Marco-Mordecai could hear the burst of conviviality which filled the ghetto on all sides: but, tired out with the excitement of the day, he was already asleep before the party broke up.

Thus after an existence of two hundred and eighty-one years and three months almost to the day, the Ghetto of Venice—the prototype and namesake of all those of Italy—came to an end.

THE LAST STAND IN THE WARSAW GHETTO

by MAREK EDELMAN

THE GERMANS FINALLY DECIDED TO LIQUIDATE THE WARSAW GHETTO. First reports of their approach came through from our advance observation posts at two o'clock in the morning of April 19, 1943. We learned that German gendarmes, with the help of Polish "navy blue" police, were encircling the outer ghetto walls, at thirty yard intervals. An emergency alarm was ordered, and within fifteen minutes all fighter units were at their battle stations. We also alerted the civilian population to the imminent danger; most ghetto inhabitants at once moved to previously prepared shelters, and bunkers in cellars and attics. Deathly silence lay over the ghetto. The Jewish Fighter Organization was on guard.

At four o'clock, the Germans began to infiltrate the inter-ghetto, uninhabited areas, in groups of three, four and five, so as not to arouse suspicion. Once inside, they formed into platoons and companies. At seven o'clock, motorized detachments, including tanks and armored vehicles, entered the ghetto. The SS was ready to attack. In closed formations, goose-stepping noisily, they marched into seemingly dead streets of the Central Ghetto. Their triumph appeared complete. It looked as if this superbly equipped modern army must have frightened the handful of bravado-drunk men; as if those few immature boys had at last realized that there was no point in attempting the impossible; that they understood the Germans had more rifles than there were rounds for all their pistols.

But they did not frighten us, and we were not caught off guard. We were only waiting for an opportune moment. Presently it came. The Germans had chosen the intersection at Mila and

Zamenhofa Streets for their bivouac area, and our fighters, barricaded at all four corners, at once opened concentric fire on them.
Strange missiles (home-made grenades and the like) began exploding all over; now and then the lone machine gun spewed bullets
through the air (ammunition had to be carefully conserved);
farther off rifles started firing. This was the beginning.

The Germans attempted a retreat, but were cut off. German
dead littered the street. The living looked for cover in neighboring stores and doorways, but the shelter proved insufficient. The
SS thereupon called tanks into action, and under their cover the
survivors of two companies began their retreat. But the bad luck
of the Germans, that day, spread to their tanks as well. The first
was burned out by one of our incendiary bottles; the rest did not
attempt to approach our positions. The fate of the Germans
caught in the Mila-Zamenhofa trap was sealed: not one left the
area alive.

At the same time a battle was raging at the intersection of
Nalewki and Gesia Streets. The fighting lasted well over seven
hours, as two combat units kept the Germans from entering the
ghetto at that point. The Germans found some mattresses and
used them for cover, but the straight shooting of our fighters
forced them to successive withdrawals. German blood ran in the
streets. Ambulances were busily transporting German wounded
to the little square near the community buildings. There they lay
in rows on the sidewalk, waiting to be admitted to the hospital. A
German air liaison post at the corner Gesia signalled our positions to their planes. But for the time being, we were invincible
on ground as well as from the air. The Gesia-Nalewki battle
ended in the complete rout of the Germans.

Heavy fighting was also in progress at Muranowski Square.
There the Germans attacked from all directions. The cornered
combat units fought back bitterly, and by truly superhuman
efforts succeeded in repulsing the enemy. Two German machine
guns as well as quantities of other weapons were captured. Fur-
thermore, a German tank was burned—the second that day.

At two o'clock in the afternoon, not a live German remained
in the ghetto. It was the Fighter Organization's first complete
victory. The remainder of that day passed in comparative quiet,

except for some bursts of artillery fire from the guns on Krasins-kich Square, outside the ghetto, and several bombings from the air.

All was quiet the following day until two o'clock in the afternoon. Then the Germans, once more in closed formation, arrived at the brushmakers' gate. A German factory guard went to open it. At precisely the same moment one of our people placed a plug into an electric socket, and a mine long ready for the Germans exploded beneath the SS men's feet. Over one hundred were killed. The rest fled under our combatants' fire.

Two hours later, the Germans tried their luck again. This time they changed their tactics, cautiously approaching in extended ranks, as they attempted to penetrate the brushmakers' area. There, however, they were suitably received by a fighter unit. Of the thirty Germans who had gotten through, only a few were able to leave. Once more the Germans withdrew from the ghetto. Once more our victory was complete. The Germans tried again to effect an entry at several other points. But everywhere they encountered the same determined resistance, each house a fortress.

Suddenly, we are surrounded in an attic. The Germans are right there, in the same attic, and we cannot reach the stairs. We cannot even see each other in the dark corners. We do not notice Sewek Dunski and Junghajzer crawl up the stairs, get behind the Germans and throw a grenade. We do not even pause as Michal Klepfisz throws himself right on top of the German machine-gun, firing from behind the chimney. All we see is that a path has been cleared. Hours later, when the Germans have been driven out, we find Michal's body, drilled like a sieve.

The brushmakers' area cannot be taken.

Then something unprecedented happens. Three officers appear, with lowered rifles and white rosettes in their buttonholes —emissaries. They wish to negotiate a fifteen minute truce with the Area Command, to remove the dead and wounded. They are also ready to promise all inhabitants an orderly evacuation to labor camps in Poniatow and Trawniki, permitting them to take all their possessions with them.

Firing is our reply. Each house remains an embattled fortress. From every store and window, bullets seek hated German helmets, hated German hearts.

Our old soldier, Diament, is at his command post, beside a tiny window on the fourth floor. His long rifle dates back to the Russo-Japanese War. Diament is phlegmatic, his movements are slow, deliberate. Boys near him try to hurry him along, but he remains imperturbable. He aims at the stomach, hits the heart. Each round finishes off another German.

At a second-story window, comrade Dworja is firing away furiously. The Germans spot her; "Look, Hans! A woman shooting!" They draw a bead on her, but miss. Apparently she does not miss often, for they withdraw quickly.

At Post Number 1, on the first floor landing, the fighters Shuster and Kazik are hurling hand grenades. The supply runs out while two Germans are still moving about the courtyard. Shuster reaches for an incendiary bottle, and hits one of the Germans square on the helmet. Instantly it catches fire, and the German is turned into a torch.

So determined is the stand of the Jewish fighters, that the Germans finally abandon all ordinary methods of fighting and resort to new tactics: they set fires on all sides of the brushmakers' block simultaneously. In a matter of minutes, fires are raging over the entire block. Smoke chokes our throats, burns our eyes. We shall have to gamble for our lives. We decide to make a break for the Central Ghetto.

Flames cling to our smoldering clothes. The pavement melts to a sticky, black tar beneath our feet. Broken glass, littering the streets, cuts into our shoes. Our soles burn from the heat of the pavement. One by one, we stagger through the conflagration. From house to house, courtyard to courtyard, half-choked, a hundred hammers beating in our skulls, burning rafters falling over us, we finally pass the area under fire. We feel lucky just to be out of the inferno.

The most difficult part of our trek remains. There is only one way into the Central Ghetto—through a small breach in the wall, closely guarded by the enemy. Five battle units will have to make their way, under the eyes of German gendarmes, "navy blue" police, and Ukrainian detachments. Tense to the breaking point, their feet wrapped in rags to stifle the sound of steps, Gutman's, Berlinski's and Grynbaum's groups get through, under heavy fire. Success! Yurek Blones's group covers from behind. While the first of this group emerges on the street, however, a German searchlight illuminates the entire section. No one else, it seems, will be able to save himself. Suddenly, fighter Romanowicz's single, well-aimed shot shatters the searchlight. Before the Germans collect their wits, our entire group manages to cross over.

We continued to fight in the Central Ghetto, together with the battle units stationed there. As in the brushmakers' area, moving freely was impossible. Whole streets were blocked by huge fires. Seas of flame engulfed houses and courtyards; wooden beams crackled noisily; walls collapsed. There was no air, only choking black smoke and burning heat, radiating from red-hot walls and the glowing stones of stairways.

What the Germans could not do, the omnipotent flames now accomplished. Thousands perished in the conflagration; the stench of burning bodies was everywhere. Charred corpses lay on balconies, in window recesses, on unburned steps. Flames drove people from their shelters, forced them from their hiding places in cellars and attics. Thousands staggered about the yards, easy prey for the Germans, who imprisoned or killed them outright. Weary beyond endurance, they fell asleep in driveways, beside doors, standing, sitting, lying, and were caught asleep by German bullets. No one so much as noticed that an old man sleeping in a corner would never awaken; that a mother nursing her baby had been dead for three days; that a baby's cries and suckling were unavailing, for its mother's arms were cold, her breasts dead. Hundreds committed suicide by leaping from fourth and fifth-story windows.

After such exemplary lessons in the Central Ghetto and the brushmakers' area, the Germans thought the other workshops would no longer oppose a "voluntary" evacuation. Consequently they set a deadline for appearing at the collection points, and threatened like treatment in the event of disobedience. Neither pleas nor threats, however, could avail by that time.

Ghetto fighters everywhere were on the alert. The first attempts to disrupt the occupation of the Central Ghetto by German units were made in the Tebbens and Schultz area. Grenades and gunfire showered on the moving truckloads of SS men from balconies, windows and rooftops. Once a speeding truck was blown up on the Aryan side. Another time, Comrade Rozowski and Shlomo the deputy Area Commander, noticed a German truck approach during an area inspection. Swiftly they climbed to a balcony, and made a direct hit on the truck with a four-pound powder charge, killing all but five of the sixty SS aboard.

Five days later, the deadline for "voluntary" evacuations expired, and the Germans once more set about "pacifying" the area. As before, they were met with stubborn resistance. Unfortunately there was no more electric current in the ghetto, and mines rigged up for just such an occasion could not be set off. But there was heavy fighting. Combatants barricaded in the buildings kept the Germans from advancing. As in other areas, each house became a battleground.

At 56 Leszno Street, Yurek is cornered at his outpost. A group of SS surround him; one throws a grenade. Adroitly Yurek catches it in mid-air, before it can explode, and tosses it back at the SS. Four are killed on the spot.

His arm wounded, Shlomo covers the withdrawal from 72 Nowolipie Street. Suddenly, their group is surrounded. All seems lost, there is no time to prevent disaster. Then Shlomo quickly pulls a sheet from a bed, and lowers everyone to the courtyard. As there is no one left to hold the sheet for him, he leaps from the second story.

In this area as in the others, the Germans finally saved their military honor by setting house after house on fire.

The Jewish Fighter Organization now changed its tactics, to attempt the protection of larger groups of the population, hidden in bunkers and shelters. Thus two fighter units escorted several hundred people from the ruined shelter at 37, to number 7 Mila Street. Thousands found shelter there for over a week.

Slowly, the conflagration died out. But now there was no

place to live. Worse still, there was no water. The fighters themselves would go down into the underground shelters occupied by non-combatants, to defend what little remained to be defended.

Armed encounters now took place mostly at night. During the day, the ghetto was lifeless. Our patrols now extended over the entire ghetto area. Our men would meet the Germans in the dark, and whoever fired first, won. The Germans and Ukrainians made a practice of patrolling the streets together, and lying in wait for us. Each night there were many casualties.

Our situation was becoming increasingly desperate. There were shortages not only of food and water, but also of ammunition. Communications with the Aryan side had broken down; consequently we could not arrange for transfer of additional weapons, allotted to us by the People's Army.

The Germans now tried to locate all inhabited shelters by means of sound detectors and police dogs. On May 3 they found the shelter at 30 Franciszkanska Street, which had been serving as an operations base for our groups from the brushmakers' area. One of the most brilliant battles was fought here for two days, during which half our men were killed. Yet even in the most trying moments, Abrasha Blum kept our spirits alive. His mere presence strengthened us more than possession of the best possible weapons could have. One can hardly speak of victory in a losing battle for survival. Yet one thing can surely be said about this particular battle; we did not let the Germans carry out their plans. They did not evacuate a single living person.

On May 8 detachments of Germans and Ukrainians surrounded the Command headquarters of the Fighter Organization. The battle lasted two hours. When the Germans realized they could not take the bunker by storm, they tossed in a gas bomb. Those who survived both German bullets and gas, committed suicide for there was no other way out. Yurek Wilner called up all the fighters to die together. Lutek Rotblat shot his mother, his sister and finally himself. Ruth fired at herself seven times. Fully eighty percent of the remaining combatants perished, among them the Commander of the Jewish Fighter Organization, Mordecai Anilewicz.

At night the few who had miraculously escaped death

joined the survivors of the brushmakers' detachments, deployed
at 22 Franciszkanska Street. That very same night, two of our
liaison men arrived from the Aryan side. Our Fighter Command
had dispatched them to our representatives there, ten days previously, to arrange the withdrawal of the fighting groups through
the sewers. Now they were back, but it was too late. For one
thing, the Fighter Organization had been decimated. But even
the pitiful remnants could not be evacuated from the ghetto all
at one time.

All night long we made our way through the sewers, crawling
through numerous entanglements set up by the Germans for just
such a contingency. The manholes were buried under rubble,
passageways booby-trapped. Every once in a while, the Germans
would admit gas into the pipes. Under such circumstances, we
waited for forty-eight hours in a sewer twenty-eight inches high,
with water reaching to our lips. Each minute, someone fainted.
Thirst was our worst hardship. Some took to drinking the slimy
sewage. Seconds seemed to stretch into months.

At ten o'clock in the morning, on May 10, two trucks drew
up beside the manhole at the Prosta-Twarda intersection. The
promised Polish Home Army cover failed to materialize, and only
three of our liaison men and a People's Army representative
patrolled the street. Thus, in broad daylight, the manhole cover
was lifted. The appearance of even a single Jew was something
of a sensation at that time. Yet one by one, armed Jews emerged
from the dark hole, before the stunned crowds.

Not all of us got out. The lid snapped shut violently, and
the trucks took off at full speed. Two battle units remained in
the ghetto. We kept in touch with them, until the middle of
June. From then on, every trace of them was lost.

PART THREE

Israelian Fruit

PLOW DEEP

by JESSIE E. SAMPTER

SEPHIERA WAS IN LOVE. FOR THE FIRST TIME IN HER LIFE SHE HAD
a secret from her sister Batya.

She lay, wide-eyed, on her back in the darkness, her full
length stretched on the cotton mattress on the floor. Seemingly
relaxed. Yet her hands were clasped tensely behind her head
among the short curls. She drew long breaths, too long, as if she
would draw all space into herself. She was warm and strong and
beautiful, feeling her strength and beauty from head to toe.
Through her thin covering and her thread-bare nightdress the
breeze from the open window stroked her, stirring on her face
and breast and curls like a live wild creature from the mountains.
She lay still and dreamed awake.

"Why is he different?" she mused, "why do I love him and
never anyone else? I like so many—they all like me and they want
to make love a little and I let them—why not? But he does not
want to make love. He draws out my soul and my heart. I am altogether his, and yet he has not asked me. He will ask me. I am
his. God—O God of my mother, if you are really God, hear me—
I am altogether his."

A bright white streak lengthened inward from the window
—the moonlight. It fell across the stone tiled floor, and gradually
it crept over Batya lying on the other mattress, fast asleep, with
her arm for a pillow, her long slim body drawn up tight like a
baby still unborn, her short golden curls turned to silver thread
falling over her chiselled face. Fast asleep.

"I cannot tell Batya," thought Sephiera. "All the others she
knows. We used to joke about it. We said we loved each other
too much. But now! We are very much alike, we *look* alike. But

we are so different. Batya would never melt, would never give
herself. Oh, I would, I would! I am ashamed—and yet proud.
Because it is to him."

Over and over she rehearsed her meetings with him.

He was English, an English Jew. Did that make the difference? The others, all Russian Jews, too much like herself. Here
in Jerusalem, was it he or was it the mountain, the light, the
mystery? Yesterday, here on the top of Mount Scopus, mountain
of seers, overlooking the Dead Sea, they had rested, sat in long
silence on the white stone wall among a riot of all colors of wild
field flowers. Below them on the west, set in bare rolling hills
green and purple and studded with olive trees, lay Jerusalem,
white walls and domes and minarets, ancient in the piercing sunlight, clear as a cameo. Blue as heaven was the jewelled dome of
the Mosque of Omar on the temple site. Eastward she looked
down over the petrified, yellow-purple, dancing wilderness of
Judaea, wild peak mocking peak, down to the bright blue sea, the
Dead Sea, like a large turquoise among the yellowish depths. And
beyond and across, dream mountains of Moab, clear though faint
as a veil drawn over invisible mysteries. There had come a tinkling of bells from the road: three camels walked mincingly with
ropes loose between them and bags of coal strapped to their
backs; Arabs alongside, with flowing gay kefiyeh, shouted and
laughed.

"Saida," called one, and Saul answered "Saida," but Sephiera
gave the Jewish greeting, "Shalom!"

They all mean peace. Then one Arab, a young man, handsome and swarthy, laughed and answered, "Shalom!"

Saul laughed. His dark eyes were pools in which Sephiera
sank, and the touch of him sitting beside her made her dizzy.

"Coal for the High Commissioner," said Saul in Hebrew.
"Plenty of work for the Arabs now there's a Jewish king on the
Mount of Olives."

"King?" she had asked, "I don't feel he's a king."

"Well, better than king," answered Saul, "brother."

And Saul Benjamin—Captain Benjamin—soldier-artist, dark,
tall, resilient, rose and walked to and fro in the white road before

her, talking again. Queer, his long silences and his outbursts of speech, like jangled bell harmonies. He spoke Hebrew beautifully, but to her it seemed strangely, because of the drawl of his inevitable English accent. Her own speech, less correct, was more crisp and fluent.

"Yes, brother! Hasn't he something of the Arab in him, the High Commissioner? Haven't I? Haven't you? Why did you wander down over the steppes of Russia, you blonde gypsy? Was it only to find a homeland? Wasn't it also to find a brother?"

He returned to the wall of loose white sandstones: "We are ancient," he said, "and the old wildness calls us. I could never live in England again—it is too civilized, too decently pale."

"Russia is not civilized," answered Sephiera, "nor I——"

She wanted him to take her hand that was pressed cold and firm on the stones where she sat.

"Look," he exclaimed, bending to the stone beside her hand, "fossils!"

Imbedded in the sandstone was a white shell, and beside it the imprint of another shell, Sephiera marvelled.

"But we are not near the sea," she said, "we are very far above the sea!"

"More than two thousand feet above the Mediterranean Sea," he answered, "and almost four thousand feet above the Dead Sea you see there. But once, ages past, this mountain was in the bottom of the sea, before Moses, before Abraham, before the fathers of Adam. These rocks are more ancient than our people. Your hand—your hand is lying on the rock of ages. Before mankind began——"

Sephiera lifted her hand as if it had been burnt. She wanted him to take it.

"After mankind has disappeared——" Suddenly he looked at her. She felt her eyes swimming, something within her flamed. . . .

"And you," he said, "you are even more ancient. Before that rock rose out of the sea, before mankind began somewhere—I already knew you. So old is the Jewish people!"

She held out her strong hand. He took it, and pulled her a

little, and she rose, and together they walked back to the house, hand in hand, swinging their arms and their bodies freely like two children. Not another word. No more than her hand.

Yet she was entirely his.

So she lay dreaming and rehearsing, his presence upon her.

The moonlight crept over, whitening the floor and filling the room with faint colors. A breeze swayed, warm, fragrant, as if the moon had an odor. And the white light crept up her body, till suddenly the vast white orb, almost full, stared into her face. The eastern moon. It ravished her, like a lover.

He was an architect, recently discharged from the army, a Jewish legionnaire who hated war as she did. But he had killed men, no doubt—he, with the compassionate eyes. And now he was making sketches and diagrams for the Hebrew University buildings that were to rise on that very spot, on Mount Scopus; working under Gates, the Scotch professor. He was an Englishman, with queer little refined English ways that seemed to her sometimes artificial, unreal—and yet he was the final reality. And she—? They had come from opposite ends of the earth for the same purpose. They had come lonely, seeking a home. They had come, with thousands of others, to live in Palestine as Jews on their own soil, and to work the land, to plow deep.

Six weeks in Palestine. It seemed to Sephiera six ages, perhaps the days of creation. More than a year ago, after sufferings and wanderings they had kissed their old mother goodbye in Riga and started out—she and Batya. Started with a group of others, boys and girls, all fellow "gymnasium" students, driven by the last desperate hope. Fellow-sufferers, but young, strong, defiant! For a year they wandered through Europe: trains, boats, filthy inns, open fields, vermin, hunger, unexpected food, silent endurances, snatched gayety, songs, comradeships. And always Batya to cling to, Batya, the older, more determined one, quiet, sure, protecting her and yet needing her.

Batya and Sephiera were the two youngest of a large family; they could not remember their father. The other children had all married and left home. Now mother was safe—a letter had already come—with Miriam and her husband in Riga. Later, she would follow them to Palestine.

"Saul loves me. O Mother, I feel that he loves me! I cannot tell Batya. Tomorrow I shall not see him. I must work in the kitchen. But day after tomorrow!"

A day is not so very long.

Batya and Sephiera took turns in the kitchen, day by day, cooking for the score or so of young people in this kevutza, or workers' group, which was engaged in putting in order the lovely but neglected garden on the land where the Hebrew University was to be built. They were camping in the one building, a beautiful but empty and forlorn stone house, which had already been bought, with the land, for the University. They loved the garden work, the fragrance, the sweat of their own brows, the earth and the sky. Even in the heat of day. And that noon rest, when Saul came! By evening he would go down to Jerusalem where he lived.

The Hebrew songs at night. The kind, pleasant boys, chatting in the Hebrew of Bible days which all of them had learnt during the long journey to speak fluently, pupils of the three or four who already knew. The merry folk dances on the stone cistern top overlooking the Dead Sea, on Saturdays, or when one is not too tired at night. Even the kitchen is not so bad; one does national work cooking cabbages. So Saul insists. To cook a cabbage well is as useful as to grow one. And Sephiera has just learned. "I hope they liked them; anyway, everyone is so grateful and kind."

Better than breaking stones on a road, as so many of the pioneers are doing all over the land. Better to be at Jerusalem. Palestine, the land of Israel, is sweet. Life is sweet. Sleep is sweet. She turns over and throws her arms across her head to shut out the moonlight. Cabbages—Saul—Mother. Sleep.

Evening after a long day in the kitchen. Full moon, Sephiera withdrew herself and wandered in the garden. Fragrances, pungent or sweet, moved about like invisible guests. The sky was blue, studded with dazzling stars, the earth clear and faint-colored and designed with the sharp shadows of the smallest leaves. Pomegranate blossoms, deep red tubes, passion flowers, trailing complex purple stars over the ground, long-needled pines, shadow and sudden light. Sephiera came to the cornerstone of the University, a kind of small pyramid in steps on the steep hillside. She stood on the lowest step and gazed down on the silver sheet of the Dead Sea and the gigantic tumbled valleys dropping down to it. Then she found a place to sit, secluded in a deep shadow.

Saul! For ever and ever he has known her, before Sodom fell, before Gomorrah was buried in fire down there in the plain. Before sin was—he knew her. She loved him.

She stretched out her bare arms and legs, taking joy in her tired body. If she could bathe in that Dead Sea, miles away! She wore sandals on bare feet, and a low-necked short-sleeved white linen smock that reached just below her knees. It was spattered with stains from the kitchen. The tepid breeze crept under. She shut her eyes, yearning, cold somewhere, in her bones, under her warm, tingling flesh.

Suddenly a rustle. Two firm hands were clasped over her eyes. She started, with unintentional strength pulled herself loose, and found Saul, laughing, already sitting beside her.

He drew her to him, not speaking, a sweeping strength and power in his action. His arm was about her. He did not speak nor move, but so sat, gazing over to Moab.

And Sephiera could not speak nor stir, overmastered by two surprises, numb with excess of feeling. The surprise of him. How had he taken possession, unasking! And yet how natural it seemed and wonderful, like the childish improprieties of dreams. And the surprise of herself. Her whole being vibrated, yearning toward him and enclosed in him. She melted, gasping faintly as with her last breath. Her head fell to his shoulder, and she seemed asleep in a wide wakefulness.

A long moment. Then he pressed her quickly to him and released her. He put his hand over his face. Sephiera sat still, watching. At last he turned to her dilated eyes.

"My bride," he whispered, in Hebrew, "you came to me out

of nowhere, and I take you as a gift of the unknown. I cannot wait for you. See, I cannot restrain myself."

He was trembling. Sephiera waited, yearning yet half repulsed by the suddenness of his passion.

He shut his eyes tight, and went on speaking, as if to himself:

"Until today, Batya, I did not even know your name. Until today at noon, until you yourself promised yourself to me as my bride, I could scarcely have touched you, you seemed remote though so near. My white girl! But now you are myself, I feel you flesh of my flesh, soul of my soul. How can I wait for the day when you will say, this shall be our wedding day? Batya, make it now, make it tonight!"

Again his arms sought her, and he enclosed her as if to break her. But she was sobbing aloud, tearlessly.

"My bride, my girl," he whispered, "why do you sob? No, I will leave you!"

He pulled himself away, watched her intensely, searching the shadow.

She raised her face and cried: "Don't you know me? Don't you know I am not Batya?"

"Sephiera! Forgive me, forgive me! I thought you were Batya! But you will understand."

"Go away," she said, and she hid her face in her hands, nor would she listen to him nor understand his pleading, troubled speech, nor look up until she had heard him move away through the underbrush. Then she shuddered and crouched down.

Sephiera lay crushed in the dust at the foot of the corner-stone, her face pressed on the cold stone, her body and soul whirling with pain. She moaned, long and stupidly . . . Batya— at noon—Batya and Saul! A crazy world!

A long, long time. She raised herself heavily and dragged into the house, into their room. Batya rolled sleepily on her mattress.

"Oh, there you are! So late! I couldn't sleep. I want you. Good night. Go to sleep."

"Good night."

"I shall not sleep," thought Sephiera, enraged, amazed, longing wildly for death, "I shall never sleep."

But her head was barely pressed into the pillow when a trance-like sleep came to save her from agony.

It seemed she was standing at the edge of a lake, in the woods. On the water floated two white lilies. She waded in, to her waist, and still she could reach only the one. And as her hand reached to take it, a black current of water swept over the second lily and carried it far off as if burying it in the lake. And as she watched the one lily, anxiously, she felt herself awakening, and heard herself calling:

"Mother, Mother!"

She sat upright, bewildered.

Batya, too, sat up.

"You called 'Mother,' " she said.

"I know. It awakened me, too."

"I was not asleep," said Batya, "I cannot sleep tonight."

Memory rushed over Sephiera.

Both girls sat upright, staring at each other in the naked moonlight. Batya's eyes shone, gray-deep as that lake in the dream. She was long and exceedingly beautiful with her tousled curls and her bare curved shoulders.

"Saul," said Sephiera.

"Do you know—do you know him?" she asked vividly.

"Why should I not know him?"

"I thought—" Batya went on disconnectedly, "it was only in the gardens at noon, when you were in the kitchen. Only a few times. And yet—I thought no one knew. It was a mystery, a wonder. It was love—Sephiera, what's the matter?"

"Nothing. Only, when you were in the kitchen and I was in the garden— There are two of us!"

"Sephiera! He loves me!"

"I love him," said Sephiera.

"But how can you? He is mine!"

"Last evening he found me at the cornerstone," said Sephiera, shuddering, "he embraced me!"

Batya sprang forward; "It's impossible!"

"He did, but he mistook me for you. He called me Batya."

"Batya!" exclaimed Batya, "it is Batya he loves. He kissed me, he kissed me," she whispered in an ecstatic voice. "But how could you let him touch you? You—when he loves me!"

"Batya, do you hate me? I love him. I did not know."

"Why do you, why? It is horrid, it spoils everything. Oh, I love you both so much."

"I could share him," said Sephiera, "if only he would take me, too! Like Rachel and Leah."

"Silly child!"

"Could you share him? No, because you don't love enough."

"Silly child, don't you see? You could share him, because you haven't got him. I can't, because he loves me. He loves me."

A passion of blind rage and self-reproach silenced Sephiera, numbed her senses.

Batya sat peering, waiting.

"What shall I do?" asked Sephiera at last, breaking into breathless sobs.

In a moment Batya sprang to her side, embraced her with strong bare arms. But Sephiera was withdrawn, smooth and stiff as marble.

"Sephiera, I love you. I love you almost as much as I do him. What shall I do? I cannot help it that he loves me."

"Don't keep repeating it. I know he loves you. Don't tell me again. And don't lie to me. Would you help it if you could?"

"No!"

"Would you give him to me?"

"No!"

"Of course not. Now answer me this, Batya. What would you do if he loved me, if he did not love you? If he married me?"

"Why talk nonsense?"

"Let me talk nonsense. What would you do?"

"I should kill myself," said Batya.

"You love him so much?"

"Yes," answered Batya.

"I love him as much as she does," thought Sephiera, "I shall kill myself."

A sharp pain and then a wave of relief swept through her at that thought. She could speak quietly now.

"There is no use talking any more," said Sephiera, "now that I have told you, you know." She shook herself gently free from her sister's embrace.

"Why did you tell me, why did you?" said Batya, "now I can never be happy. I shall always be thinking about you."

"I'm sorry I told you," said Sephiera, coldly, "but I promise you I will not make you unhappy. Good night. Let us go to sleep."

"Sephiera, you will not sleep. You are pretending."

"You asked me to pretend," said Sephiera. Then, passionately, she protested: "What do you want of me, what? Let me alone! Don't try to make me be good so you can be happy. I have to hate you, Batya, I have to hate you. But you know perfectly well that I love you."

With that she turned her back to Batya and pressed her face into the pillow, and was silent, breathing in great sobs.

At last, to her relief, Batya left her and went back to her own mattress.

So the night passed, moment by moment.

And Sephiera became aware of herself as if another had told her. She hated Batya whom she loved, she hated and wished her dead. She could have crushed her, torn her with her strong hands. But as that passion of hate swept through her, it was throttled by a passion of shame. She loved Saul, she imagined him coming to her, she remembered his embrace, and it seemed to her he was embracing her now. And that passion of love was also throttled by a passion of shame. She said to herself: "I cannot live. I am too horrible to live. I cannot endure to be with them. I shall end my own life!"

Always with that thought came a great pain and then a sweet relief. It seemed as if death would take the place of both lover and sister.

Morning. The girls conversed as if nothing had happened, yet reservedly. Batya went to the kitchen, Sephiera to the garden. She fasted. Working the earth, surrounded by warm air and sunlight, she felt faint, secure, as if already she were dead, planted in the fertile earth. But her strong body worked, powerful, capable despite sleeplessness and corroding anxiety. Her body seemed separate.

At noon she went to the spot where generally she met Saul on her garden days. She had decided on this. She had also decided, definitely and with detailed fantasy, that she would kill herself. How could she go on living near them? How could Batya marry him with her near? She would be a reproach, a ghost of dead affections. She seemed to be thinking only of them, as if with a great love.

It seemed as if she were going to kill herself for love of them, and the thought was sweet.

Saul came.

"Sephiera," he said bravely, "now let me speak to you, let me explain. You understand that in the darkness I mistook you for Batya because you are so much alike."

"I understand," said Sephiera with a soft smile.

"You know now that Batya and I are to be married. But what did you think? Why did you let me do it?"

"I thought you loved me," answered Sephiera simply. But she did not look at him.

"Sephiera! But indeed I do love you as a sister. You know I am very fond of you. You will be our little sister——"

"No," said Sephiera.

"Why not?"

"I am going away," said Sephiera, "I shall not stay with you and Batya."

"Why not, why not? We do not want to lose you, dear!"

"Because," she answered, and she looked straight into his eyes, "because, Saul, I love you, I love you very much, and so I am going away."

She wanted him to know, she wanted him to remember. A great pride filled her. And she made him take her hand and press it, she felt his pity and she did not resent it. Then she told him to go.

Youth is simple and irrevocably stubborn. It thinks life is only one life instead of a thousand lives intertwined and successive. Sephiera had made her plans. In the afternoon she pilfered a little bottle of poison from the nurse's medicine chest. Before dusk she took that and a bit of paper and a pencil, and went down toward the cornerstone. She would leave a note for Batya, a kind, loving note.

She threaded her way in the twilight among the fragrant garden paths and the white rocks down to the cistern platform, the large space overlooking the wilderness and the Dead Sea, the place where they used to dance. Her heart pounded as though it belonged to another; she seemed to be another than herself, to be watching her own motions. She stood at the edge of the platform, leaning on the broad stone wall. She laid down the paper and set the bottle on it, to keep it from blowing off in the swift breeze of the dying twilight. Twilight is short in Palestine. The mountains of Moab were dream-faint, rose-purple in the last western reflection, like a curtain of cloud, clear cut against the green-blue sky.

In a few moments they faded, the pale valley faded, large stars with garlands of smaller stars between them hung low in the sky. Yet the sky retained that deep blueness which never fades in Palestine on nights when the moon will rise.

Sephiera took the paper and the bottle. She could not write on the paper now; it was too dark. But why need she hurry? There was plenty of time to die—all night. Since one must die. She went down from the platform and felt her way among rocks and brush and dark fragrant flowers and herbs, down to the rough barren hillside. Here no one would find her. She would wait for the moon.

Her heart ached; it burned. A taut thread of fire seemed to be running from her throat to her heart, burning her life out. She sank down to rest on a sloping mound of sand that shaped itself like a bed to the need of her body. She was tired—so tired.

Saul! If only Saul would come and tell her what to do! Come and take her in his arms and let her die, her breast growing cold against the warmth of him! If only Saul would kill her! To die here, all alone, like a dog on a dust heap! To suffer. Would she suffer? But maybe it would just be going to sleep. Oh, to go to sleep is good.

She prayed. The old childhood's habit, shaken to fragments by the "gymnasium" student's skepticism, by the jolting of a crude science with a crude socialism, reshaped itself in childhood's words on her lips:

"Lord our God, let it by thy will——"

She prayed to die. She prayed for her mother. She prayed that Saul might come. She prayed: "May he find happiness; may it bring him peace and joy." Prayer is wish; and faith in God is the creative urge, the fulfilment of all desire.

Darkness envelopes her. The earth enfolds her, and even death cannot separate Sephiera from the Presence that is in all things, from the beauty that is love.

A brightness in the east, a halo over the mountains. And then into the field of her own brightness the large white moon lifts herself over the border of the plateau. Deep down, a silver streak, the Dead Sea drinking silver until it is a sheet of whiteness. Shadows shape themselves, flowers, leaves reassume color. Sephiera lies revealed, shivering, ecstatic. She sits upright. In this brightness everything is visible as by the light of a dead sun. Now she will die, and in the morning they will find her, like a broken flower on the hillside, part of the earth from which she was broken off. Earth of the fatherland. Is it a defilement to die so, to relax strong limbs that could have worked the earth? Will she never see the sun again? Feel the rain? Yes, sun and rain are substance of her substance, youth of her youth. She must not think. It is decided. This is her fulfilment of love. It must be so, since the others would have it so.

She took the paper to write on it. She found a smooth white stone for a rest.

As she touched the stone, the moonlight made sharp shadows of her fingers upon it. Suddenly she drew them away, as if they had been burned. She thought of the white fossil shells; of the ancient, ancient world. "So old is the Jewish people."

"I loved him before the world began," she thought, "I cannot escape my love by dying. I shall always love."

And then she felt anger. She looked at the little bottle. "Why am I going to die?" she asked herself, "Is it because I hate him, because I hate Batya, and I cannot bear to live with hate? No, it is because I want to revenge myself on them. It is because I cannot kill them, and I will kill myself to punish myself and also to avenge myself."

She did not know what to write. To write kind, loving words would be a lie. One cannot die speaking an untruth.

"I hate them," she said, "and I am killing myself for hate."

A thistle blew sharply against her arm, scratching it. She pressed her hand over the thistle, crunched it and cut her fingers. The pain eased her.

Thistles, thistles and thorns! She threw away the white, dry stone. Suddenly she remembered the garden, the fragrant trees, the pomegranates and passion flowers. She remembered that she had forgotten her hoe there. She had not finished her patch.

How strong she was and able to work! Those strong arms and hands! Dared she destroy them? Out of hate? Yet she had come to the land for love, for love of the land! And she loved Saul, how she loved him, how much more than she hated him! "He, too, loves Palestine; he, too, is working for our land. In the same land we work for the same love."

One never kills for love, only for hate. Love makes life, love makes to live. She was no longer ashamed, though she pictured to herself Saul coming toward her through the moonlight, for love. Was it Saul? Was it not the Jewish people, the love of her land? For them she came, for them she is here. Shame, shame to kill in hate on the barren land that cries out for love! Death no longer seemed sweet to her.

She took the bottle and, throwing it deftly, smashed it to fragments on a far rock. The sound soothed her. Then she went back to the cistern platform, and leaning on the stones, wrote by the light of the wide, white moon:

"Dear Batya and dear Saul: I am going to another kevutza to work. Maybe I shall come back. It is all the same where I work, so we all work for our land.

Your faithful Sister."

As she went back through the garden, she heard voices among the trees. Batya and Saul. So the room would be empty. She pinned her note to Batya's mattress, changed her dress, made a little bundle of necessities, tied into it a little money, and started in the moonlight down the bare road to Jerusalem. The moonlight beat upon her; she was exposed and vulnerable. Alone. And yet everywhere, under her strong young feet, the earth of the fatherland!

She had acquaintances in Jerusalem. They helped her to what she wanted. In a week she was working on a farm in Galilee, in the grain fields among another group of young pioneers.

What a strange girl, so young and pretty and bright-looking; and yet she rarely smiled and rarely talked. Friendly enough, yet distant. No doubt she would melt. They were kind.

Yet she did talk, when she was alone in the field, when she could let herself go.

She bent over, working with fine, unconscious muscles, and she talked aloud to the earth. Talked, not in the Hebrew which she had learned to chatter on her journey, but in the Jewish jargon that she used to speak to her mother.

"Oh, you earth, you good one," she said, "what do people matter after all? How many people have been here, and they are all gone, lying down inside you, so still and contented. But you are always here, always the same, always sending out flowers and trees and things to eat and all kinds of beautiful live creatures. Like that little striped green lizard there. Oh, how he loves the sunshine! But he will be content to go down inside of you again when he is dead, slithering to pieces. And so shall I, so shall I! But first I will serve you, you beautiful earth, as long as you please. Ages ago, all the old prophets and peasants and shepherds, all using you, eating of you, grazing their sheep and camels on you, standing on you to make speeches and say terrible things and then lying down inside of you, quite safe. Land of my fathers! And so many more beautiful people will come, and flowers and thistles and camels and snakes—everything out of the earth. I love my land. That is why I came. I shall love it, I shall work for it always.

"O my land, my land! You are myself, my body. Let them plow deep that the seeds may grow."

ABDUL HADI'S RIFLE

by MOSHE SMILANSKI

THE VILLAGE IN WHICH ABDUL HADI WAS BORN WAS A TINY ONE. On an arid rock, among the Judaean Hills to the South, some ten small houses perched on the slope, looking from afar like bird's nests—such is Abdul Hadi's village. And surrounding this village set in a valley are tall mountains with deep gorges cut into them, which separate it from the outside world. This village is also far from the main highway, accessible only by a narrow winding path. Years could pass without a stranger ever chancing to set foot in the village. The world doesn't know that the village exists, and the village is hardly aware of the outside world. Even the sun scarcely peers into the village. It blesses the village with its light only during the noon-hours: it rises in the morning and shines, but its light does not reach the village—the mountains to the East cut it off; and when it sets in the evening, the shadows from the West lay over the village for a long time. The sun lavishes its light on the mountains, hills and rocks; but the village is mostly immersed in black shadows.

The villagers have almost no arable fields. The narrow strips of sand and clay soil run like veins between the barren rocks, and the men raise what they can by their own hands without using any animals. The amount of grain the villagers manage to extract from the earth during the year for their sustenance is skimpy indeed. On the other hand, there are many sheep in the village, who cavort impishly among the rocks, climb the mountain crags and there find more than their fill of nourishment. All the male villagers are shepherds.

The village was far from man and it had nothing to do with

man. But about one man they used to talk there almost every day—about Ibrahim Pasha.

Their favorite topic of conversation was this hero's exploits. The old people would sit in the shadow of a huge bolder, and nearby, the youth of the village stood and listened eagerly to their stories. And tales were told there of the heroic deeds and the great wonders and the reforms accomplished by Ibrahim Pasha. In his day, the nobleman was not favored over the poor man. The pashas of the Sultan and the princes of the Lebanon stood around his table like servants, and everybody would listen and lose himself in this glorious period.

Salih, Abdul Hadi's father, was the main storyteller.

He, Salih, had fought under the banner of Ibrahim Pasha and had followed him as far as Acre, and to the Hermon, as far as Damascus, and to the Sultan's capital. . . .

Salih told of Ibrahim Pasha's mare, which he had been fortunate enough to see with his own eyes. This was the mare on which Ibrahim used to gallop back and forth, and on which he charged right into the camp of the Turks. And they could not reach her, no bullet could reach her—like a whirlwind she was gone, and none of her pursuers could overtake her, but had to return shamefacedly.

And what marvelous things he told of Ibrahim Pasha's rifle. Could you count the number of shots fired from this rifle? Certainly not. And never, never once did it miss the mark!

As he recounts these wonders, all the villagers, young and old, sit around and listen to his words as if they were new, listen and remain silent, not a sound issuing from their gaping mouths. Even the rocks, these eternal witnesses, seem to listen in awe to the words of Salih, the man from the army of Ibrahim Pasha.

The boy, Abdul Hadi, also stands and listens to the words of his father Salih, listens and dreams about Ibrahim Pasha. . . .

And sometimes the boy leaps on to a ram, grips it by the horns and goes bounding off among the rocks—leaping and frisking and seeing himself riding Ibrahim Pasha's mare. And sometimes he goes out with his bow, and imagines that he holds in his hand Ibrahim Pasha's rifle.

When Salih died, the boy, Abdul Hadi, inherited the rifle

with which his father had fought under the banner of Ibrahim
Pasha. All the youngsters of the villagers envied him. Abdul Hadi
knew what he held in his hands, and he taught his hands to use
this precious instrument. And it became famous throughout the
entire region: There wasn't another rifle like it among all the
villagers in the mountains around. Abdul Hadi loved his rifle and
he guarded it as the apple of his eye.

And Abdul Hadi grew up, married and had children. He
loved his wife and children. But all knew and said: "More than
Abdul Hadi loves his wife, his children and his sheep, he loves
his rifle."

And he really loved it. According to him, this rifle never
missed the mark. The fame of Abdul Hadi and his rifle grew
and spread beyond the borders of his village after he killed the
jackal.

This jackal had been around the village for several years.
Many villagers had tried to shoot it and failed, and they thought
it must be some ghost or phantom or evil spirit. It had cast its
terror over all the villagers who had been afraid to leave the
village alone at night. Then Abdul Hadi volunteered to kill it.
He sat up all night, he and a shepherd band, among the rocks
near the cave. The moment the jackal emerged, Abdul Hadi
took a shot at it—and his first bullet felled her.

Then everybody saw that this rifle of Abdul Hadi's was no
ordinary rifle.

Many times after that Abdul Hadi put himself to the test
and emerged victorious. Many times he was called to the villages
nearby to save them from a jackal that was terrorizing them. And
time and again he came with his rifle and did not disappoint
them; he came and saved them. Sometimes he would wait in
ambush for several nights at the jackal's cave until it would
emerge. But the moment it came out his bullet struck home.

And the fame of Abdul Hadi, and the fame of his rifle spread
far and wide. Whoever mentioned Abdul Hadi also mentioned
his rifle, for there wasn't another like it!

Now there was a sheikh who heard of the fame of Abdul
Hadi's rifle and he took a strong fancy to it.

The sheikh was a powerful and rich man and he ruled over the entire region.

And so the sheikh summoned Abdul Hadi and told him:

"Sell me your rifle and I will pay you handsomely!"

But Abdul Hadi did not answer and in his heart he laughed at him.

"I will give you ten pounds in gold!" offered the sheikh.

Abdul Hadi was taken aback at being offered such a sum beyond his wildest dreams, and he stood there as if paralyzed. For several moments he stood there silently, his eyes downcast. Finally he raised his head, looked the sheikh straight in the face and answered: "No!" And he went from the angry sheikh, sad and heavy of heart, pressing his rifle to his heart.

For almost twenty-five years this rifle had been true to him; how could he now barter it?

Let them say what they will, let people say that new and better rifles have since been invented. But he, Abdul Hadi, knows that such a rifle as he holds in his hands will be no more—only in the days of Ibrahim Pasha were they able to make such rifles.

No! He will not give his honor away to anyone, not for all the money in the world!

The sheikh did not forget Abdul Hadi's rifle, and he remembered what the owner of the rifle had done to him and it rankled within him.

And then the time came for Abdul Hadi's eldest son to be called into the army.

Again the sheikh summoned Abdul Hadi, and he told him:

"Give me your rifle, and it will be your son's ransom and he will not be conscripted."

Abdul Hadi heard this and for a moment he stood forlorn. He thought of his son whom he had raised, and of his wife. He repressed his feelings and he reached out to give the sheikh his rifle. But as soon as he touched it, he was seized with violent pangs of regret, and he lifted his head and answered with finality:

"No! I will not give it!"

The sheikh's face fell. But soon he smiled and said to him: "Well then, go in peace."

And Abdul Hadi's soul went through terrible torment. For

the first time in his life he experienced a mighty battle with his soul.

His wife wept and implored him to give the rifle as ransom for their son. The son did not say a word, but gazed at him with pleading and hoping eyes. It was harder for Abdul Hadi to bear the look of his son than the cries of his wife. And he himself went on trying to persuade himself, torturing himself awake or asleep. . . .

But in the end the rifle won once again!

Abdul Hadi did not surrender his honor and his son was taken into the army.

When the soldiers came to take his eldest son, the face of the old man was pale, very pale, but not a tear welled up in his eye.

And misfortune followed misfortune!

Abdul Hadi was summoned to a distant village in the vicinity of Hebron, to kill the jackal there, that had wrought much destruction and could not be stopped. When he came into the village and they saw the old rifle in his hand, they wanted to give him a new one. But he said not a word; only a light smile played on his lips.

That night he lay in wait for the jackal. When it emerged he aimed his rifle and pulled the trigger. The click of the pin was heard but no shot came. . . .

Abdul Hadi's blood froze in his veins—his rifle had betrayed him.

And the jackal was approaching. He should have reloaded but his hands didn't obey him. And the jackal came nearer and nearer.

It was really a miracle what happened to him here. Suddenly the jackal swung around and disappeared. But the hair on his head had suddenly turned all white.

Abdul Hadi returned to the village a white-haired man, but he did not despair and consoled himself: "This was only an accident. I certainly did not deserve anything at that moment."

But what happened to him next was even graver.

Once the tiny village was visited by the son of the rich sheikh who wanted Hadi's rifle. This young man had seen a great deal of the world. He had been to Jaffa and Jerusalem, to Beirut and Alexandria. All the villagers came and gathered round him, and he sat and told them about seafaring ships and about railroad trains that cover tremendous distances without horses and at miraculous speeds. He also told them about the new weapons, about rifles and about cannons. As proof, he had in his hands a new and shiny rifle that shot at a long range. Abdul Hadi also stood there and listened.

And the young man, the sheikh's son, laughed at Abdul Hadi and his rifle, saying:

"My father wanted to give you two hundred francs for this, but I wouldn't accept such a broken reed as a gift. Do you know, old man, what the fitting place for it is? In the dung heap!"

The color drained from the old man's face and his hands and feet quaked. If he had been told of some disgrace of his own, or of some disgrace of his wife and children, it would not have infuriated him as much as this. But from fear of answering the sheikh's son in kind, he said:

"And I wouldn't exchange my rifle for ten 'shiny-ones' like yours!"

"Maybe yours is still fit for something," answered the sheikh's son, "maybe it's fit to kill dogs!"

"Your new one is only a toy. Mine—its merit is its age!" exclaimed Abdul Hadi. "Nowadays they no longer make such weapons; only in the days of Ibrahim Pasha!"

Finally the sheikh's young son and the old shepherd made a bet as to whose rifle would shoot the farthest.

All the villagers came out to see this duel.

Both selected a distant target.

The new rifle hit the target.

But the old rifle—its bullet dropped half way.

Even the report of the old rifle, in comparison with the report of the new one, was like the voice of a decrepit old man.

The old man's face fell and his heart broke.

The sheikh's young son had cruelly avenged his father.

But Abdul Hadi comforted himself, saying:

"My rifle may not shoot as far as the new ones, but it never missed the mark."

But unfortunately, his consolation was short lived; out of his own home misfortune arose to oppress him.

Eight years his son served in the army, seeing service in every reach of the kingdom. Finally, Abdul Hadi was privileged to see him freed and at home.

All the villagers turned out to welcome him. They sat down and asked for news. And, alas, his son also told them about ships and railroad trains and new weapons.

The old man stood and listened to his son's accounts, and he began to scoff, saying that all this was only a jest of Satan's, all swindle and hocus.

Nor does he believe in the new weapons:

"True, they shoot far, but they are not accurate to a hair's breadth. So what good are they? If Ibrahim Pasha were to rise from his grave now, he would abolish all these 'newfanglednesses' of yours, that are only here to fool the people! All your weapons are not worth my one rifle!"

The son laughed and said that only in his father's experienced and sure hands does this contraption have any value at all:

"If you, father, were to take my rifle, only then would you know and feel that your weapon is a mere shard."

Hardly were the words out of the son's mouth than his father's fist was pummelling his head and face.

Nevertheless he took his son's words to heart and for three days and nights found no rest.

At midnight, when all the houses of the village were fast asleep, the old man arose from his bed, like a thief stole from his house, and made for the fields outside the village. In his hands he held two rifles: his own and his son's.

It was a night of the full moon, bright and beautiful.

The old man walked stealthily, looking back every few moments to see whether any one had spotted him and was watching him. He went farther and farther away from the village.

When he was very far away, among the rocks, he placed the

two rifles he was holding on the ground and sat down and looked back again. He looked all around—until he had convinced himself that he was alone. Now he'll see for himself; now he will convince himself and decide!

On one of the rocks—his friends, the rocks—stand a few solitary trees; they will witness the trial.

The old man raised his old rifle and took a shot at a tree.

Then he raised the new rifle and took a shot at another tree.

Then he placed both of them on the ground and walked over to the trees and examined them thoroughly—and a low sigh, a body-racking sigh, broke from his heart.

He returned to the rifles and repeated the trial.

Again he walked over to examine the trees.

And again he could not control himself—and he sighed.

And for the third time the old man performed the trial; and he saw that his son was right.

Then Abdul Hadi took his rifle, the rifle that he loved and from which he had not parted even for one day, and for which he had given up a great sum of money and his first-born son, and hurled it with all his might from the top of the rock on which he stood down into the gorge—and just stood there.

And in his ears—a noise, the sound of his honor tumbling from ledge to ledge down into oblivion.

Before the break of dawn he returned home, and in his hand —only one rifle, his son's. . . .

No one had seen him leave and no one saw him return. Only the moon and stars and the rocks and the valleys which now bore his secret.

The next day the old man fell sick. Not a week passed and Abdul Hadi was dead.

THE STORY OF A BLANKET

by MAX BROD

THE BLANKET WHICH IS THE SUBJECT OF THIS TALE LAY ONE DAY
with other blankets in a big shop window of a Viennese warehouse. In those days blankets were precious for it was the year
1915 when millions of men went to the front. This blanket was
not displayed for long in the shop window. A young Jewish girl,
just turned sixteen, passed by one day and bought it. She was a
well-built girl, with large black eyes beneath silken eyelashes, and
narrow, pale cheeks. The saleslady looked appreciatively at the
beautiful buyer as she automatically held forth upon the qualities
of the blanket. It was made of pure camel wool, was very warm
and yet very light. Its color was light brown save for a pleasant
design in dark brown running across the width on either side.
The young girl caressed the blanket tenderly—the first caress it
had ever received.

She carried the blanket home and in her little room embroidered industriously and lovingly on one of its corners a design
in scarlet silk thread. As she worked, some tears rolled down, and
a few large drops fell upon the blanket. Thus the blanket made
its first acquaintance with human distress.

After a few days the girl gave the blanket to a young man,
older than herself. He bound it to his knapsack, embraced and
kissed the girl, and made off . . . a most painful parting, for they
did not know if they would ever see each other again. The young
man, also a Jew, was off to the front.

The blanket now came into contact with all the disasters of
war. Despite great effort the dust could not be shaken out of it.
Heavy sticky mud made it almost impossible to distinguish the
pleasant embroidered border. Thick flecks of snow hardened

upon it and covered it in an armor plating. But the blanket did
its best to warm its owner; beneath the open sky, in the dug-outs,
in shelters where soldiers took cover from exploding shells and
hand grenades.

One day it was hit by a bullet which pierced it and wounded
its owner. It was far easier to patch up the blanket than to cure
the wounded soldier. Still the slight wound stood it in good stead,
for it was sent away into quarantine and cleansed of its lice which
are one of the incidental aspects of war. It even travelled with its
owner to Vienna, where it was chemically cleaned and restored
to its former glory.

On another occasion it was spread out upon a lawn by the
girl whose tears had once fallen upon it. She now smiled gladly
upon the blanket as she enjoyed the heat of the sun's rays. Both
the girl and the two boys sitting beside her felt that life was
beautiful. But life is like the weather. Sometimes good, sometimes
bad. One minute you are happy, the next you may be sad.

The blanket was again rolled into the knapsack to sally forth
with its master to the front to encounter adventures. In a very
short time things changed. The blanket could no longer be seen
suspended on the knapsack for it had been hastily stuffed inside.
The old Austrian army had collapsed. Those returning from the
front to their homes on the borders found that the new countries
that had sprung up over night had confiscated their possessions.

Save for a torn and dirty blanket the soldier brought back
nothing to the girl he met at the railway station in Vienna. No
matter how fine a blanket may be, it cannot guarantee amicable
human relationships. Still, it was often spread out on lawns pro-
viding a comfortable seat for two young people who would sit and
eat from a picnic basket and often kiss each other. At times, however, the girl would cry . . . The blanket was completely unaware of the economic crisis and of the hardships endured by
"old" soldiers trying to find work in order that they might one
day marry; it knew nothing at all of those well-to-do men who
can offer a young girl a comfortable home; it failed to understand
the sorry plight of parents impoverished by war, who prayed that
their daughter at least should be free of worry.

Day by day the daughter would hear suggestions, proposals

and warnings. In short, one day the blanket was again spread on the grass beneath the sun's hot rays. Flowers in the meadow shone among the green grass. Thousands of tiny creatures hummed above the flowers. Young men spoke words of love. But it was all different now. It was not the same as when the young girl sat beside him. True, a second or even a third love can be a fine thing, but it does not hold the fascination of a first love. Perhaps it was because the young man could not forget this first love that none of the girls who sat with him on the blanket became his wife. Life is so strange. Now he was in a position to offer a girl comfort, but the woman he so desired was long married to another. And when spring came the blanket lay over a couch instead of being packed into a knapsack. Our young man, who was no longer young, would pace his room day and night. At times people would come to visit him, but they spoke quietly as if fearing to make a noise. The cigarette smoke would hang thickly in the air, but no one would dare to open the window.

Late one night, it was actually after midnight, the owner of the blanket hurriedly packed his belongings, stuffing the blanket in too. He stole quietly out his house, and, soon, the blanket was to hear the regular and monotonous drone of train wheels. Had war begun again? It might very well be, for, after leaving the train, they trudged for some time over a rocky pathway. All told, there were four of them climbing in that steep country. At times they took shelter in caves, but often they were obliged to spend the night beneath the open sky. The nights were cold, and the skies often cloudy. The blanket on such nights tried its best to warm its owner, but the spot where it had once been wounded was becoming threadbare and it had to be handled gently; otherwise the old wound would have opened.

It wandered far abroad and naturally so, for it belonged to a Jew, whose fate it is to be a wanderer.

On one occasion it seemed to be making straight for the sun. That was when it hung drying on the rails of an overcrowded ship on which the passengers had to be most cautious about cleanliness. As the voyage neared its end, several of the passengers cut their way through the water to reach shore and in the rush the blanket was almost drowned. The young man, no longer young, was carried off his feet by a powerful wave. The knapsack which fell from his shoulders was swept away by the waves but fortunately retrieved.

The blanket now wandered through a land which its owner called the Land of his Fathers. It considered it a well deserved privilege, for it was made of camel wool. It was spread out in various huts, in orange groves, by the road sides and near houses which sprang up out of the sands. Eventually, being an industrious and loyal worker, though no longer young, the owner received a job as storekeeper of a builders' group, responsible work which appealed to him.

It thus happened that he heard of immigrants rescued from a burning ship who had been taken to Athlit. They had unfortunately lost all their belongings when being transferred from one ship to the other. Many organizations issued appeals for clothing, underwear and shoes for the refugees. Blankets were urgently required. The storekeeper's blanket, though of good quality, resembled its master, being none the better for wear. It had begun to fray at the edges, and many stains had become engrained in the cloth and would not come out. The storeman, having long since bought a new blanket, donated the old one to the refugees. Just for a moment he contemplated how the fate of that blanket was bound up with his own, but his thoughts were allowed to linger but for a short while, for the timber had already been unloaded in the store and the receipt had to be signed.

The blanket reached Athlit, and when one of the women of Athlit who arrived with her 17-year old son and 16-year old daughter saw its embroidered design she asked that it be given her, despite its frayed edges. At night she lay enveloped in the blanket and dreamed. Would she find the donor? Doubtful, for it had been collected from a central depot.

Her son and daughter had been accepted as members of a kibbutz, but the mother could not possibly think of entering a kibbutz, for she, like the blanket and its former owner, was no longer young. But she had learnt dressmaking before leaving Vienna and in her widowhood had been used to finding work to support herself and her children. Thus she became employed in a stocking factory somewhere near Tel Aviv and managed to earn her living.

If she worked in the afternoons she could not return to Tel Aviv, so she stayed with a friend of hers who lived in a store-room.

The lorry which brought material to the factory where she had recently received employment happened to return that day to Tel Aviv for a second load. The driver and his mate noticed five women standing almost frozen in the roadside, signalling them to stop. They stopped, told the women to jump in, and continued driving.

When they reached Tel Aviv the storeman caught sight of the blanket with the embroidered corner design and, with a smile on his lips asked: "Are you from Athlit? This blanket, you know, is mine." The woman who held the blanket beneath her arm made no reply. She looked at the man in astonishment; it was as if the past had come to life again. Then she looked at the embroidered border, and tears rolled once again upon the blanket. But the man did not see this. He had only noticed the movement the woman made when she turned to him, that sudden uplift of the head and penetrating look which reminded him of a woman he had known long ago.

He looked closely at the woman, leapt from the lorry, and began to speak to her. He was greatly moved. There is something, so to speak, in a first love, something which touches the roots of one's being, something which strikes deep to the heart, which the march of time cannot eradicate. That is, of course, only when it is a true first love.

Here and there the morning mist was dispersing and a blue sky broke through the clouds and shone like a pearl. The early morning carts passed noisily on their way to market. The city began to awaken. And two people stood by the lorry and spoke to each other—and both felt a new light creeping into their hearts.

THE PITFALLS OF LOVE

by YITZHAK SHENHAR

On coming to Palestine, Israel-Zvi looked around and found a group of people from different countries who wanted to cultivate the land, each man by his own efforts. Having found what he wanted, he paid in his share to the funds of the group and, when the day came, he and his fellow-members settled as smallholders on a stretch of land that had been allotted to them in the vicinity of an old established moshava. They each erected two huts—one to live in, the other to serve as a cowshed—planted vegetables, and got in some poultry.

"You ought to complete your household by taking a wife," his fellow-settlers used to tell Israel-Zvi.

And Israel-Zvi would listen and nod his head.

At first he schooled himself to hold his peace, until he had quite forgotten the secret of the rapid flow of chatter that had once been his, in the days when he had worked in a haberdashery shop. He used to wear heavy hobnailed boots that seemed to weigh down his feet and restrain the hurried jerkiness of their motion. Then he applied himself to learning how to speak to the animals, birds and plants—snatches of talk, throaty noises and shrill twitterings.

All day Israel-Zvi used to toil away, and at night he slept upon a couch whose legs sank into the earthen floor. His little hut was wrapped in darkness, silence and loneliness. His fellow-settlers smiled whenever they spoke about him. They used to say that the first time he went out to work in his fields he wore a suit of immaculate white, and that when he came back in the evening it had become a dirty gray.

Ezekiel the watchman, in particular, used to delight in recounting amusing episodes in the life of "Israel-Zvi, Tiller of the Soil." At night Ezekiel goes his rounds mounted on his mare, and looks imposing, with his eyes flashing terror. At midday, however, after getting up from his sleep and divesting himself of his abaya, he is just a weedy, sallow-faced individual with unkempt hair. He then drags himself along from hut to hut, his eyes heavy with sleep and the oppressiveness of nothing to do weighing him down like a burden. This is what he tells:

"One night I saw from afar a light in Israel-Zvi's yard. It was after midnight, all the stars were moving in their courses, and I was mounted on my mare. 'What can the matter be?' I asked myself. I drew near, and saw Israel-Zvi coming out of his hut with a lamp in his hand. He was going towards the vegetable garden . . . What for? Oh, to see how the young tomato plants in the nursery were getting on. Yes, and then he went into the cowshed. 'What on earth are you doing here at this time of night?' I asked. 'I'm worried about the chickens,' he replied. 'They climb up among the rafters of the cowshed and stay there all night. Suppose they should start laying their eggs there—why, they'd fall down and break.' Those are the very words used to me by that 'Tiller of the Soil,' honestly. But there's something more: do listen. On Saturday I found him standing motionless in the field, with his hands outstretched, looking like a scarecrow. He wanted to frighten away the birds that came to peck at the seeds. . . ."

The settlers listen with enjoyment and burst out laughing. Israel-Zvi listens too, smiles and shakes his head in silence.

Once Israel-Zvi went out to plough. It was shortly after the rains. The earth was moist and sticky, and the horses drew the plough along with difficulty. Till sunset Israel-Zvi continued to drive his furrows from end to end, his body tired and broken. The heavy clods of earth, with thorns and briers sticking to them, clung to his boots until he could not move an inch. He removed the plough from the furrow and turned it over on its side. Farmers passing by at that moment saw Israel-Zvi, his legs wide apart, standing as if rooted in the soil of his field. The disc of the setting sun had become a sphere behind his back and looked like a wide-open gate of flame. In the field there was utter silence. Night was drawing on, and lights began to appear in the nearby moshava. The sweating horses stood where they were, half closing their eyes and lowering their heads in rest. Then, when they began to feel the pangs of hunger, they started of their own accord and made straight for home. Once again Israel-Zvi was left alone, smiling, the blackness of the earth beneath him, and his toes aching painfully among the damp clods.

The years passed by. The old-established moshava continued as before, but in the new moshav members came and went. Some did not have sufficient strength to hold out, and had to leave; they went to the towns with the lament of the vanquished upon their lips, while newcomers came in their place and occupied the little huts. Young trees sprung up in the farmyards, and flowering creepers began to cover the fences. The youngsters brought a new song with them into the yards; the faces of the oldtimers were covered by a multitude of wrinkles. All the affairs of the settlement were managed by the oldtimers. Only Israel-Zvi did not cease to be young, even though his face had shrunk, his hair thinned out and his legs became like spindles.

Ezekiel the watchman still goes about from yard to yard, aiming his shafts at Israel-Zvi as of old. The oldtimers are silent and do not listen, but the newcomers are highly amused, and they slap Israel-Zvi on the back as if he were one of them.

"You ought to complete your household by taking a wife," they tell him.

He nods his head, his gray eyes looking like opaque mirrors.

In the moshava on the hill-top there lived a very aged but active woman by the name of Hannah-Leah. She was known to the inhabitants of both moshava and moshav as "Granny." Some time before she had handed over her farm to her son, since then she had devoted herself entirely to good works.

"Israel-Zvi, I shall find you a wife," Hannah-Leah once said to him when they were alone.

Israel-Zvi's face had by then become completely tanned by the sun, save for two patches of white skin behind his ears. Those promptly turned a deep crimson as Granny uttered the words.

He, however, waited patiently, the only step he took being to pile up some planks in his yard with which to partition his little hut into two rooms.

Hannah-Leah looked round among the local girls, but did not find a wife for him. She explored a distant village in the hills of Galilee, but was no more successful.

"I shall walk all the way from Dan to Beersheba on my tottering legs;" Granny comforted him. "I shan't give up. Soon, please God, I shall be going to Tiberias to bathe in the waters. There no doubt I shall be able to find what I'm looking for."

She was still engaged in making preparations for the journey when death came and closed her kind eyes. The days passed by in regular succession; the sun blazed away in the firmament, the horizon was blue and very desolate.

One day Israel-Zvi received a letter from foreign parts. It was from a young girl, a relative of his stepmother's, and she had written at great length from her distant township. She wanted to get away from there; there was no point to her life; there was not a single ray of light; no purpose in it at all. She was longing to devote all her energies to building up Palestine and to helping those who stood in the front line. She said so explicitly. And as Israel-Zvi was a veteran farmer, surely he would stand by her in her need and would not withhold from her the benefit of his advice. The letter contained a postscript in tiny letters to the effect that the writer lacked money for the fare.

Israel-Zvi read the letter and reread it, and looked out of the window at the horizon. He recollected that, while he was still quite young, he had seen a little girl who had come to visit his stepmother, and that her name was Mira. She had been dressed in white, and her slender plait had been tied round with a red ribbon. That had been many years ago. At that time the skin of his face had been altogether soft and white; there had been no callouses on his hands, and it looked as if he might still grow in stature. And now Mira wanted to come here.

Israel-Zvi went along and applied for a loan from the local "Loan and Saving Fund" and immediately dispatched the money to the far-off little town. Once again, he waited patiently, the

only step he took being to take the planks from his yard and put
up a partition in his tiny hut. A few weeks passed, and Mira
turned up at his place in the moshav. She brought with her two
tightly packed trunks, two dimples in her cheeks, and a sunny
laugh that welled up from deep down inside her.

Somewhat confused, she entered the hut, but on seeing
Israel-Zvi's face, she burst out laughing:

"Oh, how funny you are. Are you Israel-Zvi? I expected to
find someone quite different. Why, you haven't grown at all. You
look like a little 'Goy,' ha-ha-ha." Then she raised her glance,
looked round the room and said, winningly: "You won't mind
if I stay in your hut for the time being, will you?"

Israel-Zvi nodded his head and turned upon her his gray
eyes, which now looked like fallow fields that had never been
ploughed.

The first evening she sat alone with Israel-Zvi and told him
about the old town, about people who had already faded from
his memory, about his stepmother and her misfortunes. Only one
thing did Mira omit to tell him: how she intended to help those
that stood in the front line. Israel-Zvi sat opposite her, short and
straight, catching his breath and smiling.

Next day Mira rolled up her sleeves and began to get to work
upon the poor assortment of furniture littered in the hut. Mattresses were aired, and cane mats were spread over the wooden
walls. For the first time since the settlement was founded, the
sound of singing was heard from the farmstead of Israel-Zvi. From
early morning a red herchief fluttered about among the green of
bushes and trees. Ezekiel became a frequent visitor at Israel-Zvi's.
Since the hut was partitioned it seemed to have become very
spacious. Ezekiel, with a kerchief on his head, Bedouin style,
would stand his rifle between his knees and sit there drinking tea.

"Israel-Zvi, Tiller of Soil," he would say, "how long will you
continue to imprison your fair visitor in this palace? Heavens,
man, you should let her see the country, so that she can know
where she is in the world."

Israel-Zvi was busy and preoccupied and never had the time,
so Ezekiel used to offer his services to Mira and would tour the
neighborhood with her. They would walk in the hills and stay at

the nearby kibbutz. At the kibbutz there was dancing by the light of the moon; the large huts pulsated with the vitality of youth; the scent of the fields around was very near and very full.

"I wonder why you chose to join the moshav," Mira would say to Israel-Zvi on returning to the hut. "The kibbutz would suit you far better. That sort of place was specially designed for the likes of you." And she would break off suddenly with a roguish laugh: "What a pity. . . ."

Night after night Mira would disappear from the hut and would return at a late hour.

"Now that you have brought a woman to the household," the old-timers used to say to Israel-Zvi, "you ought to hurry up about it. . . ."

Israel-Zvi would nod, and the patches of white skin behind his ears would turn crimson.

The summer passed by, and the rainy season came. One Sabbath Israel-Zvi turned to Mira and said:

"Mira, to my way of thinking we can't go on like this any more. . . ." and then he fell silent.

"So?" said Mira laughing. "Well, if you don't want me any more. . . ."

"No, no, I didn't mean that." Israel-Zvi mumbled and lapsed into silence. For the first time he was sorry that he had got out of the habit of being talkative. Otherwise he would have told Mira about his way of life, about his intense loneliness, about the idea that he had once thought out so completely. Perhaps he might then have plucked up courage to tell her that since she had come, no other thought had crossed his mind.

But he did not say anything. Mira cleared the things off the table and went over to her side of the hut. From behind the partition she said:

"You are right, Israel-Zvi, we really cannot go on like this. Actually I ought to have told you this before, but for some reason or other I didn't. Well, the fact is that I'm going over to Ezekiel in a few days' time. I know, you're a goodhearted fellow, Israel-Zvi. I shall always be grateful to you, really I shall. After all, you got me into the country and altogether . . . One day we shall pay you back the money you laid out for me."

"Yes, yes," Israel-Zvi replied and nodded his head in the direction of the partition.

The wedding celebration took place in the nearby kibbutz. Carts laden with guests left the moshav, and a number of young-sters from the moshava accompanied them on horseback.

"Aren't you coming with us?" Mira asked Israel-Zvi. "After all you're the only relative we have in the country. You really won't come with us?"

"I?" asked Israel-Zvi in amazement. "No, no . . . I can't leave the farm. . . ."

THE THREEFOLD COVENANT

by YEHUDA YAARI

MY NEIGHBOR IS AN IMMIGRANT FROM GERMANY WHO CAME TO Palestine some time ago among the other refugees from race-hatred and persecution. It was just at that time that we came to live in our new flat in one of Jerusalem's modern suburbs. He lives on the lower floor, and I on the one above.

We have no personal acquaintance with each other. It has always been rather hard for me to get to know my neighbors. Several times a day I pass the door of his flat, and the name en-graved in outstanding Hebrew letters on a brightly polished brass plate gleams at me from the door as though it were alive, pro-claiming "Richard Oppenheimer."

Sometimes my neighbor and I meet in the hall in the morn-ings when I am starting out for work and he, too, is going off about his business. The moment he sees me he raises his hat in my direction, uncovers his flaming red hair, smiles at me and says:

"Shalom. Guten Morgen."

And the echo of his thick, trumpeting voice fills the entire entrance hall.

"Shalom." I return his greeting, raising my hat as well in politeness.

Apart from these infrequent morning meetings and our polite greetings there is no contact between us. Were it not for the aroma of his pot-bellied cigars ascending to me every now and then through his open window I would not know that he was there at all. He is a peaceful sort with quiet ways and his home is just as quiet. There are no noisy children, nor does as much as the hoarse voice of a gramophone or radio disturb us. If anything, it is he who must be aware of the presence of his neighbor. Not that I have either gramophone or radio or even noisy children in my flat; but I live above him and there can be no scrape of a shifted table or movement of a chair or even noisy tread in my flat which does not sound in the flat below like a clap of thunder.

Turning over the paper one morning, I noticed that, as is the custom here, somebody had sent congratulations to Richard Oppenheimer through the columns of the paper on the birth of a son. Which Richard Oppenheimer could be meant? My neighbor? Yes, my neighbor and none other. The person offering congratulations was H. Levy and I knew H. Levy to be my neighbor's business partner; for on their big shop for the sale of pharmaceutical products and cosmetics in the main street the name "Oppenheimer and Levy" was written up large for all to see. I read through the congratulation once, twice and yet a third time, and pondered upon the mysterious ways of our lives. In the very house in which I was living a woman had lain writhing in birth pangs and I had known nothing of it; a son had been born to my neighbor; and although no more than the thickness of a ceiling separated us, I had become aware of the fact only through the pages of a newspaper. Through my brain passed a sudden vision of the woman taken with the first pains, of the bewildered husband taking her to hospital, and so on.

My thoughts went directly on to other things. I forgot my neighbor and the son that had been born to him, and began to consider my daily work.

I forgot my neighbor; but that evening I remembered him

again. I had just sat down to eat supper when there was a knock at the door. I opened it, and in came my neighbor, Mr. Richard Oppenheimer.

"Shalom. Guten Abend."

I invited him in. He stood silent and nervous for a few moments and I had a chance of taking a good look at him. He was red-haired with a narrow forehead, his bronze eyes squinted slightly, his red lips looked as though they were swollen, his body was well-set and soldierly, and the back of his neck, I noticed, was fleshy and scarred. In my Polish birthplace they used to call such a countenance an Esau face. I could see that he found it hard to express himself. So I came to his aid.

"Please sit down, Mr. Oppenheimer, can I do anything for you?"

"Thanks. Yes, yes," he stammered and this time his voice was gentle and restrained, entirely different from the voice that sometimes used to trumpet a greeting at me in the hall below. "Yes, yes; I have a request to make of you. . . . The circumcision will take place tomorrow—I suppose you know that my wife has had a son. . . ."

"Yes, I heard about it, Mr. Oppenheimer. Congratulations." I shook his hand, and it immediately became easier for him to speak.

"I'll tell you quite frankly. I don't know what has to be done. I'm in a fix. I don't know how to say the blessing tomorrow at the ceremony. . . ." His reddish face grew still more flushed and something childlike and innocent about him touched me to the heart; for nothing is so touching as a strong face suddenly softening.

I took my prayerbook from the bookcase and opened it at the Circumcision Service.

"Here you are," said I.

"Hm, hm," he cleared his throat and half-smiled in still greater confusion, "But what's to be done? I don't know how to read Hebrew . . . Not so much as a single letter. Maybe you'd be good enough to write down the blessing for me in Latin characters." In his nervousness he began fiddling with his fingers.

I was nonplussed. There was something astonishing and even

startling in this confession of helplessness on the part of a man like my neighbor. He always went about with such firmness and self-assurance. His morning greeting said: I know everything, I can achieve everything; and now this confession of helplessness, of inability to read the prayerbook. I suddenly felt sorry for him and strove to overcome my astonishment. Sitting down, I wrote him the blessing in Latin characters as he had requested, in block capitals so that he would be able to read it easily. Then I read it out to him three or four times. He in turn repeated it after me with a weird German accent. "Plesset ard Dou . . . to mage our zons ender indo de Govenandt off Abraham our Fader." When he began to grow a little familiar with the blessing I rose, thinking it was finished. I offered him my hand but he did not take it.

"I have yet another request of you; pardon me, for giving you so much trouble," he stammered in a gentle voice. "Another slight request. The name, sir. We find it hard to choose a name for him. You know that my name's Richard. But for our son we want a nice Hebrew name, something out of the Bible . . . Please, do you think you could find us a nice name from the Bible?"

I took the Bible off my table and opened it at random in Numbers. The first words my eyes struck were "Elizur son of Sheneur."

"Elizur," I read from the book.

"Elizur, Elizur." My neighbor was as happy as though he had found a valuable treasure. "Elizur. Wonderful. *Grossartig*. A wonderful Biblical name. Thank you, sir, thank you. Elizur!" He gave me his hand to take his leave and simultaneously invited me to come to the Circumcision. It was a social invitation, made to do his duty, it seemed to me. Nonetheless I decided to be present, for I felt that I had a share in the festivity. I had taught him the blessing and I had found him the name; how could I do other than participate in the celebration?

It was a summer evening, hot, dry and still. I sat on my balcony to breathe a little fresh air. My neighbor sat below me on his balcony. For a long time I heard him murmuring to himself as though he were praying, repeating the blessing, "to mage our zons ender indo de Govenandt off Abraham our Fader." For the first time I was aware that we were neighbors.

The following morning I put on my Sabbath suit, took some time off from work and went to the hospital which my neighbor had mentioned to me the day before, in order to be present at the induction of his son into the Covenant of Abraham. I arrived there a bit late, after my neighbor had already said the blessing. There was a considerable number of people present. I made my way through them till I reached the Seat of Elijah. The circumcised mite was yelling at the first pain he had suffered in his life, and Reb Shlomo Jacob the circumciser, who is said to have inducted a full myriad of Israelites into the Covenant of Abraham our Father, stood bandaging the child.

Richard Oppenheimer was swathed in a new silk tallith and stood leaning against the godfather's chair. His face was set and strained and pale. I felt sorry that when he had entered my flat the evening before I had thought to myself that he had an Esau face. No, the face was now no longer that of an Esau; he now seemed to be a man overwhelmed by something fateful which could not be avoided. There was a tremendous difference to be seen in his face, and I observed it with wonder. When they reached the naming of the child his face brightened up a little. "Elizur son of Richard," he proudly told the circumciser. The latter automatically corrected it to "son of Reuben." My neighbor was perplexed for a moment; then his glance met mine. He smiled at me.

It did not take long for the entire ceremony to be completed and the yelling baby to be taken to its mother. The assembly sat down at the tables to enjoy the wine and sweetmeats. They were a noisy lot, congratulating and toasting one another, chattering, rattling their glasses and laughing. Most of them were German immigrants, of whom I hardly knew one. I sat myself down by the oldest of them all, who had been godfather. Both the expression on his face and the fact of his having been godfather attracted me. His white hair rose like a silver diadem on his head. His trim beard and moustache marked his face as though with a capital T.

He had the face of a respected man, a man of standing. Had I begun addressing him as "Herr Hofrat" he would assuredly have responded; his face told me as much. But since I was not certain I contented myself by addressing him as "Herr Doktor;" nor was I wrong.

"How was the father's blessing, Herr Doktor?"

"Very fine, very fine," replied the old man in a measured, cultured voice. "Very fine, *grossartig.*"

"I taught it him," I whispered in his ear, for I suddenly felt like vaunting myself. Or maybe I just wanted to justify my presence there.

"Indeed, indeed . . . Very fine," murmured the old man politely and poured himself a glass of wine.

"He can't read Hebrew," I continued to talk scandal to him. "I had to write down the blessing for him in Latin characters. He can't even read the prayerbook. Woe to the generation. Eh?"

The old man said nothing but finished his glass.

"I suppose his grandfather was a rabbi in one of the old German communities, and yet he doesn't even know what a Hebrew letter looks like. I'm sorry for the father who brought him up like that."

"His grandfather was not a rabbi, while as for his father, he's sitting next to you. I'm his father."

It was only now I noticed that his eyes also squinted slightly, and that there was some slight resemblance between him and my neighbor. I flamed crimson with shame and cursed myself at heart for this sudden gush of chatter. It was impossible for me so much as to open my mouth and beg his pardon. He poured himself another glass of wine, drank it slowly to the end, and went on:

"Since you taught my son the blessing, you might as well know the whole story. His grandfather was a doctor, and I, his father, am the same. I was converted to Christianity when I was a young man, but I never was a thorough-going non-Jew, for I was circumcised, you know . . . I was always a sort of half-Jew and half-Gentile; a very uncomfortable position. But as for my son Richard, I never had him circumcised, for I didn't want to make his life hard for him. I wanted him to be a complete Gen-

tile, you know . . . And now a son has been born to my son, and
I was honored with the godfatherhood. . . . Do you understand
me properly, my dear sir? I sat there on that chair, holding the
baby on my knees, and I felt that I was holding two on my knees,
that I was supporting my son as well, that I was inducting him as
well into the Covenant of our Father Abraham. . . . Do you
understand me properly, my dear sir? This was a double Covenant . . . no, no. A treble Covenant . . . I too, old man as I am,
I entered the Covenant of our Father Abraham together with
them. . . ."

The old man laughed in a way that was almost frightening,
and wiped a tear from his eyes. That moment his son Richard
came up and pressed his hand.

"Mazal tov, Abba (Good luck, father)" said he in Hebrew.

"Mazal tov," answered the old man as he rose and left me to
go with his son and bless the third to enter into the Covenant;
the baby who now lay in the next room, forgetting his pain at his
mother's breast.

IT'S SHE . . .

by HAYYIM HAZZAZ

IT WAS AT BREAKFAST THAT THE GROOM AND THE BRIDE CON-
fronted each other. The special room was decked out with divans
and rugs, colors and pictures, ostrich eggs and a portrait of Salem
—all ready to receive the young couple.

On Friday morning, after the wedding feast, the bridesmaid
brought the bride into the room and directed her to a divan in
the corner of the room. She whispered something to the bride and
departed. A little later the Mori brought the groom in and placed
him beside the bride. He poured some water on his hands,

brought the set table over to him, bent over and placed the groom's knee over the bride's, and blessed him:

"The Lord bless thee and keep thee; the Lord cause His face to shine upon thee and be gracious unto thee."

When he finished his blessing, he left the room, closing the door behind him. They were now alone, and they sat there as if they were total strangers.

Yaish sat dispiritedly, grieving in his heart. He remembered Lulwah, that beautiful girl who had been taken from him by force. Her image danced before him as he sat there pining for her. Finally he took hold of himself, shook off his reverie and put aside that whole painful episode. He arose and looked fixedly at this slip of a girl who sat mutely on the divan. She was loaded down with the fineries that others had loaned her for the occasion. His heart went out to her, and it became as two hearts.

He rinsed his hands, blessed the bread and held out a piece to her: "Eat . . ."

She shook her head in refusal.

He sat down wondering what to do next.

After a while he said: "You must eat just as I eat."

"I've already eaten," she whispered shyly.

"Eat, and don't be bashful. You have nothing to be ashamed of."

"I'm full."

"But now you must eat what I give you."

Against her will she took the bread and brought it inside the veil.

He poured a cup of arak, said the blessing and drank, then poured another cup and offered it to her.

"Drink," he ordered.

"I don't drink," she retorted a little boastfully but still looking at the floor.

"You must."

"I have a headache."

"Nothing will happen . . . d-darling."

She lifted the veil to her mouth and took a sip.

"Drink it all." He made a gesture as if to take off the tower-like tiara on her head, and lift the ornaments and veil from her face.

She turned away, pleading: "Let the bridesmaid come and take it off."

"I don't need a bridesmaid, I can do it myself."

Her face was revealed. He looked at her and saw that she was extremely beautiful, resembling Lulwah as he imagined her. He became very excited, leaped up and cried out elatedly: "It's she! It's she!"

A TALE OF TWO MULES

by SHLOMO ZEMACH

BEFORE DAWN, WHEN THE GRASSES OF THE PLAIN BEGAN TO TURN blue, the two mules did not go out to graze as was their daily habit. A sack was placed on the back of Razzala and a thick rope set about her loins. The reins and bits were set on their heads and in their mouths; and then Ali stretched his legs apart, mounted Razzala and started out. Razzala looked tremulously towards her companion, seeking support in an evil day; but she saw only the malign smile hovering between the bristles on Atra's jaw. The scents of wild grasses grew faint, grew distant and finally ceased. Their hooves struck obstructive stones. The horizon approached and it seemed as though they had entered a long gloomy cave. The hill-slopes cut off the distances. The hind leg could not find the trail of the fore-legs, and her body with Ali upon it was lifted up and aloft. The path was full of smashed chalk; there was no expanse of sky, nothing but fearsome rocks on either side.

At sunset they came out on the King's highway and stopped to rest. They drank salty water from a deep well, and then con-

tinued their journey. On every side mules, she-mules, horses, asses
and their masters flowed along with them till they comprised one
vast troop. Hubbub was plentiful; so was timidity. Long sticks
and short thick cudgels surrounded them on every side, beating
right and left; there was no refuge. The road heaved with the
beasts between the crooked, winding walls on either side.

Yet all the same Razzala soon regained her former spirits.
After all, there was much in the scene to attract her. Dozens of
donkeys brayed with weird stretchings of the throat and spread-
ings of their nostrils. The neighing of the horses could be heard
over vast distances, and they answered themselves and repeated
their neighings any number of times. The red tarbushes floated
and sank, sank and floated among the heads of the animals like
anemones among the grasses of the plain after a night of rain.
Razzala's legs grew tense; she threw back her mane and lengthened her paces. What was more, she drew her companion after
her, sniffing at her and tickling her with the bristles of her nostrils
as though trying to persuade her to cheer up and not remain so
dejected.

And Atra appeared willing to oblige her. The two mules began to forge ahead between the troops of animals until they came
out in front. At the roadsides near ploughed furrows, green
prickly shrubs could be seen, with clusters of leaves quivering
along the length of their branches. The wind blowing on the
face was moist and soft as silk. And it was good.

But as usual Atra quickly repented of her actions. All of a
sudden she set three legs firm in the ground and the fourth in
Razzala's belly for a warning. Razzala let her tail droop and, as
though she had been caught while up to mischief, started back
and also began to go slow. Her large blue eyes grew red, for the
sun, a huge crimson ball, was sinking over the hill-tops.

They entered Sidon at evenfall, and stopped to rest in a
wide open space among the other market animals. The stars of
their homeland skies did not shine overhead. Dew fell; it was salt
and burning. Razzala and Atra stood erect all night long, ears
pricked, listening startled to the tumult of the seawaves. The
noise was new and inexplicable. Something was rolling and thun-
dering. They knew those noises. But yonder in the plains of their

homeland those noises came from overhead, heralding bounteous rains and fresh green herbage in a soft, sweet pasture. Here the thunder came from the deeps of earth nearby, under their very hooves so to say. And the sea went on hammering and thudding without a break, in measured strokes, its sound never ceasing; like the pain and yearnings which had already begun to eat the hearts of the exiled mules. . . .

When dawn came it was not the grasses of the plain that turned blue. Houses became white. From the minarets sounded the long tremolo of the summons to prayer. And the city of Sidon lay before them like a very weird beast, its grey wings outspread and beaten flat to earth, with mouths in dozens yawning open to swallow all that drew near.

Only when the sun rose did Ali appear. With him was another man whom the mules did not know. Ali separated the two mules, took hold of Razzala's reins and began to run her along the open space. Then he brought her back, took Atra and did the same. He repeated this several times, showing the paces first of Razzala and then of Atra. Many men came and stood round them. Hands passed over their bodies and pinched their skins, raised their legs, forced their muzzles open and examined and counted all their teeth. They listened to a heated dispute between these strangers and their master Ali, who grew excited and pointed to each individual tooth with his fingers.

The men shouted and slapped them on the haunches. Then Ali had to run them backwards and forwards again. The men raised their eyelids and stared in; and at last the reins were placed in the hands of one man, and before the mules appeared a broad straw hat, yellow and smelling of moist straw.

Ali's tarbush disappeared. To the surprise of Razzala, Atra was in a cheerful mood. Though she did not enjoy novelties, she seemed to be happy at the change this time. In her sight the straw hat seemed to be quite worthless and contemptible. She slowly nuzzled her head along her companion's back, withdrew her lips and with her yellow teeth began to nibble at the hat. Her belly began to rise and fall like a bellows while she strove to hide her laughter and mockery. Her ears drew back and pressed against her temples, while hot mocking tears shook in the corners of her eyes. She opened half her left eye and winked to Razzala to notice what she was doing. And this time the bleary, cloudy eye showed a strange satisfaction.

Suddenly the straw hat felt what was happening, bent down, straightened up, raised its stick and thrashed mercilessly. Atra turned her head to her companion. One of her ears was cut open and ran blood. The mocking tears in the corners of her eyes dried up. Her gaze grew red and hot with shame and anger. In vain did she look round for the vast plains of the homeland. In front of her she saw only the open marketplace full of animal heads and tarbushes. But the tarbush of her master Ali was not there. Humbly she lowered her head, and whispered to Razzala: we are in a strange land, we have fallen into captivity.

In a little while the straw hat went ahead and led them out into the road. The road was paved and the two mules felt sacks of oats on their backs. They passed along hill-slopes. Fields of massed maize shone green in the distance and a sea-breeze lowered their heads before the sun. In the distance a wrinkled green water-snake twisted and twined between the rocks, held captive by plants and tall grasses. Bulrushes brushed the air with their silvery beards. There were also pools of water with buffalo-nostrils floating in them and tiny fat eyes throwing foolish glances aloft at the blue of heaven.

Afterwards they found themselves enclosed once again amid dread rocks. On either side along the road lay black stones plotting evil. Across all the hills these black patches lay scattered in heaps, adding to their fear.

Sadness began to oppress their chests once more. And there was no end to the road. They journeyed and stopped, stopped and journeyed on. They ate oats and drank water. The oats tasted good in the mouth but gave them pains in the belly. Their hooves were cut to pieces and their bellies sank down. The straw hat was silent, did not sing songs and did not say nice things, did not slap caressingly along the back of the neck; and this endless, purposeless marching on and on only increased the desolation in their hearts. . . .

But at last, as they descended a round and lofty mountain, there suddenly spread out before them a very broad flat blue

space. The sun was beginning to climb and the mountains danced
all around. The blue space moved and swayed in the scarlet light.
The two mules stood still. Razzala whinnied: the plain! the plain!
Atra was also excited, and a spark of hope shot into her dull gaze.
Both of them mended their paces and with great strides leapt
towards the sea of blue.

And their hearts wellnigh failed . . . It was a false hope
. . . That was water below, a vast amount of water. Kinneret,
the Sea of Galilee, stroked their wrinkled legs, covered as they
were with the dust of distant wayfarings. Tiny little humpy waves
stuck out long curling crimson tongues at them. They could hear
the laugh of waters, come from afar and rushing mockingly at
them. And Atra and Razzala started back. For below them at
their feet they could see, in the flowing blue-green wrinkled
patch, the faces of two vexed and grieving mules.

Ilanit, the little farming village, was built on a hill-top and
surrounded by mountain-peaks. Its houses seemed to foam down
the hill-sides till they reached the valley below. It seemed as
though at any moment they might break loose from their founda-
tions and slide down in one great pile of stones, which would in
turn be swept away by the furious rains to one of the distant
water-courses winding and twining among the mountains east-
wards. Red-tiled roofs like huge tarbushes faced the sunshine
cheerfully, and side-tracks and by-paths ran twisting and turning
in every direction; while the little stones strewn across the fields
glittered sharp and piercing. The leaves of the olive-groves shone
silver, and when the wind teased them silken veils would be
raised between the heavens and the earth. Here and there rose
a solitary eucalyptus, slender and scanty-leaved, showing the mot-
tled bark of its trunk, while hard by the houses a single silent
cypress might mount aloft, wrapped in grief and waiting for
something. . . .

It was to this village that the straw hat brought Razzala and
Atra at midnight. The mules were tired out with the toil of their
long journey and paid no attention to the spot they had reached.
They let themselves slide to the ground. They did not touch the
hay set before them, but fell fast asleep. A few hours later they

woke up, raised their heads and sought the stars in the skies. But everything was perfectly dark. In every crack and crevice lurked creaking evil spiders, chewing little pellets of dust. To right and left other she-mules stood in a long row. The ground underfoot was smooth, hard and cold. An iron chain curled round the neck, its end tied to the manger in front of them. The slightest movement brought a pleasant yet strange tinkling, as though a tiny bell had been hung at the neck. And Atra leaned over to Razzala, whispering: we are in captivity.

Razzala raised and stiffened her mane and asked: what shall we do? But through the darkness she saw the corner of her companion's half-opened eye, telling her that they would do nothing except wait and see what was going to happen. Razzala was not calmed, though, and her mane did not fall back across her neck. Instead she restrained her grief and rose to her legs.

Fine rays of light sifted through the tiles of the roof and dug into the bits of straw and chaff in the manger. Along each of these rays danced a multitude of many-colored motes, circling mazily. That was how the stars had sparkled yonder on misty nights.

The straw hat entered, slapped Razzala's haunch hard; it was a strange blow, for she did not know whether it was intended to hurt her or merely to be taken as a joke. In the stable appeared many straw hats, each of which went up to a pair of the mules standing in front of the mangers. And the sound of blows on the flesh of the haunches could be heard all down the row. Then they set on their bodies a whole network of ropes and chains. Their limbs seemed to contract and submit. And meanwhile the straw hats spoke in a strange tongue, of which Razzala and Atra could not understand a word.

They were taken out and found themselves within a large pound. In it were a cistern, waggons and many tools, sharp and flashing white fire. The mules gazed around in astonishment. And there they were, led by the straw hat to one of the waggons and harnessed to it. Razzala tried to oppose this, and of set purpose began mixing up the ropes fixed to her legs. But Atra winked at her with her left eye, which was half open and twinkling with cunning, to restrain herself; and so Razzala did. They started off, and the waggon dragged behind them. The wheels rattled. The chains jingled. The hooves hammered. Razzala's ears twitched up to a point. What were all these noises? And the mules went down the slope.

The wheels pushed them as though urging them on; and they hastened their stride, for something heavy began pressing on the back of their necks and seemed to choke them at the throat. Razzala's eyes opened wide. Here was Ilanit village with its houses, red tarbushes on their heads; it was nice to drag this waggon, to let it down and pull it up as you desired. She tried to hinder the running of the wheels and stop the sound of the jingling. She stopped. Atra also stopped. And how remarkable! So did the waggon. The rattling stopped, and there was a silence.

Razzala was already preparing to start off again when a sharp hiss cracked overhead. A long, coiled, strangling snake curled about her neck, and at one point along the back of her neck dug in its fang and left a sharp, searing sting. For a moment she did not know what they had done to her, till Atra signed to her in great concern: let us run for our lives! They are threshing our flesh with whips!

But Razzala did not know what to do. She stood astonished, for no whip had ever touched her before. The network of fine veins that spread over her grey belly suddenly swelled up, she trembled and a tremendous tumult deafened her ears. She turned her head, gazed contemptuously at the straw hat and asked it: do you intend to beat me?

At that very moment the loud hiss sounded again, and the coiled snake twined once more, this time round her belly. It was even more painful than the first time. Once more the fang stung and burned in the back of her neck. Atra moved her legs and urged her as well to hurry along. But Razzala had lost her senses. The ancient blood, proud and free as the stormwind of the plains, with its training in warfare and racing, boiled in her veins. Atra with all her cunning, her wisdom and carefulness now mattered to her no more than a fly. Razzala lifted up her hindlegs and showed the straw hat her hooves. Her haunches broadened, her back shrank together, her tail began switching and her eyes filled with blood. With a single movement the harness was

snapped, the crosspiece broke in two, and Razzala's body shot sideways like a keen arrow down the slopes of the hill which was
strewn with glittering gravel. Pillars of dust rose and hid her;
then they collapsed in the morning breeze and fell to earth; and
the same instant far beyond that spot, others were born in
which flashed a black light-dappled patch.

Atra stood harnessed to the waggon, deep in her own
thoughts. She could not understand what had happened at all.
That light-headed Razzala! Such strength and such enthusiasm!
It was true, as Atra knew very well, that her companion's uprising
and revolt were all in vain. Yet such strength and enthusiasm!
Atra shook her head.

She saw the storm that had been raised round about. Out of
every house-door came straw hats armed with pitch-forks, cudgels
and whips. And when she saw the pillars of dust rapidly growing
more distant and all but at the slopes of the hill on the horizon,
she quivered with expectancy. Maybe Razzala would succeed in
escaping from her pursuers. And so she stood bowed of head,
holding back with all her strength the waggon which pressed
upon the back of her neck as she stood on the slope; and her
short thick legs trembled.

But it was no use; in a little while the pillars of dust grew
quiet and small and began to return to Atra. She understood
what had happened. Razzala had fallen into captivity once again.
The pitchforks and the cudgels surrounded her on all sides, and
here was Razzala taking tripping sideward steps. Her mane was
arched as though she had gone out on some triumphal procession.
Deep wounds gaped along her skin, and the foam of her lips was
red. Even at a distance her burning gaze rested on Atra.

And Atra could not face that gaze. In it seethed contempt
and a secret complaint, and she seemed to hear her voice saying:
Atra, my friend since childhood, why did you leave me in the
hands of these strangers without coming to my aid?

But now she had come up to the waggon again. They stopped
her beside it, fixed the harness afresh, and the straw hat ordered
her to go on. The two mules moved off. The wheels rattled, the
chains clanked. And this time Razzala was full of speech. She
emptied out all her heart to her companion. They had thrown

stones at her. She had already been a long way off when suddenly a red tarbush had appeared and stood in front of her. It was her master Ali, she said to herself, come to deliver her from those who pursued her; the plain and all its wonders had appeared before her. She had approached the tarbush and he had taken her reins. But he had betrayed her and handed her over to her pursuers.

Razzala's voice shook. This time Atra did not mock at her. Her lips drew near those of Razzala, which were flecked with pink foam, and she licked them compassionately. With her tongue she licked the wounds on the other's body. And each of the mules after her own fashion remembered the dear plains of their homeland, their freedom and their youth. A pleasant melancholy weighed down on the chest. The waggon rattled. A sea-breeze blew. The two mules dragged the waggon, lowering their heads under the weight of memories, while the storm passed out of their hearts. And the sun stood high in the midst of the heavens.

Thereafter Razzala and Atra lived the lives of all the mules which slept together with them in the stable. Every morning the man with the straw hat would come in, slap them on the haunches, put on the harness and lead his beasts out to the day's toil. The two mules rapidly learnt all the duties of field and farmyard. In the rainy weather when the storms covered the meadows of the valley with a soft carpet of grass, they both plodded the length of the furrows, dragging the plough after them and astounded to see the green being destroyed and transformed into brown. In summer, during harvest time, the waggons with the crops were brought with especial pleasure to the threshing floor. It was true that the straw hat used to crack the whip just over their heads, but he never actually touched them.

And the days passed. There was work in the fields and rest and food in the stable. Now and again they met young darting foals at the fences; and the foals would send their bright moist gazes across to them. Of Razzala they approved. And sometimes a foal's head would approach her own and the bristles of the nostrils moving against one another would awaken some secret, baulked and painful longing.

At bottom Atra was jealous of her companion but she over-powered this feeling. Indeed, she concentrated all her thoughts on finding methods for lightening Razzala's heavy labors. During one cold winter night, when raindrops beat on the tiles and the floor was cold, and the mules were half-asleep, standing on three legs with the fourth slightly bent and as though hanging in the air—on one of those winter nights this was the thought that came to Atra: when she works let Razzala show her liveliness and diligence while Atra of set purpose behaves as though she were the slothful and backward one. Razzala started at the suggestion: but they will beat you! said she. But Atra cunningly screwed up the corners of her eyes and pressed out of them a mocking smile, as though saying to her companion: my thick skin doesn't fear the whip and all its crackings.

And it became a regular practice. When they climbed up the hill and the waggon was heavily loaded, or when they ploughed heavy, thick clay soil, Atra would suddenly dig her four feet into the ground and refuse to budge, while Razzala would tug within her harness as though she wished to pull Atra after her and urge her to go on working. Then came the turn of the whip. It ploughed deep ribbons in Atra's coat, but made no difference. She stood fast, not a single part of her body even flinching. Her belly alone swelled up. Her ears lay back flat against her temples and her ribs widened with laughter and the desire to annoy. Then she turned her eyes on Razzala, and when she saw that the patches of sweat on her companion's skin had evaporated and that she was once again breathing normally, she would start work again of her own free will and not at the behest of the whip.

But now something happened which Atra herself could not understand, nor how and when it began to happen. She had grown so accustomed to half-close her left eye and look out through it sideways as though waiting for a foe, that it had be-come her normal way of looking. When she ploughed or did any other work she would now secretly and without attracting atten-tion loosen the harness.

It was a sort of weakness which she could not overcome. Atra seemed to start out first, followed by her companion; but she knew very well that Razzala was carrying the whole load. Razzala would tug at the waggon with the last remnants of her strength. Her coat began to shine, the dappled hair of her haunches seemed to curl, while drops of sweat gathered in the wrinkles of her belly and dripped to the ground. When they returned to the stable and Atra saw the stumbling gait of her companion, she suddenly regretted what she was doing, and a gleam of guilt shone in her cunning eyes; but she would not give up her game, and next day went on as before. She tried to silence her sense of guilt by giving Razzala part of her own food. But it did not help. Her companion's appetite decreased and she did not even finish the fodder that was set before her.

The trick did not pass unnoticed by the straw hat. Razzala's leanness and weakness had awakened his concern and he sought the reason until he found it. Early one morning the mules returned from the fields, dragging after them a waggon-load of peas. As usual Atra let slip one of the ropes. Razzala stiffened, breathed to the bottom of her lungs and took all the load upon herself; her slender legs trembled with weariness. And then suddenly came the cracking of the whip over their heads with a jubilant sound and a great noise. The end of the lash touched Atra's neck only slightly, but this time there was tied to it an iron wire as sharp as an awl; and where it touched it drew blood.

Atra jumped from her place. It was not the pain that started her. But they had discovered her cunning trick, and how would she be able to look Razzala in the face now? In order to discover whether it was not just an accident, she tried to slip her harness once again. This time the storm of blows raged overhead in a torrent, crack and slash, one after the other. There was no doubt about it. The secret was out.

Thereafter she changed her behavior. She took upon her shoulders the whole burden of the work. Some pathological liveliness came into being within her and almost reached the point of madness. All her heavy strength burst outward. With lowered head and waggling chest and bottom she dragged the plough almost, one might say, enthusiastically. At the shout of her master she would start up hastily, and a tremor would run down her spine, as though she were preparing to do her duty once again

during a long hard day. Now her eyes were wide open, and a
new flame flickered in them. One dim feeling filled her; she would
atone for all her sins against her companion by hard, bitter, un-
remitting toil.

But she was too late. Razzala's health had been thoroughly
undermined. Leanness did not cease to consume her flesh, and
her bony skeleton could be distinguished clearly under her thin
coat. The same mincing gait as before it was true, could be observed in her walk, and the muscles still twitched on her haunches
and her chest. But these were only vestiges, smoking firebrands
plucked from the great burning which was now dying down in
everybody's sight. She wearied at a moment's notice, sweated
amain, stopped in the middle of her work and was compelled to
gasp for breath with dilated nostrils; while the light of her eyes
and her whole body grew fainter from day to day.

One morning, when the straw hat came in as usual to summon them to work, it found Razzala's manger full of fodder
which had been set before her the day before. She was lying
doubled over, her head turned backwards and her eyes wearily,
wearily straying hither and thither. He tried to shake her, but
she did not respond to him and did not rise. The straw hat rested
a despairing gaze upon her and turned away. On the floor lay a
pile of useless bones. He went up to Atra, took her rein and
prepared to take her over to another part of the stable and pair
her with one of the other beasts there. But suddenly he felt his
arm gripped as in a vice. Atra's yellow teeth were set in the flesh
of his arm, which she held unyieldingly, in vicious silence. He
wailed aloud. Atra almost closed her eyes, as though she were
enjoying some tasty morsel; but she did not let go.

At the cry of her master all the grooms and waggoners in
the stable rushed over, and blows descended upon her from every
side. But Atra would not give up her spoil. She went on creasing
up her eyes, and the cunning smile lurked in their corners. Only
after she was satisfied did she open her mouth wide and quietly
plunge her muzzle into the manger before her, calmly beginning
to chew stalks of grass left over from the night before.

That day she did not go out to work. She remained standing
by Razzala. She stood bent over her, breathing her warm breath.

There was an emptiness in her heart. But she stood where she was, without moving all that day and all the night through.

Before dawn, when the morning star arose, she suddenly became very frightened. The warm breath from her companion's nostrils was gradually growing more chilly. It seemed to her that it had stopped. She could hear only the creaking of the spiders in all the corners and cracks. Across the odds and ends of straw a weasel hastened with tiny paces, dragging her prey behind her. Through the darkness she could see only one of Razzala's eyes, blinking and rolling. In it there were so many yearnings and entreaties, so much helplessness. Atra carefully loosened the chain which tied her to the crib. She went right up to Razzala and lay down beside her. She licked her neck, and as in those happy days yonder on the plains of their homeland, next to the tent of Ali under the star-strewn skies, she placed her head on the back of her companion's neck.

"What ails you, Razzala?" she quietly asked.

"Nothing. All is well. I am in the plains of my homeland."

"Indeed. Indeed."

"And spring has come to our country."

"Who told you this Razzala?"

"The starry little blue flowers peep at me from the grass. And the flies have awakened to disturb my rest."

Atra remembered the rain and the taste of the grasses in the meadow. Her mouth began watering. She leaned further over Razzala and asked in a whisper:

"And are the stalks of the thistles still sweet?"

"Very sweet, Atra. But tonight a great herd is resting at the camp."

"How do you know?"

"All the grass is covered with droppings, and there is an evil smell."

She became silent, turned her head aside and stretched out her legs. Her eyes went on blinking very fast indeed. But the cold of her body increased, and the rigid, outstretched legs froze. Atra approached her and touched Razzala's jaw with her bristles, only to start back in fright. The soft grey smooth jaw which she had so loved was also as cold as snow. Its bristles had become chilly too, and sharp as the spines of the artichoke on the Syrian plains.

Then she understood what had happened. Here was Razzala lying in front of her; but there was no breath of life in her any longer. Atra sprang up. At first she wished to get away from her companion, and the chain began to make itself heard. But she changed her mind and remained where she was.

Once again she lowered her head. Memories, many of them, began to sprout one after the other. They grew larger, grew together and filled her entire skull. The plain. Nights filled with dew and stars. Ali and his tent. The city of Sidon and the waves of the sea. The straw hat. The sea of Galilee and the angry, weary faces of mules. Razzala's revolt. Work. Work. Work.

Little by little she felt a new world opening before her. A feeling of orphanhood and loss was already part of her. She suddenly felt how all her life long she had cozened, tricked and evaded her share. She had loved Razzala with all her mulish spirit. Razzala had been her all in all, with her naughtiness, her simplicity, her liveliness, her bursts of emotion, her gentleness and her beauty. Together with her there had been good reason for her caution and her shrewdness. They had only existed for the sake of Razzala and on her behalf. Now they had no meaning. They no longer had any value. There was an empty feeling within her, like the sense of a great hunger. The corners of her eyes wrinkled tight. Out of them squeezed round salt tears. But these were not tears of mockery. They were new, different. She had never known any tears like them.

So deep was she in her mulish musings that she did not notice the straw hat stealing up and placing a muzzle of iron wires over her jaws. But when she did, she remained quiet. When they came to put the traces on her back she offered no resistance. Calmly and indifferently she left her place in the row and prepared to do her master's will. When he called her she tugged at the harness alone, forsaken and submissive, with all her strength. This time, she felt, they harnessed her to a very heavy load. But she felt too weary to turn her head according to her usual habit and see what they had done with her. Absolutely submissive, she lowered her

head, tensed her flanks, breathed deep and strong, took hold of
the soft ground with her hind legs and strode forward.

The load dragged behind behind her, hesitated, sank in the
soil and dragged again. She half-closed her eyes out of habit, but
there was no cunning smile in them any longer. Now they showed
deep grief, despair and indifference. And she went out to work
alone, forsaken, solitary, with a sense of orphanhood searing her at
heart.

For she did not know that it was the carcass of Razzala her
companion that she was dragging away to the fields, far from the
houses and their dwellers, to be carrion for the jackals, food for
the kites and the crows.

GROWING UP

by LEAH GOLDBERG

THIS TIME I FOUND HIM IN A RESTAURANT. HIS FEET WERE STRETCHED
out confidently in front of him, and his upper lip sported a thin
moustache. He had the expression of a person who found it not
unusual to be sitting in the company of grown-ups.

"How is the guest?" I asked.

"The guest is relaxing," he answered in an adult way.

I offered him a cigarette. He took it hesitantly, but then
puffed on it with ostentatious enjoyment. It is such a simple matter to be seventeen and a half. His young mother kept throwing
merry, knowing glances at him from the corner of her eye. I
remember how I once took him to the theater when he was seven
or eight years old. It was a performance for children. We walked
along the road hand in hand. And now, here he is sitting with me
smoking in public. And now——

Our conversation is not running smoothly. What can I tell him? I know that in thirty minutes the bus will take him to his station, and tonight he will be standing guard on the border of his colony, doing his duty whatever it may be. He had no ambition to do brave things. He loved plants, animals and little children. Soon he will get up and go. What do I know about him? What does his mother know, looking at me with that secret expression of adoration? Whom is he worried about there at night? About himself, us, all of us? Are we the only ones worried about him? Perhaps someone cares for him, perhaps his life is dear to some young girl. The mystery of growth, the mystery of boy becoming man, the mystery which becomes more complicated every day. When everything which is so simple is no longer simple.

He answers our questions unwillingly, with a minimum of words, in a way devoid of all emotion.

He knows all types of weapons well. "But I have never hit anybody." And after a long pause,

"Thank God."

Soon he will get up and leave, soon his mother's merry look will sadden, soon I shall begin talking in his absence on the usual topic: our young people. . . .

And we? We the witnesses of growth, we who wonder about these simple things in nature, we whose maturity should protect them. We are now protected by them.

THE PRISONER

by URI AVNIERI

THE ENEMY'S RESISTANCE HAD BEEN BROKEN, AND HIS TROOPS HAD evacuated the village. He was now confining himself to ineffectual sniping from the ridge of hills on the other side. Now and then an occasional bullet would whizz far above one's head, like a lazy bee. The enemy's snipers were firing at random without even bothering to raise their sights. There was no longer any fear of a counter-attack.

The lads dispersed in groups into the narrow alleys of the village looking for prisoners, ammunition and souvenirs, especially souvenirs. They were not out for anything valuable—just a kufiyeh (kerchief used as a head-covering), tarboosh or string of beads. The sapper who turned up with an ornate narghileh created quite a sensation.

Rafi went off by himself: he wanted a little solitude. He wandered along a deserted alley and entered a house. He stood there a while, plunged in thought, until a commotion outside interrupted his reverie. He was out of the room at a bound. At the end of the alley he saw an Arab boy struggling to elude the grasp of several soldiers. The boy must have been about twelve years old. He was putting forth all his strength, his eyes dilated with fear. His hair and eyes were black; but despite his dirty and dishevelled appearance and expression of fear, his face retained a certain beauty. There was a pride in his features that was at variance with the fear in his eyes.

"What d'you want of him?" Rafi asked.

"He's a spy," one of the soldiers replied. "I tell you, he's just a dirty spy. We found him hiding in a dark corner of a room. He was going to sneak out across the lines at night and give away our positions to the Egyptians."

"You can't do anything to him," said Rafi. "You heard what Yisrael said last time: he'd pitch in to anyone who touched a prisoner. We must take the boy to him."

The lad said nothing during the interrogation. He hadn't left the village because it was *his* village. Just that—*his* village! Yisrael, the Company Commander, who was asking the questions in broken Arabic, looked at the lad in astonishment. He had never heard such a simple, yet astounding, statement from an Arab prisoner.

"What shall we do with him?" Yisrael asked. One of his endearing qualities was that he used to consult his men, just like in the old days of the underground, when the Army was still the Hagana. "I think we ought to send him off to join the other refugees. Even if he stayed behind to spy, he couldn't tell the Egyptians anything they don't already know."

The lad, who did not understand a word that was said, looked with fear-stricken eyes at the knot of unkempt, bearded soldiers. "It's my village," he mumbled in Arabic, "mine, mine!"

Rafi gazed at the lad. He began to take a liking to him. The poor boy might be an orphan. If he joined the refugees he would starve like them. An idea crossed his mind. "How about letting him stay with us?" he suggested.

The others looked at him as if he had taken leave of his senses—an understandable reaction just after a battle. "What do you mean, let him stay here? What'll we do with him? He's liable to go off at any time and give information to the enemy."

Rafi tried to reason with them. "That's simply nonsense about spying. You've just got a crazy idea into your heads. If you let him stay with us," at last he stumbled upon a convincing argument, "he can be our servant. He can bring us our food, wash dishes and make himself generally useful. Why should we let him go and serve the Egyptians?"

"That's an idea," said Shmulik. Thereupon a general discussion ensued. The men divided up into pro-Hasan and anti-Hasan factions (Hasan was the lad's name). Strange to say, it

was the "toughs" who espoused the pro-Hasan cause most warmly.
They decided the issue, and Hasan stayed.

The village was perched on a curiously formed hillock. The
hillock was one of the tells (mounds) dotted about the southern
countryside beneath which lie buried the ruins of many an
ancient Israelite or Phoenician town. Most of the houses were
built on the slope. On the top of the mound, which afforded
a view of the entire area, were ruined buildings of older date.
At its foot, near the spring and a cluster of trees, were some
recently built houses, apparently belonging to the wealthier
inhabitants.

The Company H.Q. was, of course, situated in the best
houses, near the spring. In its immediate vicinity were the kitchen,
mobile shower-room, canteen and No. 1 Platoon. The other two
platoons were quartered on top of the hillock, and their men
furnished the sentries.

Hasan's main task was to bring the men on top their meals
from the kitchen. He did his work to the general satisfaction of
the company. Three times a day he would appear on the hill-top
riding a white donkey, which carried the food and utensils.
Between meals he would be occupied in washing dishes, cleaning
out the shower-room (he himself used it only occasionally),
polishing boots, and similar tasks.

All his actions were characterized by a natural pride which
caused general amusement. He never refused to do what he was
bidden; but he did it with a kind of strange aloofness—as if he
were a host performing the duties of hospitality towards his
guests.

By and by, everyone took to spoiling him. Those who in-
dulged him most were the "toughs." They brought him slabs
of chocolate from the canteen, and even taught him to smoke.
The others claimed that he served to salve the conscience of the
"toughs"; but they themselves spoiled him as well.

Hasan used to accept the gifts of chocolate with the same
air of royal condescension with which he performed his menial
tasks. He did not make friends with anyone but Rafi, and to

Rafi his attitude was that of a slave towards his master. He cleaned his boots and washed out his uniform without being asked. He seemed to derive particular satisfaction from the thought that his master would look clean and neat. The fact that Rafi was a mere private did not lower him at all in Hasan's estimation. Although the lads used to crack jokes about Rafi and his servant, they gradually grew accustomed to the idea that Hasan belonged to Rafi the way Nero, the pup, belonged to Moshe.

As the summer drew to a close, the peaceful atmosphere of the place was broken. First came the jeeps. They appeared almost daily, harassing the villages in no-man's-land and probing the enemy's strength. After them came the scouts, and then staff officers from Brigade H.Q., and all the other types whose appearance usually heralds a push on a particular sector of the front. Finally operational instructions came through: in two days' time a force of two battalions was to attack and mop up the area as far as the range of hills.

Next morning the jeeps turned up, and a general discussion took place at the canteen concerning the details of the coming operation.

"The Egyptians haven't got wind of anything yet," said Rubka, a jeep-driver who wore a red kerchief in place of an army cap. "We were over there just now, and the farmers scuttled off after the first bursts. The Egyptians hadn't even put in a force to hold the place. I tell you, this time it's going to be as easy as winking."

"If you don't stop messing about in no-man's-land they'll smell a rat," said Moshe in a querulous tone: the superb self-assurance of the men in the jeeps grated on his nerves.

"Leave it to us," Rubka laughed. "They think we're simply chasing them."

"What's up? Where's the food?" It was the hoarse voice of Yanek, commander of the 2nd Platoon on the hill.

"Oh, stop bothering me. You'll get it," replied Yisrael in a preoccupied tone as he replaced the receiver. He was busy digest-

ing the details of the operation. "Hey, Dudik," he called, poking
his head outside the door, "tell Hasan to hurry and bring up
the food."

A few minutes later, Dudik's head appeared in the doorway.
"Don't bother me now," Yisrael mumbled. "Can't you see
I'm busy?"

"Hasan's vanished," Dudik announced.

"Perhaps you want me to go and look for him?" asked
Yisrael sarcastically. "Go along to the kitchen or canteen and
you'll find him. Make it snappy, the boys up there are hungry."

Dudik didn't budge. "I've hunted all over," he said, "I can't
find him anywhere. The donkey's gone as well."

Yisrael looked up with a start. "Call Rafi. Quick. And tell
Moshe to get the jeep started."

Rafi appeared, looking pale. Dudik had told him the news.

"When did you see him last?" Yisrael's sleepy voice was
now curt and incisive, as it used to become in battle.

"I don't know . . . He was in the canteen about three
hours ago. What are you going to do?"

"What is there to do? I'll chase after him in the jeep."

Rafi hesitated a moment. Then he said: "Yisrael, take me
along."

Yisrael looked at him with something akin to pity. "Listen,
my boy," he said with unwonted gentleness, "you'd better stay
here. One shouldn't pal up with anyone at the front: it only
causes trouble, especially if an Arab is involved. It was a mad
idea from the start. I shouldn't have let you do it. Now it may
cost the lives of our boys. If I find him too close to the Egyptian
lines, I may have to try a long shot at him." Yisrael was one of
the crack riflemen of the Brigade.

"All the same. . . ." pleaded Rafi.

"All right. But remember, I've warned you. You're too
sentimental for such matters."

When they got to the main street of the village, they found
the donkey by itself. Rafi jumped down and made for the houses.
Yisrael switched off the engine and followed him.

Rafi stopped and listened. He could hear sounds coming

from a room in one of the deserted houses. He drew nearer on tiptoe, his rifle ready to be fired. Outside the window of the room he stopped and peeped cautiously inside.

At first he could distinguish nothing in the gloom. Then, as his eyes got accustomed to it, he saw Hasan crouching down beside a recumbent figure in a dark corner.

"Abu Musa," Hasan said. Although he spoke in a whisper, his words carried across the room. "Can you hear me? It's me, Hasan ibn Darwish."

An inaudible mumble came from the recumbent figure: apparently it had not heard what Hasan had said.

"You must remember me. I'm Hasan. You taught me to read and write."

"Hasan," the old man became more animated. "Hasan ibn Darwish. God bless you."

"They've all run away," Hasan sobbed, "all of them. And the Jews are laughing at them. Only you are left."

"If God wills," the old man mumbled. It was not clear whether he had understood.

"I've brought you food," Hasan went on. "Good food. I took it from the Jews. I'll bring you some more tomorrow. I'll bring you some every day."

The old man stroked the boy's head and said nothing.

Rafi started. Something had touched his back. It was Yisrael. He had also been standing by the window.

They cautiously withdrew and returned to the jeep.

When they were in the jeep, Yisrael burst out laughing. "Another sentimental fool like you! You've infected me." But his laughter sounded forced.

"Never mind. The main thing is that he'll come back," he said as he turned the jeep round.

THE GUITAR

by BATYA KAHANA

THE YOUNG MAN WITH THE GUITAR—WHO DOESN'T KNOW HIM in the Emek? Actually, he isn't even a young man, only a boy. Black, deep-set eyes, pale face, a smile that seems to have been fixed forever on his thick, youthful lips.

Morning found him in Tel Yosef; by noon—he was in Ein Harod; in the evening—there he was in Kfar Yehezkeel; and to be put up for the night—why!—he was already in Merhaviah.

So he went from kibbutz to kibbutz, from settlement to settlement, summer and winter, the guitar on his shoulder. Along narrow field paths between waving stalks, half blinded by the dazzling sun and the sheen of the vegetation, covered with perspiration that rolled down from under the keffiyeh tied around his brow—he went in whatever direction happened to please him. He knew all the ways and byways. And he never got lost.

In winter he tramped over the mud that squirted and oozed under his feet.

The path is invisible then. But he, the young man, he had a compass—no—not in his pocket! Right before his eyes—Mount Tabor.

Where he worked, where he lived—no one knew. At Balfouriah they said he works in Bet Alfa, and at Bet Alfa—that he works in Tel Adas. But actually, no one knew. Not even Leah with the slim figure and the big, haughty eyes. Or perhaps she did know, but wouldn't tell.

From settlement to settlement he tramped, from kibbutz to kibbutz. Every now and then he came to the large kibbutz whose tents are pitched at the foot of the mountain and whose bungalows are on the mountain. He would go from tent to tent. All were happy to see him. They crowded around him and treated him with great fondness. He tersely answered their questions, his usual smile on his face.

"Hi, Yuval!" they would greet him. No one knew his real name and they had named him after the inventor of the first musical instrument.

"How are you, Yuval?" they asked.

"Fine."

"What are you doing?"

"As usual. . . ."

"Brought any new songs?"

All at once his face would light up and his eyes would widen. "If it's song you want, then make way for Yuval!" He spoke clearly and loudly. Ah! How beautifully he sang! Is it possible to tell how the grass grows in the broad meadowland? Is it possible to determine exactly where rain comes from? Well, it is as little possible to find the source of Yuval's song. One song after another he sang, airs of every land and people, airs gay as a bright summer day in the woods and sad as the soggy fields in winter. Melodious as the song of the lark, soft as the flight of a bat at twilight.

He knew songs of every sort, Yuval. A big crowd would gather to hear him sing. As many as possible would crowd into the tent, and the rest, young and old, would stand outside. These were members of the settlement who, for one reason or other, had not gone out to work on that day. Also present were the guests of the settlement, parents and relatives, artists and writers seeking in the kibbutz material for their paintings and stories. These were also the people on kitchen duty who had left the soup to boil, and those on laundry duty, bringing with them the smell of soap and steam. As Yuval sang those who were working in the vegetable garden straightened their backs and walked over to the tent. The attendants in the dispensary were also unable to resist and finally, they, too, came.

The mules had been brought in from the fields that day and were waiting patiently for somebody to unhitch them. A cow seemed to complain silently to her neighbor that they had forgotten to milk her. Lonely and forlorn the hens sat in their hutches, a bit hungry, while the ducks cried out despairingly to them.

Everyone came to hear Yuval's songs and guitar, except Leah. Perhaps that is why Yuval would go most often to that tent near the edge of the camp where Leah and her sister lived. No one knew if he spoke more to Leah than to her sister, but in Leah's presence his singing really rang out, and his playing— how beautiful it became! Leah awaited Yuval's arrival impatiently, and when he came, she lowered the flaps of her tent so her comrades would not see him.

Leah's sister heard her telling him: "Play softly so no one can hear. You must play only for me, you hear, only for me."

She heard Yuval answer: "I want to play and sing for you, for all of them, for everybody."

And then she heard them kissing . . . or thought she did.

It was early spring. The flanks of the Gilboa mountain were decked in a fine carpet of green embroidered with an exquisite array of patterns of every hue and tint. The ground was still damp from the rains that had only just ended, and the mud stuck to the shoes. The flowers in all their gaudy colors were just opening, thirsty for the spring rains that had been tardy in arriving that year. There was gaiety throughout the land, as group after group of boys and girls came from Metulla and the Negev to roam the hospitable Emek. One day in this early spring Yuval arrived at the kibbutz after he skirted the newly planted field. He made straight for the tent at the edge of camp.

It was a holiday. His arrival was immediately noticed.

Yuval is here! From one end of the camp to the other went the news. Leah's tent instantly became filled with people.

Yuval sat down on her narrow white bed, mopped his brow, and looked around at the company. His usual smile hovered at his lips.

"Good thing you came, Yuval. We're having a holiday today," the members of the settlement told him.

Yuval played. That day his playing and singing were exceptional. Everybody joined in the singing. When some got tired others took their turn. Only Yuval didn't tire.

On his right sat Leah. Her long eyelashes shaded her haughty eyes, and she was frowning.

The company sat on the beds, some on the table, and others on the floor. It was a magnificent day, and the air was vibrant with the singing and the sounds of the guitar. But the crowd was restless, perhaps because of the approaching spring rain. For a long while they sat and listened until the third bugle call reminded them it was time for supper. As if coming out of a powerful spell they gradually got up. Yuval stopped playing and his bulging eyes retreated back to normal size.

"Let's go eat," they called to Yuval.

He arose, lifted the guitar before him, and hesitant about where he should put it, looked from side to side.

"Put the guitar on my bed," Leah came to his aid. "Don't worry, no one will touch it."

Nobody took any notice then of her face which had turned white. Supper went along with gay chatter. Suddenly, Leah abruptly stood up and answered Yuval's wondering look with, "I think it's raining, I'll go see." When she returned her eyes were bright and mischievous. The raindrops glittered like jewels on her dark, curly locks. She was laughing and went right on laughing.

"What a rain," she kept repeating, "what a marvelous rain!"

After supper they said to Yuval, "What luck it's raining, now you won't be able to leave and will have to spend the night here. What luck!"

"Yes," answered Yuval. "I'll get my guitar. I have some new songs that I've never sung for anyone. You hear, Leah?"

Leah looked away and said nothing.

Everybody went with him to get the guitar. It was a holiday and there was no cause for hurry. When they entered the tent Yuval reached his hand out to pick up his guitar, and in its place—shattered pieces of wood and splinters.

A long, despairing "Oh" burst from dozens of mouths; then there was silence. The rain beat down with mounting intensity on the canvas of the tent. Yuval knelt—perhaps he had made a mistake—and tried with trembling hands to assemble the pieces but to no avail.

A few moments passed in dead silence. Suddenly, a dry, strange voice broke the silence: "Odd! . . . But what's to be done?"

It was Leah who spoke. Everyone felt uneasy.

Yuval gave her a long, penetrating look. His eyes darkened and he didn't say a word. The smile left his face and looked strange to his comrades; they had never seen him like this. He took the keffiyeh and turned to the tent opening. Silently they let him pass.

"Yuval, where are you going?" Leah sharply asked.

But he ignored her. She remained standing there, her arm stretched out to Yuval who kept on walking, his head bare to the warm rain. He never once looked back and soon vanished in the distance.

Yuval never again visited the kibbutzim. No one knows where he is. Some claim to have seen him in the quarries near Jerusalem. Others say he got a job in a sheet-music store in Tel Aviv. But these are mere rumors and no one actually knows. It is only known that Yuval will never return to the Emek, for there they broke his guitar.

Every now and then they remember him, tell the new settlers about him, but Leah doesn't care for these stories. She remains silent and the color drains from her face.

What's a guitar? For money you can buy another guitar. Leah—she knows that Yuval's whole heart was bound up with his guitar.

It was in early spring, when the fields were fresh and sweet, and caressing zephyrs brought on their wings peace and tranquility, and people were happy at the gay patter of the spring rain. It was then that Yuval's heart was broken, broken, and no one knew.

SERGEANT SHMUELI RIDES A DONKEY

by ARYEH TABAKAI

SERGEANT SHMUELI HAD EARNED THE FURLOUGH HE HAD BEEN looking forward to. He had been at the North African front for a long time with all sorts of people and had returned to Egypt with a renowned outfit. Only a night's ride now stood between him and the land of Israel, between him and his wife and his boy after days and days of longing. The Egyptian tailor had had to use his best workmanship and skill for, when he wanted to, Shmueli had a sharp eye for uniforms and especially his own.

His uniform and all its accessories stood ready, like a cast. The three stripes on each sleeve were fixed exactly where they belonged. He even managed to get exactly the right shine on the buckles and the insignia on the collar and shoulders that decorate official uniforms in peacetime. And when the day for his departure arrived everything was ready and packed and covered against the dust and dirt of the roads.

There he was, sitting in the corner of a coach near the wall, so that he could lean on it and sleep. With his eyes closed, he reviewed over and over again the schedule he had prepared for his ten-day furlough: what he would do, where he would go and whom he would visit. He had worked out a full program. He wanted to see all his acquaintances: those who had known him in his good days and bad, those who had known him as manager of the Beham estate, his comrades on the illegal immigrants' ship, workmen and guards of the Sharon, and the owner of the farm who had worked him like a slave and whom he had left in order to join the army. He felt like a young farmer who could not help showing off his astonishing success on his return home. In arranging this program of visits he was anxious not to waste one

of the few precious days he had at his disposal. So precious.
Maybe only half a day would do for this, or that. For, how long
does it take to go to the kibbutz and get the child? While he
was out of the country, his wife had taken Yosi, their boy, and
put him in one of the kibbutzim in the Emek, and she had gone
and found herself a job in Haifa. Of course, in her letters she
never stopped praising the kibbutz where Yosi was placed—and
for such a reasonable price—and their son was so satisfied. What
else should she write?

Personally, he didn't hate the kibbutzim. There were even
some kibbutz members in his outfit. They seem to be the simplest
and nicest of people. But there was some invisible barrier between him and them, a barrier which could never be crossed.

On the first day of his furlough, Shmueli woke up from
his sleep as the sun was setting. He saw his wife walking silently
in the room. He remembered that he was on a holiday which
he had not yet even begun to enjoy—and already he was counting
the passing days. One day gone!

But if his day had gone by in a profound sleep to ease the
weariness of a night's ride, well, he still had the whole evening
ahead of him. An evening in Haifa. Who can describe the joy
that these words conveyed to him after being away so long.

All spruced up, tall, broad-shouldered, with an impressive
red moustache, and in good spirits, he took his wife by the arm
as they walked down the stairs into the bustling evening street.

"Where shall it be this evening?" he asked her in a gracious
manner.

"Let's walk a little."

"Alright, let's walk." Shmueli seemed to agree but on the
next block as they stood before one of the cafés he suggested:

"Shall we go in?"

"Let's." She wanted to be seen with her husband.

They pushed through the crowd and squeezed in at one of
the tables. The new arrivals attracted some attention only because of the inconvenience they caused those already seated—
who had to get up, move this way or that, crowd together as
much as possible, but no sooner were they all seated than they
returned to their conversation. They had often seen a woman

coming into the café with a soldier—a private, a sergeant or an officer. They've seen everything, these city people, and nothing surprises them. They no longer look up in the street when they see an airplane. It is not worth the bother. Only soldiers are interested in them and watch them until they disappear. They will go on watching them to the end of their lives.

Shmueli kept looking around for acquaintances, scanning every table. His wife sat beside him like a stranger, cold and reserved, and saw his mood getting worse by the minute. His eyes grew smaller and more irritable, and his voice was no longer clear. He looked the crowd over as he eyed his men when he was angry: Is this the way to welcome a soldier just back from the front? He had heard soldiers complain about this coolness on returning to duty.

But what bothered him went deeper than that. He had not had a chance to get over the feeling of estrangement that had come from his total separation from his previous life. Somehow it seemed to him that he had lost the way to his home and his wife. He envied the couples he saw around him. Everything was so natural to them. How simply they get up from the table and walk out, as if things had never been any different in the world. Calm, tranquil, secure. Oh, if they only saw how, in only a matter of hours, people's fates were determined and the welfare of nations decided—if they only saw all that, with their own eyes, they wouldn't go about as if all this were coming to them. They don't even know—Shmueli continued to reflect bitterly— how close they had been to disaster, and what a great miracle had happened. They did not seem to know that the men with him had prayed for just one thing: Whatever happened to them at the front, let our country be saved from the approaching enemy. At that point Shmueli thought: Who knows, maybe we shouldn't have said that prayer. If only the enemy had broken through. Then, then all these people sitting here and all the other thousands and tens of thousands would have risen up to fight to their last breath. As a country "wounded" in the fighting, they could also have taken their full share in victory. Shmueli searched the faces of the people and tried to estimate the potential of each in his battle of "a wounded country" which he pictured to himself.

Suddenly, he heard a lively and vivacious voice which startled the café from its reserve:

"Smuleni! Smuleni!"

"Eiger! Eiger!" Shmueli reached out toward this man, who had once been a salesman of agricultural machinery in Czechoslovakia. Back in those days, he had often hidden from him when he came to sell his wares, but now he lifted him up and kissed him on the mouth. Eiger was small but his voice was loud and booming. After freeing himself from Shmueli's embrace, he drew back a few steps, as a painter eyes a picture and began to roar his admiration.

"Whom do I see before my eyes? What a glorious soldier! What a serviceman!"

He pulled himself together and cried:

"A sergeant! And since when have Jews of this country started making that rank?"

He patted his brow as if he had just hit upon a really important discovery:

"Tell me please, aren't you a member of that Hebrew unit that got a ten-day leave on account of its bravery at the front?"

"That's the outfit," answered Shmueli and sat down on his chair. Eiger also pulled up a chair, and faced Shmueli with the demand written all over him— Tell me something!

"And what do you think of my Hebrew?" Shmueli would not let pass this other aspect that Eiger hadn't noticed at first.

"On my life! You're talking a real Hebrew, but a real Hebrew!"

"It's very simple," Shmueli said, "very simple: we sat in trenches and studied Hebrew. It was an order from the commander." Shmueli knew that such an order was praiseworthy and that he would also get his share of praise. And, having started, he went on telling stories of the front until midnight.

Very encouraged, Shmueli took his wife's hand when they got up to leave. Outside he told her with great satisfaction:

"Quite a nice café, quite *nice.*"

"And what do you say to my Hebrew? What do you think of your daddy's talking to you in Hebrew?"

Shmueli was really thrilled to be able to spring such a surprise on his son. The child, who showed no signs of developing a physique like his father's, looked, in compensation, more independent and mentally alert. His father almost humbled himself in his effort to win the boy's heart. In his first hour in the kibbutz he realized that he would not take the first bus back to town. Certainly, he could not leave without having lunch. Besides, the supervisor of the children's house had informed him that she had started preparing for Yosi's birthday party, which she had postponed when she heard that his father was coming.

As he walked about the camp, he learned that two members of this settlement were in his unit from the time it was first formed. Well, that makes him more than just a visitor coming for an hour and going again! He is a member too! He is one of the big family, to whose arrival they had actually been looking forward! He will not only have lunch here, a visitor's lunch, but also the afternoon snack and dinner after the lovely party at the children's home. The children followed him wherever he went and became attached to Yosi's daddy more than to Yosi himself.

After lunch the members of the kibbutz wanted him to give a talk on his experiences. They asked him to tell the group about everything he and his comrades had gone through from the day they left the country until today. He didn't get up on any platform to speak. Instead, he sat, satisfied and relaxed, in the neat after-supper room with the two families of the soldiers who were members of the kibbutz. He immediately felt the family warmth about him—and with family, a person isn't shy about talking. Soon more people gathered around behind the seated families, and behind these, more and more. Shmueli did not make a speech but he talked and talked.

After that, and after spending the night there, he felt he had paid all his debts to these very dear hosts and prepared to start out to the first place in his program of trips and visits— Herzliah. There he had spent almost all the years since arriving in the country, as a hired laborer on the farm of a lawyer who lived in Tel Aviv. There he had been seen, day after day, driving a cart full of jugs to the dairy like one of those servants of his on the estates he had managed abroad. He felt that the people on the street considered him a thickheaded peasant.

He wanted to put in an appearance on that very street, but under completely different circumstances! He would sit leisurely on the terrace of a café, smoking a cigar and watching the street through the smoke. He would get up occasionally to pace comfortably back and forth. He would talk to people in a condescending manner, as soldiers on furlough should. But he wouldn't even glance at the farm he had worked on, though he was very curious to know how it was getting on without him.

From Herzliah he would go to Tel Aviv and pay the lawyer a friendly visit. He, his wife and the boy. This visit was worth making. That lawyer should know just who it was that had once served him. "We are now staying in Tel Aviv," he would tell him. He would spend three to four days in that city, in Tel Aviv, and then go on to Haifa. After breakfast he went to the children's house and took his son by the hand.

"Yosi, get your best clothes and let's take a little trip to Haifa, to Mama. From there we'll take a nice trip to Tel Aviv."

"I don't want to."

"Why don't you want to go?"

"I just don't want to."

Shmueli knew that his child was a little different from other children but not to the extent that he would be willing to give up a trip.

"Why don't you want to travel a little with daddy?" he pleaded.

"It's so nice here, daddy."

Again Shmueli took his son's hand in his, and walked with him in a very affectionate way around the grounds of the children's home and the lawn of the dining hall. But instead of him leading, he found that he was being led. They stopped at the cattle shed. And here, near the donkey section, the son showed his deep affection for the place.

"Daddy, put me on this donkey, on Shifra!"

"Ah, boy, boy! If you could only see the bicycle I have back there in Egypt," the father tried to distract his son from the beast. "I have a bicycle on which I do fifty miles an hour!"

The donkey that had earned that lovely name "Shifra" was really pretty. It was grey, pleasant to look at and somewhat mischievous. Yosi had long ago taken a liking to it. Perhaps this love began when Yoske, the biggest boy in the kibbutz, had started training him for riding. Yoske rode and galloped, with all the children running after him. Now, Yosi wanted to take advantage of his father's general popularity and get his heart's desire.

They went inside and approached the donkey. At first Shmueli's approach was more with his hands than with his feet: he put his heavy hand on the animal's neck, moved it over its back and ribs down to the legs. Then he put his hand at the base of its strong ears, and stroked it with a circular movement of his fingers around it. The donkey felt this hand on him and started to pay attention to it. Shmueli felt this living thing under his hand, so humble and meek, and became somewhat more reconciled to the idea of mounting his son on it. Then he also realized that this was the first pleasure he had been enabled to grant his son. He grasped the opportunity.

"And where would you like me to lead you?" he asked heartily. It seemed that even on this score the boy had ideas of his own. At first he only wanted to go to the saplings he, together with his friends, had planted on the slope of the hill. But on the way there, with his father walking by his side, the boy, all thin arms and legs so different from his father's, became excited and wanted to roam all over the area.

"What a bad deal," Shmueli muttered under his breath. "You've gotten yourself a full week's program of visits in the kibbutz."

With a kind of hatred, he purposely avoided looking at the fields on either side of the lane, the gardens and orchards, as if to say: "Me, I haven't the slightest interest in that." They completed their tour of the hill slope. Yosi pointed out every shrub that he and his friends had planted and informed his father how long each had taken to grow.

They decided to go to the vineyard. There they tied up the

donkey in the shed and went over to see the workers. It was
almost lunch time and the workers had stopped work a short
while before because no one was rushing them. Or rather, because they were doing one of those jobs that "must" be done,
and which are therefore postponed at every opportunity. They
sat down to lunch in the hut near the shed and were enjoying,
as usual, the informality of a meal outside the dining hall. During
the meal, Shmueli told them about the grapes in Egypt and
Lybia which, in his opinion, did not grow well. As to the grapes
in Palestine, he didn't know the first thing about that.

Just as the workers took their time about coming into the
hut—because they would have to wait a little for the table to
be set—so they took their departure leisurely. Yarkoni, the
kibbutz oldtimer, showed Shmueli around the vineyard. His
voice was a little muffled, as if it were coming from a distance,
from years and years back. And these years became increasingly
real as the strollers went deeper into the vineyard: the twenty
years, in which the kibbutz workers had first set out with the
plough and ten teams of mules. Those strong winds that had
lined their faces became vivid—there are no such winds any
longer in the country. Yarkoni knows every wind, every special
season that is important to the field and vineyard, orchard and
garden, the woods and beast.

To Shmueli all these things were interesting even though
he appeared to shrug them off and even looked a little irritated.
As they walked, they talked about the different varieties of seeds,
how they were sown, what harvests and vintages they produced,
and so on, until they were back at the shed where the donkey
was waiting. Then they realized that they had lingered too long.
Shmueli untied the donkey, mounted Yosi on its back, and as
they were about to set out, Yarkoni remembered something else
he could do for Shmueli. Shmueli, too, could have a donkey. He
could ride Sasson, who was standing in the shed beside Shifra!

Shmueli laughed at Yarkoni's kindness. "It would be a fine
thing for a soldier to go riding an ass. Real glorious!"

All the way home Shmueli felt secretly displeased and
irritated while Yosi was happy and jolly. Shmueli looked like
a man whose whole fortune was going to pot and Yosi—like

someone whose fortune lay ahead of him. Yosi said: "Daddy, tomorrow you'll take Sasson and we'll ride to the banana groves. It's very far!"

"Yosi, I see you're planning to keep me here all week. I still have to see some other people before I return!"

"Alright, so go."

Shmueli now knew that he had "buried" his whole furlough in this place. Still, he made one more try.

"And what about Mama, I went away and didn't return."

"Mama will be coming tomorrow. She comes here every Sabbath. She has already made some good friends here and they even give her a room to herself when she comes," the boy replied.

The next day Shmueli's wife came to the kibbutz. She waited two hours for her husband and Yosi to return from the fields. And when finally the two riders appeared, she couldn't control her laughter. There was Shmueli out in front, riding the donkey, all flushed and sweating, with the hooks and buttons of his dress tunic open. The tunic looked as if it had been rolled up, all wrinkled and creased, and it suddenly seemed too small to contain his huge bulk. And the hat, that very serious looking hat, bounced on the back of his head to the jogging of the ass. The woman could not control herself and burst out laughing. Her laughter was infectious and under Shmueli's moustache a smile began to form. Shmueli then began to relax.

A little later, his wife arranged the room they had given her, opened the valise containing his clothes that she had brought with her from Haifa—plain army shirts, clean and full in cut, not like the snug coat he was now wearing. He took a shower and washed, put on those fresh clothes, and went to the dining hall. He was happy at that moment, for he felt it was a good custom to rest on the Sabbath in the kibbutz if there was only time.

He did not pass his Sabbath here like a guest but as one who belonged. And all because of his Yosi whom everybody liked. From that day through the rest of his leave, he was never irritable again, though he was still tempted a little by Haifa, Tel Aviv and Herzliah. But now he began to doubt the wisdom of his original plan. Go to whom? What for? As he reflected on this he practically forgot the talks he had had with his buddies in the trench across the empty highway on which the enemy kept a constant eye. That empty and quiet highway had so tantalized them. They wanted so to be riding on it, to be moving freely along it at high noon, or at dusk, like a man strolling leisurely, or a farmer riding an ass in peace-time. And recalling that longing for a donkey, he enjoyed more and more with each day the ride that his son had forced on him. He started paying attention to all that was going on on both sides of the path that cut through the field. He touched a mule's harness, a pitchfork with green corn impaled on it, a cart passing in the kibbutz. And as he walked, he kept repeating over and over to himself:

"If only we could find a piece of land to live on when we get back from the war— Just a small piece of land."

SPEED THE PLOUGH

by ASHER BARASH

Yair, himself of farming stock and a member of the youthful moshav in the Emek, went out at dawn to plough his portion of field. He had stood on guard with his rifle in the trench under the starry skies until the third watch. When he had handed over the rifle to his relief, he dashed off for his horse and plough.

He proposed to plough for a couple of hours, since his portion was small. By the time morning was well advanced he would have finished the work and could return to his shack and his wife Hemda, as though he were just coming back to rest from his night on duty.

Bowed between the two handles of the plough, pressing down with the full weight of his body, Yair plodded along the furrow, and as he went a straight course he could not turn his eyes away from the rising sun. It rose high in the distance over the mountains. As it mounted it dispersed the rose-colored mists as though by a wave of the hand; and clear and hot it came forth to give light to the world. Swarms of birds all wet with dew descended to the overturned heaps of earth, whirled and danced along the waves of air and welcomed the ascendant day with joyful song. Myriads of tiny eyes of light gleamed and glistened from the unopened wild flowers. The wild grasses began to thaw after the frozen night and gave off a faint incense.

Yair felt that the darkness which had been gathering in his heart during the days of bloodshed was also being swept away, that the sun of a vast happiness was rising within him. The wife he had wedded eight months earlier was now sleeping on their bed, and within her the tracery of his living seed was taking final shape. Strong arms she had, an upright heart and much experience of toil and poverty. He had taken her from Upper Galilee, from a poor peasant home, and had brought her to the village he was helping to build. Yesterday the eldest of her sisters had come to stay with her until after the birth, so that she no longer needed to do anything but light work about the house and the yard. When Hemda went to the hospital her sister would take charge of everything. This sister was a widow whose husband had been killed in the field during the first month after their marriage. She was a widow and childless, but very brave of heart. Whether the child would be son or daughter, a name had already been decided upon by the three of them; a name that would be fresh and musical as the song of yonder birds to the rising sun. It was only another month.

As Yair ploughed straight towards the rising sun, with only a third of his portion left, an echoing shot burst from ambush, and a bullet pierced his back, coming out through his chest and hitting against the iron plough. He fell forward upon the plough between its two handles. And the horse stopped, pricked up its little ears and stood frozen and immobile like a statue.

The sound of the shot brought the men of the village running to the spot. Among them were the four guards of the night watch. One of these was the man who had taken the rifle over from Yair at the end of the third watch.

They lifted him up and laid him flat on the earth. Then they kneeled down and listened to his heart. One of them pulled out a fine thread of wool from his coat, and set it under the nostrils of the murdered man. The thread did not stir. Then the men rose and stood to attention on either side of their dead comrade. Their faces were stony, tears froze in their eyes and their lips were tight.

They turned the plough over, cut green branches from the neighboring oak, set the branches along the plough and placed the dead body on the living green. The horse jerked forward and made for the village, his head bowed, dragging the burden of his master.

The funeral was held at sunset as the evening breezes blew. Many came from the surrounding villages to do the last kindness for Yair, who had fallen at his plough. Never had so silent a procession been seen. The whole of the Emek seemed to be holding its breath. The fields wore a scarlet prayershawl. That day the first grave had been dug in what was to become the gathering-place for all who live. A few furious words were said, a few words of pain were whispered. Hemda gave one brief scream but no more, for her sister's hand stopped her mouth from utterance.

Silent and bent they returned to their places. But the four guards marched at the roadside with firm stride and heads erect, as they had been taught.

The setting sun kissed the moist and solitary grave and a wing of the evening breeze caressed it lovingly. A small star lit up, in memory of the soul.

That night the two sisters lay on the bed in the room of mourning. They fell asleep only after midnight; and when the first ray of light edged through the window Hemda roused herself suddenly and awakened her sister.

"Did you hear anything? It seemed to me that the horse went out of the courtyard pulling the plough . . ."

"Hemda, my love, what ails you? Calm yourself. You must have been dreaming."

And the weary woman turned over and fell asleep again.

But in a little while Hemda shook her by the shoulder a second time. "What, did you not hear it this time either? The horse has come back. . . ."

The light of dawn shone grey through the window-space against the wall of the shack. The sister got out of bed.

"It's dawn already. Time to milk the cow and feed the chickens."

Hemda remained lying on her back, her gaze turned to the ceiling where the shadows were forming themselves into the visions of her dreaming eyes.

When the sister passed through the yard she saw the plough in its proper place. But her heart, despite all her bravery, hammered strongly within her; and she could not refrain from going to look at the horse. So before proceeding to the byre she went into the stable. In the light of the rising sun which reddened the entrance she saw, aghast, that a white foam covered the horse, which quivered and panted as it stood. She passed her hand over its flank. Her hand came away wet with the warm lather.

In the morning the field of Yair was found entirely ploughed.

And to this day no man knows whose hand it was that sped the plough.

THE BOY PROPHET

by EDMOND FLEG

IN THE SOLITARY WASTES OF JUDAEA, IN AN ARENA OF ROCKS, BOYS and maidens of Israel, clad as in the kibbutz, were paying homage to the six million martyrs before the young shoots of their future Forest.

On the bare peaks the torches of mourning were alight.

Blue stars, borne on white banners, descended the hills. From the
weeping urn before the grotto rose a dark plume of smoke.

Flutes and horns. Muted drums. Deep-throated songs. Tales
without words. Soundless weeping . . . Intimacy with the sublime. . . .

Then the mighty drama of the Ghetto, victor and vanquished, lapsed into silence.

On the lofty stone a form appeared and the voice of Ezekiel
conjured up once more the Vision of the bones:

"Behold, O my people, I will open your graves, and cause
you to come up out of your graves and bring you into the land
of Israel."

And in the echoes of that voice the bones of the valley stirred.
Nerves and flesh and skin grew upon them. Breath entered into
them and they rose up. They were a living, marching people.
And the voice said:

"And ye shall know that I am the Lord when I have opened
your graves, O my people, and brought you up out of your
graves, and shall put my spirit in you and ye shall live; and I
shall place you in your own land: then shall ye know that I
the Lord have spoken it, and performed it, saith the Lord."

Two thousand five hundred years had passed since that
prophecy and here was the past returning to life in it. The people of the living were rising again; and the Forest of the future
would raise the dead, the six million dead. But, if the Forest of
Trees was not yet whispering, the Forest of Souls was already
there. And they seemed to say:

> . . . Yes, it is a beautiful thing, a great and sacred thing
> you have prepared for us in your fervour and medita-
> tion, O children of Israel. What the Brute has made of
> our bodies there below, you know; but where they are
> or not, neither you nor we can know. And here in their
> memory you plant these verdant sepulchres, so that their
> martyrs may enrich Israel's joy . . .
>
> But is it truly our memory that you will perpetuate?
> Will it not indeed be yours? Of us you have but one

memory, our death. And yet we lived before we died!
Will our memories of our lives also find a place in your
memories?

There were some among us who cherished countries
that gave us refuge and a welcome, work and pleasure,
knowledge, glory and beauty. Will they remain strange
to you? Will the final maledictions drown the blessings
that went before? Or will you let them grow and grow
again with our branches and our leaves?

There were some among us who lived with the faith
of Abraham. Will you banish it because it was the faith
of banishment? Will you see in the land of Israel only
its soil and not the spirit with which time has imbued it?

Are Man and God to be driven from the Promised
Land? Is the Forest of Remembrance to be a mere Forest
of Forgetfulness?

In thus questioning the dead, was I not investing the dead
with the sufferings of the living?

The word "Israel" still stood, until recently, for all the
Jewishness of Israel. It seems that in the past five years it has
come to mean only that of the State of Israel. By the same token
many of the dispersed professed themselves opposed to the In-
gathering of the Exiles; and many, today, among those Ingathered
profess themselves opposed to the existence of the Exile.

Is it not conceivable that one spirit, old and new, might
unite them once again?

I knew once a child of fifteen years, whom I called the Child
Prophet. He used to say, timidly, to his old rabbi:

"Ah, these practices, these Feasts—if only they were meant
to turn our thoughts more to the Messiah, to help him to come
more quickly, to persuade God to send him sooner! All would
become so clear! We would understand it all! . . ."

What has become of the Child Prophet? Have the Nazis
carried him off too?

And then, one night, I had a dream. And in my dream, the shadow of a breath stirred the sound of the bones. And in my dream I saw again the Forest. And the six million trees had grown. And their branches, earthly and heavenly, covered the mountains of Judaea, and the continents, and the oceans.

And, standing in front of me, small as at fifteen years and tall as at twenty-five, the only living being with me in front of the six million souls of the six million trees, the Child Prophet asked them:

"Will you give us back the heart of Abraham? Will you give us back the heart of Adam?"

And the six million trees with the six million souls replied:

"Let a new Ezekiel raise up the living, if they are dead; we shall be their Prophets, we, the dead, who are the living!"

PART FOUR

Spices of Yesteryear

THE LEGEND OF THREE AND FOUR

by HAYYIM NAHMAN BIALIK

KING SOLOMON HAD A SWEET AND LOVELY DAUGHTER WHOSE LIKE was nowhere to be found. He loved her as his own soul and guarded her as the apple of his eye. But she was passing strange, differing from all other maidens of her years, disdaining the clamor of pleasure-houses and rather desiring to walk alone and silent through the gardens of the king; or to rise betimes and wander far and wide along the tracks that twined among the vineyards, her spirit absorbed and her eyes gazing far ahead; always did she seem to be dreaming while awake, and there was none that knew her heart. When her time came to be wed, princes from far and near arrived to entreat her from her father; but the king's daughter turned her face away from them and never paid heed to their words; so that they returned one and all, shamed with hanging heads, to their own countries.

Time passed; and when they saw that the maiden persisted in hardening her heart, the princes despaired of her and ceased entreating for her. By reason of this, the king was troubled in spirit on her account and went up to his roof by night to gaze at the stars and perceive who the prince might be that was designed of God for his daughter; and when he would come. He studied the signs of the heavens and discovered that neither king nor prince was matched by God with his daughter, but a poor and needy youth of honest stock would come to her at the appointed season, and take her to wife.

Now this vexed the king exceedingly, and he sought for a stratagem to foil the purpose of heaven. And he decided to hide the maiden away for a while, until the time foretold in the stars should be past and the decree of fate could no longer come about.

So he sought him a lonely isle in the sea, far from the ways followed by the ships in their traffick. There he had a lofty castle built, with many a hall and many a chamber; and he ranged a buttressed wall around it on every side, and set his daughter in the castle with seventy Elders of Israel to keep watch and ward over her and serve her every desire; plentiful provision for them did he make, storing them all manner of food and drink and the delights of the world, nothing lacking. Then he closed all the main gates and postern gates and portals and doors of the castle from without with bars of iron and locks and seals so that none might enter or leave; and he said, "Now shall I see the feats of God and His deeds, and whether the intent foretold by the stars shall be brought about or no."

So the king's daughter dwelt within this castle, with the seventy elders mounting guard over her, keeping watch and ward day and night and hastening to satisfy the least as the greatest of her desires. She was permitted whatsoever pastime she might wish, for the king had ordered that she be amused that her loneliness might not oppress her. One thing alone was beyond their power; out of the gates of the castle she could not go since the castle was enclosed from every quarter, none entering and none leaving. If she felt strait and confined within the building she would ascend to the roof and take a turn to and fro in the open air; or would lean against the coping of the battlements, gazing at the width of waters round about and hearkening to the medley of the waves; and she would be eased.

On the wall stood a watchman night and day, his eyes wide on the sea round about, observing the isle lest any ship approach or any strange foot be set on its strand. Twice a day, morning and evening, a speedy skiff would come within bowshot of the isle, one sitting therein who was sent by the King to ask the weal of the maiden. The one in the skiff would wave the white cloth in his hand and ask whether all was well with the king's daughter. And in reply the watchman would wave a white cloth back, signifying that all was well. Then the skiff would straightway turn about and vanish on the horizon.

And the closer came the season which the king did fear, the more did the elders pay heed to their watch and their ward; they stayed awake at their posts by the sealed posterns and gates and portals, their eyes wide, their nostrils sniffing, their ears twitching, starting at the buzzing of a fly as it knocked against a pane of glass or at the scratching claws of a lynx striving to scale the wall; for they were good men and true, such as would not think to deceive while about the king's business.

Now a poor lad of good stock who belonged to a family of scribes forsook Acre his city, for he suddenly found that the home of his needy parents was too small for him; and he turned his face afar. He left his home with empty hands, carrying nothing with him save his staff and his body; nonetheless he had no concern and his spirits never fell, since his bones were springing with youth, and his heart bounded with visions and high hopes, and his locks curled and happiness thudded within him all the way, so that he sang as he went. Crossing the fields he watched the grasshopper hopping and the joyous birds at song and the cony of the rocks and the clambering, darting lizard. Every green tree attracted him, and every forgotten booth in a forsaken vineyard. He sustained himself as might a bird from his gleanings in the generous fields, and slept on the ground with a stone for pillow. And wandering wide, passing through villages and cities, he would lend his ears to the converse of the wayfarers, gathering traditions and parables from the people and the elders of the people and storing all such away in his memory; this comforted him in his poverty and restored his soul in his wanderings.

But one day the sun set upon him while he was alone in a desolate, forsaken spot; the evening was rainy and cold, the lad was hungry and thirsty and naked and barefoot, so that frost consumed him and his strength all but vanished. In this plight he saw the carcass of an ox near by and rejoiced, saying: "Blest be God Who hath revealed me a couch in this place; lying therein, I shall grow warmer maybe." So he crept between the ribs of the skeleton, curled himself up and fell asleep.

During his sleep a huge eagle descended, picked up the skeleton in his beak together with him sleeping within it, flew off and set them down on the roof of the princess' castle, where it began to pick the little that was left of the carrion from the bones. Then the youth came out and drove it away, afterwards sitting on the roof all night long, weary and trembling by reason of the cold and the rains.

Morning came and the heavens cleared. The king's daughter mounted to the roof as was her daily custom, saw the strange youth, stood at distance and asked:

"Who are you and who has brought you hither?"

And he replied very simply:

"Prithee fear not, O maiden, and be not angered with me. An Hebrew am I, a son of poor folk who dwell at Acre; last night the rain caught me in the fields in my hunger and my thirst, with never a garment to cover my flesh; so I lay me down in that skeleton yonder, and the eagle flew away with it and set it down here. Now I do not know the fashion after which I can depart hence, for there is nothing but the sea round about and never a ship in sight."

The king's daughter pitying him, brought him in secret to her bower, where she bathed him and garbed him and gave him to eat and to drink; and thereupon the brightness of his countenance returned to him with his high spirits. She gazed at him, found him handsome and pleasant, rejoiced in him exceedingly and was fain that he should be her companion. So she concealed him in her chambers and the elders knew nothing, since she had not revealed his coming to them and they would not venture to enter her chambers save if they were summoned. Thenceforward she went forth twice a day to them to report her weal; and the elders paid no attention, thinking it but a whim. And they remained diligent and wakeful about their charges, each remaining in his position as he had been ordered, his eyes darting hither and thither, his ears wide to catch a stirring, his nostrils quivering to sniff; for the men were exceeding faithful, doing the king's behest with faith and an entire heart.

The king's daughter perceived the wisdom of the poor youth, his good understanding and his pureness of heart, and loved him with all her heart and all her soul. And there came a day when she said to him:

"Am I fitting in thine eyes to be taken for thy wife?"

And the youth rejoined:

"Wherefore dost thou ask? I am thy slave to wash thy feet."

Then the maiden told how great her love was for him; how he was more desirable and precious to her than all the princes in the world; how God Himself had brought him thither on the wings of the eagle; how from the moment she saw him her soul did cleave to him; how in his lack her life would not be a life. Many such words did she utter from her ardent heart, and he answered her with the like, seventy and seven fold; and they made them a covenant of eternal love. The youth arose, let blood from his arm, and wrote with his blood the matter of the covenant on a scroll, signed and sealed, betrothing her according to law, saying: "Witness be the Lord, and witnesses His Angels, Michael and Gabriel."

And meanwhile the elders knew of all these matters neither much nor little, though there were none such as they, honest and upright men who turned night into day and remained awake and exceedingly watchful at their posts.

When the season revealed to Solomon by the stars had gone by, he bethought him of his daughter shut into the castle; and he resolved to bring her home again. So he went down to the sea in a ship and came to the isle with its castle; he examined the bars of iron and the locks and the seals on the gates and the posterns and the portals, and found that none had tampered with them and they were whole; so he ordered them to be hacked through and the gates and the portals swung open. Thereupon he entered the castle and the elders sprang up before him, then made obeisance and greeted him with peace.

And the king asked: "Is all well with my daughter? And where is she?"

And the elders replied: "All is well with her, O lord king, and she is within her bower."

Then the king proceeded to the maiden's bower, the elders following. They opened the door; and there was a handsome youth facing them. And the elders quivered and quaked, and their hearts perished within them.

"Who is this?"

But the elders could not make any answer, for they were so astonished that they might have turned to stone. They stood silent and pale, their heads drooping.

Then the king stamped his foot and cried in fury:

"Answer, or you shall be cut down one and all and hewn in pieces!"

The elders fell on their faces before him and answered in fear and trembling:

"Alas, our lord king. What is there to say and how shall we speak? As God lives we have kept watch and ward over the king's daughter with all our might; we do not know the fashion in which this lad is come hither."

The king turned to the maiden, breathing hard with anger as he asked:

"Wanton, say what this lad is doing here? Who brought him hither?"

The maiden fell at his feet, replying:

"Not in thy wrath, my lord and father! For this thing is come about only from God. He sent His messenger the eagle to bring me this youth my beloved, whose wife I am become. Take him and bless him, O my father!"

Then the king asked the youth:

"Who art thou? And after what fashion art thou come hither?"

And the young man stood erect before the king and answered without fear, relating all that had befallen him. The king observed how fine a youth he was and treated him in friendly fashion, conversing with him and finding him versed in all wisdom and parables more than all the scribes in his entire kingdom. So he enquired his name, his city and the house of his parents; and the young man answered directly and truthfully to all his questions telling him of his poverty and his wanderings, and the wonderful manner in which the eagle had brought him to the roof of the castle, and how the maiden had pitied him and taken him to her, entreating him graciously. And he produced the scroll which he had written and signed with his blood and showed it to the king, in token of the eternal love existing between him and the king's daughter. And Solomon hearkened to all these wonders and understood that he must be the poor youth of whom he had been forewarned in his stargazing; and he said:

"Now indeed do I know that there is no wisdom nor understanding nor counsel that shall withstand the Lord."

When the elders perceived that the king was no longer in a fury their spirits returned; and they rose from the ground and raised their heads aloft to heaven, saying, "Blest be the Lord Who giveth a man a wife."

Then Solomon brought his daughter and her husband to Jerusalem, where he made them a seven-day feast and rejoiced with them greatly. When the feast had come to an end Solomon said to his son-in-law:

"See thou art the son-in-law of the king, and my domains spread far and wide. Choose thou whatsoever high office thy heart may desire and it shall be thine."

But the youth replied:

"My lord king! Since my childhood I have been but a poor man of letters; my forefathers were scribes and learned of the Lord one and all, never aspiring to greatness nor acquainting themselves with pleasure-houses. Therefore if I find favor in thine eyes, let thy servant be given a secluded home on the seashore, where I may dwell with my spouse, conning the works of God and studying His ways like my fathers before me."

The king granted his request, setting him in charge of the royal scribes. So he dwelt in his home and gathered together all the words of wisdom, proverbs and parables, which Solomon uttered from time to time, and recorded them in a book. Further, the king's son-in-law wrote down some little of his own wisdom, which he had learnt or had fashioned in his meditations; adding them after the proverbs of Solomon the king; these being the words of Agur son of Yakeh.

And among his sayings is to be found:

> There are three too wonderful for me,
>   Four and I know them not.
> The way of an eagle in the heavens,

The way of a serpent along the rock,
The way of a ship in the heart of the sea
And the way of a man with a maid.

THE ROMANCE OF ESTHER
A Biblical Tale

Adapted by LEO W. SCHWARZ

THE FOLLOWING EVENTS HAPPENED IN THE DAYS OF XERXES WHO reigned over one hundred and twenty-seven provinces from India to Ethiopia. In the third year of his reign King Xerxes made a seven days' feast in his castle in Shushan for all his princes, nobles and commanders. After he showed them the riches of his glorious empire, they assembled in the Court of the Garden of the royal palace. There were marble columns and white stuff of cotton and blue hangings, fastened to silver rings with cords of fine linen and purple, couches of gold and silver stood on a pavement of porphyry, marble, mother-of-pearl and precious stones. The guests were served in golden beakers of which no two were alike, and the royal wine was abundant and poured according to each man's pleasure.

At the same time Queen Vashti made a feast for the ladies in the royal palace.

On the seventh day of the feast the king's heart was joyous with wine. He commanded his seven eunuchs to bring Queen Vashti with the royal crown in order to show the princes and the peoples her great beauty. But the queen refused to come to the banquet.

Xerxes' anger burned within him and he was greatly enraged. He called the seven chief princes of Persia and Media,

Carshena, Sethar, Admatha, Tarsgish, Meres, Marsena and Memucan, and asked:

"Because she has not done the bidding of King Xerxes, what shall we do to Queen Vashti according to the law?"

Memucan replied,

"Vashti has not done wrong to the king only, but also to all the princes and all the peoples in the empire. For the behavior of the queen will be reported to all women, who will likewise look down upon their husbands. If it please your majesty, let a decree be written into the laws of the Medes and the Persians so that it may not be altered, and let it be known that the king has banished Queen Vashti from the court and that she be replaced by another who is better than she. So when the decree shall be published throughout the great empire, all the women will give honor to their husbands both high and low."

As this proposal was approved by the princes, the king followed the counsel of Memucan. He sent letters to all the royal provinces, into every province according to its form of writing and to every people according to its language, that every man should be master in his own house and should speak whatever seemed proper to him.

Then the king's counsellors said,

"Let the king appoint officers in all the provinces of his empire. Let them gather all the beautiful young maidens to the castle in Shushan and let them be placed in the custody of Hegai and given every beauty treatment. Then the king may choose the maiden who pleases him most to be queen in place of Vashti."

The plan pleased the king, and he did so.

Now there was a certain Jew in the castle at Shushan whose name was Mordecai. He was a descendant of those whom Nebuchadnezzar, the king of Babylon, had exiled from the kingdom of Judah. He had brought up a daughter of his uncle, whose Hebrew name was Hadassah but she was known as Esther. When her father and mother died, Mordecai adopted her as his own daughter. She was fair and beautiful.

When many maidens were gathered together in the castle at Shushan, Esther was also taken and placed in the custody of

Hegai, keeper of the women. She was most pleasing to him and he was very kind to her. And he removed Esther and her serving maidens to the best apartments in the harem. Esther had not made known her people or her kin, for Mordecai had commanded her to keep them a secret. He used to walk back and forth every day before her apartment to learn how she was faring.

It was the custom of the king to entertain each of the maidens for a day so that he could make his choice. When the turn of Esther came, she won favor of all who saw her. The king loved her more than all the other maidens. In the tenth year of his reign, during the month of Tebet, he took her into the royal palace, set the royal crown upon her head, and made her queen in place of Vashti.

Then Xerxes made a great feast for all his princes and ministers, and called it the feast of Esther. And he proclaimed a holiday throughout his empire and distributed fine gifts in all the provinces.

In these days Mordecai used to stay near the gate of the royal palace. There he once overheard two of the royal guards, Bigthan and Taresh, conspiring against Xerxes. Mordecai revealed the plot to Queen Esther, and Esther told the king in Mordecai's name. Accordingly the affair was investigated and when the guards were found to be guilty, they were both hanged on a tree, and, in the presence of the king, this was written in the Royal Book of Chronicles.

After these happenings King Xerxes promoted Haman, the son of Hammedatha, the Agagite, and raised him above all the other princes. The king also commanded that all the people should show Haman respect in accordance with his high position. So they bowed down and did obeisance to him. But Mordecai would neither bow down nor do obeisance. Thereupon the king's servants at the gate of the palace said to Mordecai;

"Why do you disobey the king's command?"

They spoke to him of this every day, but he did not listen to them, for he said a Jew must not bow down to a man. So they told Haman. He was filled with anger, but he thought it beneath him to lay hands on Mordecai alone. He decided to destroy all the Jews throughout the empire of Xerxes.

It happened to be the time when the people cast Pur (which is the Persian word for the "lot") before Haman. So he said to King Xerxes;

"There is a certain people scattered among the peoples of your empire who have different laws from all other peoples. Nor do they observe the king's laws. Therefore I do not think it fitting to leave them alone. If it please the king, let it be decreed that they be destroyed. I will pay ten thousand talents of silver into the king's treasuries."

The king took his signet ring from his hand and gave it to Haman, the son of Hammedatha, the Agagite, the enemy of the Jewish people. At the same time he said:

"The silver is yours, and you may do with the people as you please."

Haman had the royal scribes write letters to the satraps of the provinces and the princes of the peoples. He commanded them, in the name of Xerxes, to slay, destroy and wipe out all the Jews, both young and old, infants and women. This was to be done in one day, the thirteenth day of the twelfth month which is the Hebrew month of Adar. And they were to take all their possessions as plunder. The letters were sealed with the king's signet, and couriers carried them forth throughout the empire so that every province should be ready for that day.

At the same time the decree was given out in the castle at Shushan. The king and Haman dined together; but the city of Shushan was perplexed.

When Mordecai found out what had been done, he tore his clothes and put on sackcloth with ashes, and went into the center of the city and cried out with loud and bitter lamentation. Even though it was not permitted to dress so in front of the palace, Mordecai went there. Likewise, throughout the empire where the king's decree was proclaimed, there was great mourning among the Jews, and fasting and weeping and wailing; and many lay in sackcloth and ashes.

When Queen Esther's servants told her of this, she was greatly distressed. First, she sent a servant with clothes to Mordecai, asking him to take off his sackcloth. But he did not accept them. Then she ordered Hathach, one of the king's servants, to ascertain the reason for his conduct. Mordecai told him all that happened and gave him a copy of the king's decree. He asked Hathach to show it to Esther and request that she go before the king and plead for her people.

Esther reminded Mordecai through the messenger that whoever goes to the king without being summoned is subject to death (unless the king holds out his golden scepter). She said that she had not been summoned by the king for thirty days.

Mordecai then sent this message;

"Do not think that you will escape inside the royal palace any more than all the rest of the Jews. If you remain silent now, then deliverance will come from elsewhere; but you and your father's house will perish. And who knows whether you have not been made queen for such an emergency as this?"

Thereupon Esther sent Mordecai this reply,

"Go, gather all the Jews in Shushan and fast for me. Neither eat nor drink for three days, night or day. I also and my maidens will likewise fast. Then, contrary to the law, I will go to the king, and if I perish, I perish."

So Mordecai left and did just as Esther commanded him to do.

On the third day Esther put on her royal robes and stood in the inner court of the palace directly opposite the king's apartment. The king was then sitting on the royal throne. When he saw Queen Esther standing in the court, he was pleased and extended to her the golden scepter. Esther drew near and touched the top of the scepter.

"What is your wish, Queen Esther," the king asked. "It shall be given to you even to half of the empire!"

"If it please the king," replied Esther, "let the king and Haman come to a banquet that I have prepared for him."

The king commanded,

"Bring Haman immediately that he may fulfil Esther's wish."

Both the king and Haman came to Esther's banquet, and as

the wine was being poured he asked the queen to make her request. But Esther only asked that both of them attend another banquet which she would prepare for them on the morrow. Then she would make her petition.

Haman left the palace joyful and happy. But when he passed Mordecai at the palace gate and Mordecai neither stood up nor moved for him, his wrath was even greater than ever against Mordecai. Nevertheless, he restrained himself and went home. There he bragged of his riches and his position to Zeresh his wife and many friends. He also boasted,

"Even Queen Esther permitted only me to come to the banquet, and tomorrow also I am invited by her together with the king. Yet even this honor does not satisfy me so long as I see Mordecai the Jew sitting at the palace gate."

Then his wife Zeresh and all his friends proposed this;

"Let a gallows fifty cubits high be erected and in the morning persuade the king to hang Mordecai on it. Afterwards go merrily with the king to the banquet."

Haman was pleased with this plan. He had the gallows built.

That night the king could not sleep. He had the Royal Book of Chronicles read to him. And he listened to the account of how Mordecai had saved him from the two guards, Bigthana and Teresh, who had plotted to murder him. Whereupon Xerxes asked,

"What honor and dignity have been bestowed upon Mordecai for this?"

The courtiers replied that nothing had been done for him.

"Who is in the court?" asked the king.

It so happened that Haman had just entered the outer court of the palace in order to request that the king put Mordecai on the gallows he had prepared for him. When the king was told of his presence, he asked Haman to enter. And the king asked him,

"What shall be done to the man whom the king delights to honor?"

Now Haman thought: Whom would the king delight to honor more than myself? So he replied,

"For such a man, let the king's own robes and horse and crown be brought. And let the robes and the horse be delivered

to one of the king's most noble princes. Then let the man whom
the king delights to honor be clothed by them, and placed on the
horse and be led throughout the streets to the cry of 'Thus shall
it be done to the man whom the king delights to honor.' "

Then the king said to Haman,

"Hurry and do all you have said to Mordecai the Jew who
sits in the palace gate. Let nothing fail of all you have spoken."

So Haman did as he was commanded. Afterwards Mordecai
returned to the palace gate. But Haman hurried home, like a
mourner with his head covered. He related to his wife and friends
what had happened to him. They said that if Mordecai belonged
to the Jewish people, then his plans would be defeated. While
they were speaking, a royal messenger arrived and summoned
Haman to the banquet which Esther had prepared.

So the king and Haman dined with Queen Esther. On the
day of the second banquet, the king again asked Esther;

"What is your petition, Queen Esther? Tell me, and it shall
be granted. Even if you ask for half the empire, it will be given
to you."

"If I have found favor in the eyes of the king," replied
Queen Esther, "and if it please the king, grant me my life and the
life of my people. For I and my people have been sold to be
slain and to perish. If we had been sold only as slaves, then I
would have been silent and not disturbed the king. But we are
to be destroyed."

"Who and where is the man," Xerxes demanded, "who dares
presume in his heart to do this?"

"An adversary and an enemy," said Queen Esther, "this
wicked Haman!"

Haman was terrified. When the king rose and went into the
palace garden, Haman stood up and begged for his life from
Queen Esther. As the king returned, he saw Haman prostrate
upon Esther's couch.

"Will he violate the queen even while I am here!" cried the
king.

No sooner had he uttered these words than the servants
covered Haman's face. And one of the attendants, Harbonah,
added;

"There are also the gallows fifty cubits high, which Haman built for Mordecai."

"Hang him on it!" the king commanded.

So they hanged Haman on the gallows that he had made for Mordecai. Then the king's anger abated.

On that day King Xerxes gave the house of Haman to Queen Esther. And he took the signet ring which he had taken from Haman and gave it to Mordecai. And the queen put Mordecai over the house of Haman. So it came about that Mordecai was next in rank to King Xerxes. He was great among the Jewish people and a favorite with the mass of his fellow-countrymen, for he sought the good of his people and the welfare of his countrymen.

In remembrance of the deliverance from destruction by Esther and Mordecai, this day was declared a day of feasting and gladness. It became known as Purim and was celebrated by Jews everywhere. As a thanksgiving for the sorrow that was changed to gladness, it became the custom to exchange gifts and share one's bounty with the poor. And the Scroll of Esther, which became part of the Bible, is now read on Purim in remembrance of this great deliverance.

THE DESTRUCTION OF BEL
An Apocryphal Tale

Adapted by LEO W. SCHWARZ

KING ASTYGES DIED AND CYRUS OF PERSIA RECEIVED HIS KINGDOM. Daniel was close to the new king, and was honored above all his friends.

Now the Babylonians had an idol called Bel to which they

provided every day twelve large measures of fine flour, forty sheep and six vessels of wine. The king worshipped Bel and went daily to give it his praise. But Daniel worshipped his own God.

Once the king said to him,

"Why do you not worship Bel?"

He answered,

"Because I may not worship idols made with hands, but only the living God who created the heavens and the earth and rules over all creatures."

"Do you not think that Bel is a living god?" the king asked. "Do you not see how much he eats and drinks every day?"

Daniel smiled and said,

"O king, be not deceived. This idol is but clay within and brass without. He never did eat or drink anything."

The king was furious. He called for his priests and said to them,

"If you do not tell me who it is that devours all the food, you will die. But if you can prove to me that Bel eats and drinks what is sent to the temple, Daniel shall die for he has spoken evilly against them."

"Let it be as you command," said Daniel to Cyrus.

Now the priests, aside from their wives and children, numbered seventy. And Daniel accompanied the king to the temple of Bel. Then the spokesman of the priests said,

"O king, we are leaving the temple, but you may set the meat on the altar, make ready the wine, shut the door and seal it with your signet. And tomorrow when you enter, if you find that Bel has not eaten up everything, we will die; if not, it shall be Daniel who accuses us falsely."

Of course they were not very much concerned for they had made a secret entrance under the altar through which they always entered and ate the food.

As soon as they had left, the king set the food before Bel.

Now Daniel had ordered his servants to bring ashes which they strew over the floor in the presence of the king alone. Whereupon they went out of the temple, shut the door, and sealed it with the king's signet. And so they departed.

In the night the priests with their families came in accordance with their custom. They ate and drank everything.

The king and Daniel arose early and went to the temple.

"Are the seals whole?" asked the king.

"Yes, O king," replied Daniel, "they are whole."

As soon as he opened the door, the king looked at the altar and exclaimed,

"Great art thou, O Bel, and with thee there is no deceit at all."

But Daniel laughed. He held the king so that he should not enter, saying,

"Look at the floor and notice well whose footsteps are there."

"I see the footsteps of men, women and children," said the king.

Cyrus was burning with anger. At his command the priests showed him the secret door where they entered to eat the food, and he had them killed. He delivered Bel into the power of Daniel who destroyed the idol and his temple.

THE AKIBA STORY

Adapted by MICHAH JOSEPH BERDITCHEVSKI

LISTEN TO WHAT A PIOUS WOMAN, THE DAUGHTER OF RICH PARENTS, once accomplished.

There was a man in the land of Israel named Kalba Sabua. He was named thus because if a hungry dog had come to his house, he would have fed him. Akiba was the shepherd of his sheep. Kalba had a beautiful and charming daughter, whose love Akiba won.

She said to him: "Make me your wife."

He answered: "I will do as you wish."

When this was told to Kalba Sabua, he was pained to the death, and he vowed to God that he would give his daughter nothing of his wealth for having been attracted to an ignorant man.

The daughter, however, paid no attention to this and married Akiba. He comforted her and said: "We are very poor and suffer need, but be strong and trust in God; when I have become wealthy, I will buy you a golden bandeau."

Once, as they were speaking thus, someone came to them and begged: "My wife is in the pains of childbirth, and there is nothing in the house for her to lie down on; will you not be kind to me and give me some cloth?"

Akiba had only straw and gave the man his own share. He said to his wife: "You see that God is good to us."

After many days, Akiba's wife said to her companion: "Listen to me, my lord. Take my advice and dedicate yourself to learning."

Akiba obeyed her and left, going to Rabbi Joshua and Rabbi Elieser, to partake of wisdom with them. He remained there for twelve years, and then returned to his own city, followed by twelve thousand pupils. There he heard someone tormenting the deserted wife, saying: "I know what your father did to you for having chosen a shepherd as husband, a boor who was not worthy of you. After he had married you, he left and has not returned these twelve years; you are a widow during his lifetime."

Akiba's wife answered: "It is my wish that he remain away twelve more years, and not return as a boor."

When Akiba had heard her reply thusly, he returned to his study halls and gave twelve more years to learning.

Now he returned to his own land, accompanied by twenty-four thousand pupils. The elders of the city put themselves out to receive him properly; he was the recipient of many honors, and no one knew that it was Akiba. He informed his wife of his arrival; she wanted to go to meet him but she had only torn garments. One of her neighbors asked her to borrow a dress from her, but she replied: "A just man knows the ways of the poor."

She went to meet her husband and fell on her face before him. Akiba's pupils wanted to push her away, but their master said: "Do not touch her. She has suffered bitterly. It was she who brought me and you the teachings of God."

In the meantime Kalba Sabua learned that a wise man had come to the city and hurried to meet him, to ask that he release him from the oath. He was saddened by the break with his daughter who was suffering great need. Akiba asked him his desire, and Kalba Sabua told him of his vow. Akiba said: "Why did you do this?"

Kalba Sabua answered: "Because my daughter took someone as husband who was not worthy of her, without an occupation and illiterate."

Akiba said: "If he had been such as I, would you not have made that vow?"

Kalba Sabua answered: "God forbid! If he had only been able to read one paragraph, I would have bestowed half my wealth on him."

Akiba said: "I am your son-in-law, your daughter's husband."

Kalba Sabua rose, kissed Akiba's head and embraced him. Then he gave him half his wealth.

Thus Rabbi Akiba became wealthy and had a golden bandeau made for his wife, as he had promised her.

You will see what great honors this man won because of his wisdom. But he had gleaned his wisdom in great poverty.

Akiba's Student Years

It has been said of Rabbi Akiba that even at the age of forty he still had no learning. When he married Kalba Sabua's daughter, she said to him: "Go to Jerusalem and study the Scriptures."

Akiba answered: "I am forty years old, how much learning can I acquire?"

One day he was standing before a well in Lydda and saw that the stone at the well was grooved. He asked how this hollow

had been cut into the stone. He was told that the groove had been
made by the rope rubbing against the stone when the pail was
drawn up. Akiba began to evolve deductions from the immediate
to the remote. He said to himself: "If soft matter can hollow out
hard matter, how much more will words of learning, weighty as
iron, groove into my heart, that is of flesh?"

Others narrate the following.

Akiba's wife said to her husband: "Turn to learning."

He answered: "I will be laughed at, because I am so old
and still so ignorant."

His wife said: "You will soon see a miracle."

Then she said: "Bring me a donkey with a flayed back."

Akiba did this. His wife covered the beast's back with earth
and sowed seed in it. After a while flowers blossomed on it. Akiba
led the donkey to market, and everyone laughed. He led the
donkey to market the second day, and people made fun of it. On
the third day he once again led the donkey out, and by this time
no one paid attention to it.

Akiba's wife said to him: "Go and devote yourself to learning. On the first day people will laugh at you, on the second day
they will laugh, on the third day they will say: 'That is the man's
way.'"

It was said of Rabbi Akiba that during the years of his study,
he gathered wood daily and made a bundle of it. Half of the wood
he sold for his upkeep, the rest he carried to his house and
burned them for light that he might study by. One day his
neighbors were disturbed by this and said:

"Akiba, the smoke is doing us harm; will you sell us the
wood and buy oil for illumination?"

Akiba answered: "I derive many benefits from the wood; I
study by its light, I am warmed by its flame, and the money it
brings me buys me nourishment."

Wandering Death

Rabbi Akiba was once passing a graveyard and saw a man
with a bundle of wood on his back running as swiftly as a horse.

The man's face was as black as a smithy's. Akiba ordered the hurrying man to stand still and said to him:

"My son, what is the reason for your working so hard? If you are a slave and your master has placed this yoke on you, then I will release you and return you to freedom; if you are poor, then come with me, and I shall make you rich."

The man whom he was addressing answered: "Sir, let me go on, I am not supposed to stop."

Akiba said: "Are you man or spirit?"

The man said: "He who speaks with you is a dead man. Day after day he is sent out to chop wood, so that this wood may be used in his immolation."

Akiba asked: "What did you do on earth?"

The dead man answered: "In my lifetime I was a rent collector; I was considerate of the rich and strangled the poor, and as if this were not enough, I once, on a Yom Kippur, violated a young woman who was engaged to be married."

Akiba said: "My son, have you never tried to find out from the demons to whom you have been turned over, whether there is no surcease for you?"

The dead man replied: "Sir, do not speak to me, or my guards will punish me even more, for that is the way of chastisement. Nothing can help me, but I heard them say that only one thing might bring me surcease, but it is something which cannot be accomplished. The demons said that if I had a son and if this son, during a common prayer, sang out praise to God, whom all praise, and if the congregation called out Amen to his prayer, the sinner would be freed of torment. But I have no son. I left a widow who was with child at my death, but I don't know whether she gave birth to a boy or to a girl, and if it is a boy, who is going to teach him Scriptures? I have no friend in all the world."

Akiba asked the dead man: "What is your name?"

He answered: "Akiba."

The teacher asked further: "What was your wife's name?"

The man answered: "Sisna."

Akiba asked: "What was the name of your city?"

The dead man answered: "I lived in Laodicea."

Akiba went there and asked after the dead rent collector. When the residents of the city heard his name, they cried out:

"May the villain's bones be ground to dust."

Akiba said: "Let me find out everything you know about him."

The people answered: "He had a son born after his death, and the son is uncircumcised."

Akiba had the boy brought to him and circumcised him. Then he began to teach him Scriptures, and tried to familiarize him with the table blessings. But the boy grasped nothing of his teachings. Then Akiba fasted forty days because of the boy. A voice came down to him from above and called: "Akiba, have you burdened yourself with fasting because of this creature?"

Akiba answered: "Lord of the Universe! I have vouchsafed this boy to you."

Then God opened the heart of the boy, and he learned "Hear, O Israel," and the eighteen blessings. Akiba brought him to the synagogue, and the boy cried out: "Praise be to God, whom all praise!"

The whole congregation responded with an Amen. At once the dead man was relieved of the punishment that had been put upon him. That night he appeared to Akiba in a dream and said: "May your spirits be at peace, since you have brought me rest."

Akiba said: "Praise be to the Eternal, who does the will of his believers."

Last Days and Death

When the Romans issued a decree forbidding Israel to teach the Torah, Akiba assembled students and plain folks and taught the Torah.

One day Pappas, the son of Judah, approached him and asked,

"Akiba, are you not afraid of these people?"

"Pappas," replied Akiba, "are you the one they call wise? You are really a fool. Let me tell you a parable.

"A fox was walking along the banks of a river and in the

water he saw the fish fleeing in every direction. 'Why are you fleeing so?' he asked. They replied, 'To escape from the nets which are cast for us.' 'Come up upon the dry banks,' said the fox, 'and we will live together just as your fathers and my fathers did.' 'Are you really the most cunning of all animals?' they said, 'You are only a fool. If we are afraid here in the water which is the place of our life, shall we not be even more afraid on dry land which is the place of our death?'

"So it is with us, Pappas," continued Akiba. "If we are afraid of studying the Torah which is our life, shall we not be even more afraid if we cease from studying it?"

Soon afterwards Akiba was arrested and thrown into prison. The Romans also arrested Pappas and put him in the same cell with Akiba.

"What brought you here?" asked Akiba.

"You can be happy," replied Pappas, "for you are in prison for the sake of the Torah, but I am here for a trivial offense."

When they led Akiba out of prison to his death, it was the hour for the recitation of the "Hear, O Israel" prayer. The executioners tore off his flesh with iron combs, but he prayed and accepted the flaying with the love of the Torah.

His students cried,

"O Master, it is enough, enough!"

But he answered,

"Every day I prayed and wept over the words, 'And thou shalt love the Lord, thy God, with all thy soul.' I asked myself, 'Will that moment ever come for me?' Now that the moment has come, shall I not fulfill my desire?"

And when Akiba recited "The Lord is One" he lingered on the word "one" until his soul left his body.

At that moment a voice from heaven was heard, saying,

"Happy is Akiba, whose soul went forth still proclaiming My oneness. For this Akiba is destined for the world to come."

LEVIATHAN AND THE FOX
A Medieval Fable

Adapted by LEO W. SCHWARZ

ONCE THE ANGEL OF DEATH ASKED FROM GOD THE POWER TO KILL all living things, but God only said to him, "Throw a pair of each member of the animal kingdom into the sea and then you will have power over all that remain of each species." The Angel did this immediately.

When the fox saw what he was doing, he wept.

"Why are you weeping?" asked the Angel.

"For my companions," replied the fox, "whom you have thrown into the sea."

The Angel asked the fox where his companions were. The fox called his wife and ran to the seashore and pointed to the water. The Angel saw the reflection of the foxes in the water, and he thought that he had already thrown in a pair of foxes. He called the fox to his side and said, "Go your way!" The fox and his wife fled and escaped to the woods. There they met a weasel and the fox related what he had done; so the weasel went and did likewise.

At the end of the year Leviathan, king of the seas, called together all the creatures living in the water and he saw that the fox and the weasel were missing. He sent a messenger and through him ascertained how they had escaped. The fish were delighted with the fox's cunning, and they began to taunt their king. Disturbed and envious, Leviathan sent an embassy of great fishes, commanding them to trick the fox and bring him to his throne at the bottom of the sea.

They found the fox near the seashore. Seeing the fishes play-

ing near the bank, he ran toward them. They looked at him as if
surprised and asked him who he was. "I am the fox," he said.
They told him that they had come to tell him that there was a
great honor in store for him.

"What is it?" he asked.

"The Leviathan is sick and on the verge of death. He has
heard that you are wiser than all other animals and has appointed
you to rule in his stead. We have been sent to offer you this great
honor and to ask you to come with us."

"But," answered the fox, "how can I go into the sea without
being drowned?"

The fishes assured him as follows: "You can ride on one of
us, and he will carry you above the water so that even the soles
of your feet will not get wet. Come with us and be our ruler.
You will not have to search for food nor will you be threatened
by man or beast. You will be happy all your life."

The fox believed them, and rode on one of them over the
water. Soon the waves dashed over him, and he began to see that
he had been deceived.

"Alas!" he wailed, "What have I done? I have played many
tricks on others, but these fishes have played one on me worth all
mine put together. How shall I free myself now?"

Then he asked the fish, "What do you intend to do with
me?"

"To tell the truth," they replied, "Leviathan heard of your
cunning and fame, and he plans to tear you apart and eat your
heart so that he will become wise."

"Oh!" said the fox, "why didn't you tell me that right away?
I should then have brought my heart with me and given it to
Leviathan and he would have honored me. But now you have
failed in your mission."

"What!" You haven't brought your heart with you?"

"Certainly not," the fox continued slyly. "I always leave my
heart at home when I go out for pleasure. When I need my
heart, I take it; when I don't, it remains at home."

"What shall we do?" asked the fearful and bewildered fishes.

"My home is not far from the seashore. Take me back to
where we met, and I will get my heart and will return again with

you. I will present my heart to Leviathan, and he will honor you and me with great rewards. But if you take me without my heart, he will be angry with you and devour you. I am not afraid for I shall tell him that I wanted to bring my heart but you refused."

The fishes took his advice. They carried him back to the same place on the seashore. The fox jumped off the fish, ran on the shore and danced for joy.

"Hurry!" cried the fishes, "fetch your heart and come back."

"You fools," replied the fox, "how could I have come with you without my heart? Are there any animals among you, who go about without their hearts?"

"He has tricked us," the fishes moaned.

"Fools! If I could trick the Angel of Death, I can certainly trick a school of silly fishes."

Shamed and heartbroken, they returned and told Leviathan what had happened.

"Truly," said Leviathan, "the fox is cunning and you are simple. You remind me of a saying in the Bible. 'The confidence of fools shall destroy them.' "

Then Leviathan ate the fishes.

EMPEROR BASIL AND RABBI SHEPHATIAH

by AHIMAAZ BEN PALTIEL

IN THE YEAR 868, BASIL THE FIRST WAS ELEVATED TO THE THRONE of the Byzantine Empire. He seized the throne by bloodshed and deceit and, in his zeal for the Christian faith, he planned to destroy the people of Israel or make them submit to conversion. He sent legions of cavalrymen to all corners of the empire to compel Jews to change their religion. A company of them disembarked at the port of Otranto in Italy, and after making known the dread decree of the Emperor, they sailed to Oria. They brought with them a letter from the Emperor Basil to the honored Rabbi Shephatiah. Breaking the royal seal of gold, he read as follows:

"I, King Basil, request that you, Rabbi Shephatiah, appear before me. Pray do not fear to come for I have heard of your great wisdom and I yearn to see you. I swear by my life and my crown that you will be given safe-conduct. I will receive you with the same honor as my own kin and I will grant bountifully whatsoever you may request."

Rabbi Shephatiah immediately embarked for Constantinople and he was housed in the palace as a royal guest.

The Emperor soon after the Rabbi's arrival engaged him in a discussion of religious subjects. He introduced the topic of the comparative merits of Solomon's Temple in Jerusalem and the Church of the Hagia Sophia in Constantinople. Which had required greater wealth to build? The Emperor contended that the Church was the greater of the two because untold treasure had been used to build it. Rabbi Shephatiah requested that a copy of the Bible be set before them.

"There you will find the facts," he said, "and you can then judge which structure consumed more wealth."

The Emperor immediately sent for a Bible. He computed the figures recorded by David and Solomon, and was soon satisfied that the treasure expended on building the Temple in Jerusalem was greater by one hundred and twenty talents of gold and five hundred talents of silver.

"The wisdom of Rabbi Shephatiah," exclaimed the Emperor, "has prevailed against me."

"Nay," replied Shephatiah, "it is the Bible, My Lord, not I, that has prevailed."

Soon afterwards the Emperor invited him to a royal banquet. The table was overflowing with fruits and delicacies; and savory food was served to Rabbi Shephatiah in golden dishes so that he might eat in accordance with the dietary laws. These dishes were lowered on silver chains but the place from which they were lowered was invisible.

After the banquet the Emperor spoke to Shephatiah about his daughter who was the apple of his eye. She was tormented by a demon and no cure could be found for her. The Emperor implored his aid and Rabbi Shephatiah agreed. He said that he would do so with the aid of Almighty God, but that he must have a place free of the impurities of idol worship. The Emperor readily made available the beautiful Garden of Bukoleon in a palace facing the Sea of Marmora. Rabbi Shephatiah took the girl there.

He prayed to God and conjured up the demon in His name. The demon cried aloud,

"Why are you helping the daughter of a man who visits his wickedness upon your people? God has placed her in my power so that I may humble her. Now go away—I will not leave her body."

"I refuse to listen to you," replied the Rabbi. "Come out, demon, in the name of God come out, so that the Emperor may know that the God of Israel lives."

The demon came out of the girl's body and tried to flee, but the Rabbi seized it, and put it in a leaden jar. He sealed the top with the name of God and then flung the jar to the bottom of the sea. Whereupon the Princess became calm, regained her health, and happily returned to the Emperor and the Queen.

Rabbi Shephatiah now sought the Emperor's permission to return to his home. Basil put his arms around the Rabbi's shoulders and led him into his private chamber. There he tried, by persuasion and the offer of wealth, to induce the Rabbi to abandon his faith. He argued, cajoled, threatened. But Shephatiah, although oppressed by pressures applied by the Emperor, resisted.

"O Mighty Lord," he cried, "you are breaking your word and subjecting me to violence!"

The Emperor relented. He agreed to let the Rabbi go but asked him before leaving to visit the Queen who was anxious to bid him farewell and present him with gifts.

Remembering what he had done for the Princess, the Queen was grateful. She talked with him about his own family, inquiring whether he had any children.

"Your servant," replied Shephatiah, "is the father of a son and two daughters."

The Queen offered the Rabbi her earrings and her jewelled scarf and urged him to accept them.

"I give them to you as tokens of my regard for your wisdom. They are priceless. Give them to your daughters." The weight of the earrings was a litra of gold, and the scarf was of equal worth.

Then, ready to depart, the Emperor summoned him and said,

"Shephatiah, ask of me whatsoever you desire. If it is not wealth you wish, you shall have an inheritance of cities and provinces. I wish to fulfill my promise."

"If my Lord wishes to favor Shephatiah," the Rabbi replied earnestly and almost in tears, "allow those engaged in the study of our Law to continue without interference. Do not oppress them and make their lives miserable. If my Lord cannot grant me this, then it is my wish that at least my own city be free of persecution."

"If I had not given you my word," the Emperor replied angrily, "I would make an example of you here and now. But I wrote the letter and cannot break faith with you."

So the Emperor issued an edict and commanded that there should be no religious persecution in the city of Oria. And he sent Rabbi Shephatiah home in peace and honor.

THE CLEVER GIRL

by JOSEPH IBN ZABARA

A KING WITH MANY WIVES ONCE DREAMT THAT HE SAW A MONKEY among them. His spirit was troubled and he seemed downcast. He thought the dream meant that a foreign king would invade his

kingdom and take his harem for plunder. One of the royal
officers told the king about a clever interpreter of dreams, and
the king sent the officer to find out the meaning of the threat-
ening dream.

He set out on a mule. Meeting a farmer on the road, the
officer said to him, "Carry me or I will carry you." The farmer
was amazed for they both were riding mules. Noting his amazement, the officer replied, "O tiller of the earth, you are earth
and you eat earth." As they rode along, the officer suddenly
commented, "There is snow on the hill." Since it was summer,
the farmer laughed. Further along they passed a road with wheat
fields on both sides. "A horse blind in one eye has passed here,"
remarked the officer, "loaded with oil on one side and with
vinegar on the other." Then they saw a field covered with golden
corn and the farmer praised it. "Yes," said the officer, "if the
corn is not already eaten."

They rode on a little further and a high tower loomed into
view. The farmer remarked that it was well fortified. "Fortified
without, if not ruined within," replied the officer. A funeral
passed them. "As for this old man whom they are burying," said
the officer, "I cannot tell whether he is alive or dead."

The farmer was now convinced that his companion must be
mad to make such strange remarks. They approached the village
where the farmer lived and he invited the officer to stay with
him overnight.

Late in the night after the officer had retired, the farmer
told his wife and daughter that though the officer looked intelligent he was a fool, and repeated the remarks he had made.
The farmer's youngest daughter, a girl of fifteen, said, "No, the
man is no fool. You did not understand the real meaning of his
words." The farmer was surprised and asked his daughter to
explain. She said, "The tiller of the soil eats food grown from
the earth. By the 'snow on the hill' he meant your white hair
and you should have answered, 'Time caused it.' He knew 'a
horse blind in one eye' had passed because he could see that the
wheat had been nibbled on one side of the road and not the
other; and as for its load, he saw that the vinegar had parched
the dust while the oil had not. His remark, 'Carry me or I will

carry you,' means that he who diverts a journey with stories and riddles carries his companion, relieving him from boredom. The corn of the field you passed," she continued, "was already eaten if the owner was poor and had sold it before it was reaped. The high and fortified tower was in ruins within if it was without the necessary supplies. About the funeral too his words were true. If the old man left a son, he was still alive; if he was childless, then he was really dead."

The next morning the girl asked her father to give the guest the food she would prepare for breakfast. She gave him thirty hard-boiled eggs, a dish full of milk and a whole loaf of bread.

"Tell me," she asked of the officer, "how many days old is the month? Is the moon new and the sun at its zenith?"

He noted that the farmer had eaten two eggs, a small piece of bread and sipped some of the milk, and answered,

"Tell your daughter that the sun is not full nor is the moon, for the month is two days old."

Transmitting these answers to his daughter, the farmer laughed. "You see, my child, I told you he was a fool! Aren't we now in the middle of the month?" She asked her father whether he had eaten any of the food she had given him. He told her exactly what he had taken. "Well, then," she said, "now I know for certain that the man is really wise."

The royal officer was amazed at the wisdom of the young girl, and told her of the king's dream. She told him that she could interpret it correctly but that she would do so only directly to the king. So he returned with her to the palace.

He praised her wisdom to the king who immediately summoned her to the throne and asked her the meaning of his dream.

"Search your harem," said the girl, "and you will find among the women a man disguised as a woman."

He conducted the investigation personally and found that her words were true. Immediately he ordered the man and the women of the harem to be executed.

And the king married the farmer's daughter. She became his only queen, for during the rest of his life he never took another wife.

TALES OF DEMONS AND DERVISHES

Retold by MICHAH JOSEPH BERDITCHEVSKI

1

The Golden Table

IN THE DAYS OF THE TALMUD THERE LIVED A CHILDLESS MAN named Abba. This man was esteemed by the king and was one of his advisers; he had free access to him. Among the king's treasures was a golden table; on it stood a golden tree from which hung a precious jewel that could illuminate the whole world. The king boasted about this jewel to all the other rulers.

It so happened that the king became a widower. His councillors advised him to marry again, but he was not attracted by any woman. They showed him the daughter of a king of an old aristocratic line and very beautiful. But she refused to marry the king until he had shown her all his wealth; if she succeeded in finding therein some rare thing that did not exist in her father's house, and if the king gave this to her as a gift, then she would become his wife. When the king heard of this, he had the young woman led through his treasure houses. Here the princess saw the golden table and asked the king to bestow it on her, then she would marry him. The king asked for time to meditate on the matter of the table, and the princess consented.

Moreover, the king held counsel with his sages. At this time Abba was not present. The elders advised the king to entrust the Jews in his country with discovering another such table. If they did not do this, the king was to destroy and exterminate them, including Abba. The king hearkened to the advice of his sages and commanded those of that race to produce another table such as his, or else all would die.

There was great mourning among the Jews of the land; they closed their shops, fasted, wept and prayed. When Abba returned, his brethren reported to him what lay before them. Then he hurried to the king and said:

"What have you done, oh King, in laying this heavy burden on my people and allowing them so short a time for the task?" The king replied:

"What am I then to do?" Abba said to the king:

"My advice is that before all else you remove the obligation you have laid on your protégés; I will take it on myself to produce a second table for you. Give me letters to the neighboring princes, asking them to show me their treasures, and allow me one year's time. Also, let me take along gold for the voyages and for the purchase of the object."

The king prepared a letter for Abba, and Abba signed it also. Then Abba set out on his travels. As he was leaving, a voice called from the heavens:

"A son will be born to you, who will shed light on half the world, like a precious jewel."

Abba traveled a long time and had nowhere found a table and a jewel, such as the king wanted. He was greatly worried and asked the princes whom he was visiting for advice. They told him that there was a queen in the west, who herself held a throne, and that he would find this treasure there. Abba took the advice and travelled to the distant country, where the queen permitted him to see her treasures. Here he confirmed that among her treasures was a golden table with a tree and jewel on it, of the identical size and appearance as his king's table. Abba spoke to the queen and said:

"If you will sell me this table, I will give you anything you want."

The queen replied:

"Not for all the wealth in the world will I part with this table."

But the queen was an astrologer and understood how to

read heavenly omens. She saw that Abba had been chosen to show a son that would illumine half the world. So she tried to persuade him to stay with her, and said:

"If you do as I wish, I will give you the table and the jewel."

Abba was in great need, so he resolved to accede to the queen's desire, thinking to himself that it is better to sin on behalf of a good cause than to follow an order without any devotion.

Thereupon there was much displeasure in the upper regions, that such a son should be born to a heathen. That night a column of cloud appeared and brought Abba to his own home. This was the very night after his wife had taken her ritual bath in the spring. Abba knew his wife, and she conceived a son by him, who was later known as Samuel, the almanac scholar. Morning came, and the column of smoke returned Abba to the house of the queen, who had noticed nothing. But the queen knew that Abba's own wife was already blessed with a son, and said:

"It must be that the stranger has divine powers, since he was able to traverse this great distance back and forth in one night."

So she refused to lie with him and gave him the jewelled table. Abba esteemed the queen and parted from her joyfully.

In the meantime three months had passed, and the news spread in the city that his wife was pregnant. The townsmen said:

"She has whored, since her husband has not been home for a year." The woman was brought before a court and sentenced to thirty-nine heavy lashes. While she was being whipped, the child hid his head in such a way as to prevent its being touched.

When the hour of birth had come and the angel arrived to snap the boy in the nose, so that he forget everything that his spirit had experienced of divine knowledge, his face remained hidden, and the angel could not touch him. This was Samuel, son of Abba, the first among mankind to remember everything that he had learned in the womb.

2

The Dervish and the Transformed Mouse

There was once a dervish who served God as a pious, righteous man, and his prayer was constantly hearkened to; even if he had desired the world to be returned to its primitive state, his desire would have been granted.

One day, while the dervish was sitting on the banks of a river, he saw an eagle flying high above him, with a mouse clasped in its claws. The bird flew low in the vicinity of the dervish, and let the mouse drop, which fell at the feet of the man. He was merciful to the thing and covered it with his coat. He wanted to take the mouse home, but was afraid that his neighbors would despise him and oust him. Then he prayed to God that the mouse be transformed into a girl. The Lord hearkened to the pious man's prayer, and the mouse was transformed into a majestically beautiful young woman. The dervish took her home, and she stayed with him. His wife, however, did not sense that the girl had previously been a mouse, and kept her as a slave that her husband had bought.

When the girl was twelve years old, the dervish took counsel with himself:

"The young woman has reached the age when she can take on the responsibilities of womanhood; she should not remain without a husband any longer, she needs a bread-winner. But I will return to the service I have always carried on."

He said to the girl:

"Find someone you would like to have as husband."

The girl replied:

"I want for my husband a hero of great strength, possessing more power than any man." The dervish said:

"I don't know anyone but the sun that has this power; I will therefore pray to the sun to betroth you to whoever is its master."

The dervish wished, and implored the sun:

"Oh Sun, pure and luminous, who bestows light on human beings through the kindness of a generous God, I beseech you to give my daughter as wife to him who determines your ways, since she wants the strongest of the strong and the mightiest of the mighty as husband."

The sun answered:

"I have heard your words, and I will not let you leave me without fulfilment, out of respect to the appearance that God has given you, in preference to all other beings. I must show you who is stronger than I."

The dervish asked:

"Who is it?"

The sun answered:

"It is he who commands the clouds, which have the power of covering me and darkening my light."

The dervish went to the place where the clouds rose out of the sea. He called out their lord and told him what the sun had said. The prince of the clouds replied:

"I have understood your words right; I am truly in possession of such strength as is granted only to angels. Yet I must send you to someone who is stronger than I."

The dervish asked:

"Who is he?"

The prince of the clouds replied:

"The wind, which drives me from one end of the heavens to the other, and whom I can neither force nor oppose."

The dervish betook himself to the prince of the winds and talked to him as he had earlier talked to the lord of the clouds.

The prince of the winds replied:

"I am strong and mighty, but you must go to someone who withstands me, and whom I cannot bend."

The dervish asked who this was, and the prince of the winds answered:

"It is the mountain near you."

The dervish turned to the mountain and said:

"I want to give you my daughter as wife, you great giant."

The mountain replied:

"What you have been told is true; I am strong and unbending. But I will show you someone before whom I am powerless."

The dervish asked:

"Then who is this?"

The mountain said:

"It is the mouse, who can undermine me."

The dervish went to the mouse and spoke to it as he had spoken to the mountain.

The mouse answered:

"I am truly the one who can undermine the mountain. But how can I woo someone of human origin, since I am but a mouse and live in a hole?"

The dervish returned to the girl and spoke to her:

"Do you want to have a mouse as husband? There is none so powerful; I have talked to heroes and giants, and they all sent me to the mouse. Do you want me to implore God to let you become a mouse again, so that you may be companion to the mouse?"

The girl replied:

"Do as you wish."

Thereupon the dervish prayed to God, and the girl became a mouse again. The dervish led it to the hole, where she became wife to the man who was her equal.

3

The Dancing Finger

During the time of a famous kabalist the following incident occurred in the Holy Land. Several boys had gone for a walk in the fields. As they rested for a moment, they suddenly saw a finger rise out of the earth and move forward. One of the boys wantonly said:

"Who will put his ring on this finger, as one does at a betrothal?"

Immediately, one of the boys offered to do this; he placed his ring on the leaping finger and uttered the words prescribed for a betrothal. At once the finger and the ring disappeared. The boys were stunned and returned to the city in a state of confusion.

Some time passed, and the event was forgotten. The boy who had been so bold became engaged to a girl. On the wedding day the community gathered to read the seven prayers before the bridal pair. Suddenly a woman's voice was heard to wail:

"What stain did the bridegroom find on me that he wants to marry another, when he has already promised marriage to me? Summon judges and give me what is mine, or else I will kill the bridegroom and the bride. Look, the ring is on my hand."

The strange woman showed the circlet to the assembly, and it was recognized as belonging to the bridegroom, since his name was scratched on it. The bride's father hurried his daughter away and to their home, and the day of joy became a day of mourning.

The story was brought to the kabalist, who summoned the boy and said to him:

"If you are willing to marry the ghostly woman, then do so, but if you are afraid of her, then I will save you."

The boy said:

"Who would be so mad as to marry a devil? But what can I do against my evil destiny? If I had only broken a leg that day and not left the house!"

Herewith the rabbi called in his servant and asked him to fetch the witch. The messenger searched everywhere for the devil, but could not find her. The rabbi said:

"She has remained in the boy's home, and is in hiding for fear of me. Go there again, stand before the ladder that leads to the roof, and say: 'I have been sent here by my master. If you come along, very well; if not, then I will excommunicate you and your kin.' "

The servant betook himself to the designated place, and spoke the words that the rabbi had asked him to say. The devil came down from the roof and followed the messenger. The rabbi said to the spirit:

"What have you found in this boy that you want to become

engaged to him? Find a husband for yourself from among the spirits, such as you yourself are."

The woman answered:

"Is this then your judgment? Am I to marry another, even though one has already become betrothed to me?"

The rabbi repeated:

"Your betrothal to the boy has no meaning, since he did not see your face, and could not know that you are a devil; he placed the ring on your finger only in jest."

But for this also the devil had answer, whereupon the rabbi shouted at her and said:

"Although the law does not require it, I will command the boy to give you a divorce. If you do not accept it, I will excommunicate you and all that is yours."

He called the scribe and had the divorce papers written. The spirit woman had to accept the papers; the rabbi further placed her under anathema, so that she could not ever injure the bride and groom.

THE GOLEM OF PRAGUE

Adapted by MICHAH JOSEPH BERDITCHEVSKI

IN WORMS THERE WAS A RIGHTEOUS MAN NAMED BEZALEL. ON Passover night a son was born to him. It was during the year 5273 after Creation, and Jews were suffering severe persecution. The nations among whom they lived were accusing them of using blood in the preparation of the Passover bread. As Bezalel's son came into this world, his birth brought immediate benefice. When the mother was gripped by birth pangs, neighbors ran out into the street to fetch the midwife, and thus interfered with the purpose of a gang of villains who were lugging a dead child in a bag, with the idea of charging Jews with its murder, by throwing it into the street where Jews lived. Then Bezalel prophesied over his son and said:

"He will comfort us and free us of torment. His name in Israel is Judah Arieh, according to the verse in Jacob's benediction: 'Judah is a young lion; when my children were rent asunder, he roved high.'"

The boy grew and became learned in books and a wise man to whom all branches of knowledge were entrusted, and who mastered all languages. He was made Rabbi of Posen, but was soon called to Prague, where he became Chief Judge of the community.

His mind and his thoughts were directed toward helping his oppressed people and freeing them from the blood libel. He asked Heaven to tell him in a dream how he could overcome the priests who were spreading the false accusations. He had a nocturnal command:

"Make a man's image out of clay, and you will destroy the evil intent."

The master summoned his son-in-law and his oldest pupil, and confided the celestial reply to them. Also, he asked them to help him in the undertaking. The following four elements were needed to make the Golem: earth, water, fire and air. The rabbi said of himself that the strength of the storm lived in him; his son-in-law was one of those who are fire incarnate; his pupil he saw as the image of the waters, and so he hoped that they three would be fortunate in the work. He took a vow not to disclose anything of the scheme and to prepare himself seven days for the task.

The appointed time was over on the 20th day of Adar, 5340. Four hours after midnight the three men set out for the stream which ran outside the city, on the banks of which there was a clay pit. Here they kneaded a human figure out of the soft clay. They made it three ells in height, carved the facial characteristics, then the hands and feet, and laid the figure on its back on the earth. Now the three placed themselves at the feet of the clay image, and the rabbi asked his son-in-law to pace seven times around it while reciting stanzas he had composed. When

this had been done, the clay figure became as red as glowing coals. Then the rabbi asked his pupil also to circle the image seven times and to recite other stanzas. The glow subsided, the body became damp and sent out vapor, and it could be seen that nails had sprouted from the finger tips, hair covered the head and the body and face of the figure seemed to be those of a thirty-year-old man. Now the rabbi himself paced around the figure seven times, and the three men in unison recited a verse from the Story of Creation: ". . . and God breathed into his nostrils the breath of life; and man became a living soul."

As they finished speaking the verse, the eyes of the Golem opened, and he looked at the rabbi and his disciples with a glance of astonishment. Rabbi Loew spoke aloud to the image, and said: "Arise!" The Golem rose to his feet. Then the men dressed him in garments and shoes they had brought with them —the garments were such as were worn by synagogue employees —and the rabbi said to the man of clay:

"You must know that we made you out of the dust of the earth, so that you may protect the people from the evil that they must suffer at the hands of their enemies. I name you Joseph; you will live in my courthouse and do the work of a servant. You must hearken to my commands and do everything that I ask, even if I command you to walk through fire, to jump into the water or to throw yourself from a high tower."

The Golem nodded his head at the rabbi's words, as if he wanted to express his consent. In general he had human attributes; he could hear what was said to him and understand it, but the power of speech was denied him. So it was that on that memorable night three men left the rabbi's house; but when they returned at six in the morning, there were four.

The rabbi told his neighbors that on his way to his morning plunge he had met a beggar who seemed to be honest and innocent of any wrongdoing, and that he had taken him along. He wanted to put him to work in the study-chamber, but he forbade that any housework be allotted to him.

The Golem sat constantly in a corner of the room, his head bowed into his hands, and he was motionless, as if he were a being whom intellect and comprehension had deserted and who paid no attention to what was going on in the world. The rabbi said of him that neither fire nor water could harm him, nor sword wound him. He had named him Joseph after the Talmudic figure Joseph Seda, who was half man and half spirit and who had served scholars and often aided them in distress.

Rabbi Loew availed himself of the Golem only when it was necessary to combat the blood libel under which the Jews of Prague were suffering especially. Whenever Rabbi Loew sent the Golem somewhere where he was not to be seen, he put an amulet on him written on deerskin. This made him invisible, but he himself could see everything. During the Passover festival the Golem had to pace through the city every night, stopping everyone who was carrying a pack on his back. If the pack contained a dead child which was to have been flung into Jews' Street, he bound the man and the carcass with a rope he always had with him and led him to the City Hall to be turned over to the deputies. The Golem's strength was supernatural and he fulfilled all he undertook.

At this time there were two rich men living in Prague, business partners. Together they acquired a large house and lived side by side in loyal neighborliness. But in one matter their destinies were not identical. Whereas the one had children who were healthy and gay, the other man's wife could bring forth only weaklings. Thus the woman who was afraid for the lives of her children, grew envious of her friend. She did not show her feelings, but the midwife who attended both women at childbirth, understood what was in the heart of the less fortunate one, and looked for ways and means to serve her.

It so happened that both women took a cleansing bath on the same day and became pregnant at the same time. The births occurred simultaneously, and both women were delivered of sons. But since one child was stronger than the other, whose survival was in doubt, the midwife exchanged the children during the night, while the residents of both houses were asleep.

The two women suckled the children, and neither one suspected that the child at her breast was not her own. The boys grew and did not know that those whom they called father and mother were not their parents. Nor did anyone else discover the truth, for the midwife kept her secret diligently and betrayed nothing of her deed. One day she died suddenly, and the event sank like a stone into the sea.

Meanwhile the time neared for the offspring of the two neighbors to marry. The man who was rich in sons and daughters made varying arrangements. But in connection with the youngest son he came to his neighbor, to engage the son to the neighbor's daughter. The engagement papers were prepared, and the marriage was to follow soon thereafter. Chief Rabbi Loew was asked to read the ceremony and he appeared at the wedding. But as he raised the cup and was about to read the blessing, the cup fell from his hand and was shattered, and the wine spilled. A second glass of wine was brought him, but this also fell from his hand. Rabbi Loew paled at this unusual circumstance, and all those present were frightened. Joseph, the Golem, was sent to fetch more wine. The Golem ran across the courtyard to his master's cellar. The wedding guests watched him and saw him exchange nods with something invisible. When he arrived at the cellar door he suddenly stopped, and ignoring the cries of the people who were urging him to hurry, he turned toward Rabbi Loew's courthouse. There he wrote a few words on a slip of paper, and returning, handed the note to his master. On it was written: "Bride and groom are brother and sister." Dazed with shock, Rabbi Loew glanced questioningly at the Golem, who beckoned him to follow. Rabbi Loew told the guests that the marriage could not occur on that day and that the food was to be distributed among the poor. He left the wedding hall with the Golem. Before the synagogue window he saw a ghost standing, who had told the Golem of the kinship of the bridal pair. Rabbi Loew resolved to clarify the mystery. The next day, when the members of the community had come to pray at the synagogue, he asked them to remain after the service. He had already had built a wooden box. After the prayers were over, he and two assistant judges, who were still wearing their prayer-shawls, stood themselves before a table. He sent an old synagogue servant to summon the bridal pair and the parents, and when these had arrived, he ordered the Golem, before the whole community, to go to the cemetery and call up the dead midwife. He gave him his own staff, with which to beat on the grave and awaken the sleeper. Fear gripped the assembly when they heard these words. But the master said:

"Be calm. Nothing will happen to you."

After a short while the Golem appeared. He handed Rabbi Loew the staff and pointed to the wooden box, as if he meant to indicate that he had fulfilled his mission and had brought the soul of the dead here. The assembly was again frightened; people closed their eyes and sat as if in a trance. Then they heard Rabbi Loew's voice saying:

"We, a court on this earth, have decided that you must explain how it has happened that the engaged pair are brother and sister."

The ghost began to speak and reported accurately what had happened that night many years back when both children were born. The assembly heard only the voice of the ghost; the words were indistinguishable, but the judges, the parents of the bride and groom and the bride and groom themselves were able to understand everything. The dead woman continued, and said that in the twelve years that had passed since her death, she had found no peace in the grave. Only because of Chief Rabbi Loew had she been allowed to disrupt the wedding, since she had thus been given the opportunity to make good her misdeed. At the end of her speech she wept, and the assembly with her.

Rabbi Loew conferred with his judges as to what decision to hand down. It was decided that first of all the guilty person had to apologize to the bridal pair for the public disgrace to which they had been subjected. When they had forgiven her, she would be clean and free of all guilt. Again sobs were heard; the dead woman was asking forgiveness of the bridal pair. The brother and sister assured her:

"We forgive you."

Then the court said:

"We, earthly judges, declare you to be free, and hope that the heavenly court will be lenient. Go in peace, rest in peace, until the Messiah comes."

Then Rabbi Loew ordered that the wooden box be hacked

apart as a sign that the dead woman was no longer there, but that one board be nailed to the grave marker of the midwife, as a memento of the occurrence. He had the synagogue ledger brought to him and entered the event, from which entry future generations learned of it. The judges who were present had to set their seals on the entry. Chief Rabbi Loew also commanded that the boy and the girl who had grown up together and been always known as brother and sister, should marry one another. Both were pleased, and the parents consented. Thus the marriage was celebrated, and the newlyweds were a happy pair.

Not far from Prague, on the road that led to the city, there was—in the time of Chief Rabbi Loew—a neglected ruin, in which demons carried on their doings. Wayfarers were afraid to go past this spot at night. Some thought that they had heard an orchestra playing; others claimed that they had seen a man on the roof, blowing a trumpet, as if he were summoning warriors to battle. Still others saw a pack of black hounds circling around the ruin. For this reason travelers avoided this public spot.

It once happened that a Prague Jew, whose livelihood was derived from peddling in the neighboring villages, passed the desolate house at night. A black dog leaped at him, circled him several times, barking, and ran back to the ruin. Dread and horror gripped the man, and almost fainting with fright he dragged himself home. Here he told his family what he had experienced, and prepared to go to bed. But during the night the family were awakened from sleep; they heard the man barking like a dog. They hurried to his bed and awakened him. The man was drenched with sweat and broken with what he had seen in his dream: It seemed to him that he was in the midst of a battle with other men, all of whom were sitting astride black dogs and were themselves barking like dogs; they forced him, too, to bark like a dog, with all his strength. The next night the same apparitions appeared, and the peddler again bellowed loudly like a dog. This was repeated night after night, and the man grew quite weak from the torment he had to endure.

When he realized how badly off he was, he gathered his

strength and with his wife and children went to see Rabbi Loew.
He implored him for help and told him of the trouble he was
in. The rabbi told him to examine the talith katan that he
was wearing. Several threads were missing from the fringe and
had to be replaced. Then the rabbi had the scribe prepare an
amulet of deerskin, which the peddler was to bind around his
forehead before retiring. Moreover, the man was not to spend
the night in his own home for a week, but in the courthouse, on
the Golem's pallet. On the other hand, the Golem was to sleep
in the peddler's bed. This was arranged. On the Golem's couch,
the peddler regained peaceful sleep, and was no more pursued by
evil dreams. After this he returned to his own home and recovered his health. To the Golem the rabbi gave a bundle of
straw and a fuse, and ordered him to set the ruin afire. This
was done, and the place ceased to be a spot of corruption.

After a decree was issued, declaring the blood accusations to
be groundless and forbidding all such charges, the spirits of the
people were quieted, and Rabbi Loew resolved to take breath
away from the Golem. He had him placed on a bed and ordered
his pupils to pace around him seven times, repeating the words
that had been voiced at the time the Golem was created, but
in reverse sequence. As the seventh circling came to an end,
the Golem once again turned into lump clay. The clothing was
removed from it, it was wrapped in two old prayershawls, and
the clay image was put behind a heap of old, faulty books in the
rabbi's attic.

Rabbi Loew said that while he was about to blow breath
into the Golem, two spirits appeared before him: Joseph the
devil and Jonathan the devil. He chose Joseph, who had already
come to the aid of Talmudic scholars. He could not endow the
Golem with the faculty of speech, because in his innermost being
there was only a life urge, but no soul. He possessed a certain
amount of judgment, but wisdom and deep insight were denied
him.

Although the Golem had no soul, one could still see,
strangely enough, that on the Sabbath his face was more friendly
than on weekdays. There were some who said that on the day

before the Sabbath Rabbi Loew would remove the shield bearing the name of God from under the tongue of the clay image, because he was afraid that the Sabbath might make him immortal and that men would worship him as an idol.

The Golem had no desires within him, nor good, nor evil. All that he accomplished was in answer to the urge to be obliterated again. He could reach with ease anything that was ten feet above or ten feet under the ground, and nothing could prevent his completing a task he undertook.

THE LITTLE MAN IN THE JAR
A Ghetto Tale

Retold by S. S. KOTELIANSKY

ONCE UPON A TIME THERE LIVED TWO SCHOLARS. THEIR LEARNING and wisdom were so great that they were known all over the world. One of them was Rabbi Moses Maimonides—blessed be his memory!—and the other was Aristotle, the great philosopher of the gentiles. They were great friends and all their lives studied together. After many years of study and thinking they discovered that if a certain tiny vein were cut out from a living human being, and put into a jar and kept among certain herbs, the little vein would begin to grow and grow until it became a man. And the man, so grown from the little vein, would live forever. At first they intended to cut out the vein from one of the people they knew. But as that meant death to the persons so operated upon, they finally decided that the best thing would be for the little vein to be cut out from one of the two learned friends. Then they drew lots, and the lot fell on Aristotle.

After a time the little vein in the jar began to grow, and

Rabbi Moses Maimonides—blessed be his memory!—perceived that the man who was to grow up from the little vein and live eternally, would be made into a God by the people; that the people would abandon the living God and serve the eternal man whom Aristotle and himself had created. Maimonides felt terribly distressed on that account; but as he had given his hand to Aristotle not to interfere with the growth of the man in the jar, he could not destroy the jar and thus prevent the little vein from becoming an eternal man. The more marked became the signs of the little vein turning into man, the more grieved and distressed Maimonides became, for he had no longer any doubt that the people would turn the eternal man into God and serve him and worship him.

After many months of deliberation, prayer and fasting, Maimonides came to a decision. He told the servants to let into the room, where he prayed and studied, and where on a shelf stood the jar with the little vein, all the chickens and cocks of his household. Maimonides then put on his long praying cloak; and as his habit was to walk about the room while praying, as soon as he began to pray the chickens and cocks got frightened by the waving of the cloak, and began to jump and fly about the room. At last a big cock jumped on the shelf where the jar stood, and upset the jar. The jar fell to the ground and broke in pieces. And when Maimonides saw that the tiny little creature pointed a tiny finger to him as a sign that he had broken his oath to Aristotle, Maimonides wept bitterly, and all the rest of his life prayed for forgiveness.

THE SALVATION OF A SOUL

Retold by S. S. KOTELIANSKY

WHEN THE BAALSHEM—BLESSED BE HIS MEMORY!—WAS ABOUT TO
die, he called together his friends, disciples, and followers to
have his farewell talk with them and to advise them what each of
them should do and how he should live. To his beloved disciple
Rabbi Jacob he made this bequest: that he should wander about
all over the land, from city to city from town to town, from
village to village, and tell people the events and happenings of
the Baalshem's life. This advice seemed unusual to Rabbi Jacob,
who was the favourite disciple of the Baalshem, and who was
looked upon by everyone as the Baalshem's successor. Now he
was to leave everything, his wife and children, his studies and
meditations, and to wander over the land as a beggar and to
tell stories from the life of the Baalshem. But as the Baalshem
had laid upon him this mission, Rabbi Jacob had to accept it.

When the Baalshem passed away, his disciples and followers
started on their work, each in the way he was told, and Rabbi
Jacob also started on his pilgrimage. The way he made it was
this: he would arrive at a town or village, go into the synagogue
and announce to the people that he could tell stories from the
life of the Baalshem. The people, eager to hear those stories,
would gather together either in the synagogue or in a house,
listen to the stories, thank Rabbi Jacob, and then make a collection for him to enable him to carry on his work. And so he
went about from one place to another, always on the move, always telling the wonderful stories of the glorious life of the
Baalshem—blessed be his memory.

Once he arrived in a big city; he went to the synagogue and
announced that he could tell stories of the Baalshem. Then the

people said to him that there lived in that city a rich and very respected Jew who was so fond of hearing stories of the Baalshem that he paid a golden sovereign for each story told him. Rabbi Jacob called on the rich Jew, and repeated to him what the people in the synagogue had told him. The rich Jew welcomed Rabbi Jacob, and said it was true. He also invited Rabbi Jacob to stay at his house for several days, and as the rich Jew was very busy during the week—so he told Rabbi Jacob—he would be free to listen to Rabbi Jacob's stories on the Sabbath. Then the rich man summoned his servant and told him to put up Rabbi Jacob in one of the best chambers in the house, to buy fine clothes for him, and to do all his bidding.

On Friday before nightfall the rich Jew and Rabbi Jacob went to the synagogue to the evening service. After prayer the rich Jew told the beadle to announce that a distinguished guest, a disciple of the Baalshem, who had been with the Baalshem for many years and had witnessed many glorious events of his life, had arrived at their city and was staying at the house of the rich Jew; that the disciple was going to tell them stories from the life of the Baalshem; and that the rich Jew invited all who cared to call at his house to listen to Rabbi Jacob's stories.

The congregation was delighted at the pleasure of passing the time at the rich Jew's house, listening to stories about the Baalshem. So they gathered at the house of the rich man; they sat down to table, blessed the wine and ate and drank. When the meal was over many other people called at the house of the rich man, all eager to listen to Rabbi Jacob's stories. Then said the rich Jew to Rabbi Jacob: "Now, Rabbi Jacob, you may begin telling us your stories!" When Rabbi Jacob opened his mouth to begin a story, no words came out. He suddenly found that he had forgotten everything. He sat dumbfounded, disgraced, not knowing what to say. The rich Jew encouraged and comforted Rabbi Jacob. But no word came from him. The guests began to laugh at him and to tease him. But the rich Jew forbade them; and to Rabbi Jacob he said: "Surely, you must be tired. You had better go and rest, and tomorrow you will probably remember a story and tell it us."

Rabbi Jacob went to his chamber and lay down, but he could not sleep. All night long he tried to recollect the stories he so well knew, but could not recall to his mind even the very fact that the Baalshem ever lived. In the morning the rich Jew and Rabbi Jacob went to the synagogue to pray; and after prayer the people gathered again at the rich man's house to the midday meal, to eat and to hear Rabbi Jacob's stories. But this time, too, Rabbi Jacob could not remember a single thing, and, disgraced, he sat in silence. The rich man, too, felt grieved, and said to Rabbi Jacob: "You must be still tired; rest yourself; perhaps you will remember some story in the evening." Rabbi Jacob retired to his chamber, ashamed and heartbroken. But what could he do if God had punished him so bitterly. All the other disciples sat peacefully at home, each doing his appointed work; and he, Rabbi Jacob, had to be a wanderer in strange places, and unknown, an exile; and now, too, to undergo the disgrace of having forgotten all the stories of the Baalshem. All day long, in spite of the Sabbath, Rabbi Jacob was in great distress and wept bitterly; he would rather have died than encounter the people again and go through the shame of being taken for a liar. As he was so sitting, absorbed and distressed, the servant called to ask him to the evening meal. After the meal the people asked him again why he kept silent. Then Rabbi Jacob said to them: "Do with me what you will. I am not a liar. I have been for many years with the Baalshem and with my own eyes witnessed many events in his life; but now I have forgotten them all." The people, convinced that Rabbi Jacob was an imposter, wanted to drive him out of the house; but the rich Jew stopped them. The Sabbath over, Rabbi Jacob called on the rich Jew and said to him: "I must take my leave now. Do not be angry with me for having given you so much trouble. But God is my witness that it is not my fault." The rich Jew comforted him and said that he was not at all angry, and that he would very much like him to stay on with him till Tuesday; perhaps he might after all remember one of the stories connected with the Baalshem. If, however, he could not recall any story, he would not detain him any longer.

Rabbi Jacob prayed and wept during the next two days

and nights; but it was of no avail. On Tuesday morning he went into the rich Jew's apartment to say goodbye. The rich Jew gave Rabbi Jacob some money, shook hands with him and they parted. But no sooner had Rabbi Jacob crossed the threshold of the house than he suddenly remembered a story of the Baalshem. He rushed back and said to the rich Jew that he could tell him a story which he had just remembered. The rich Jew begged him to tell it. And Rabbi Jacob told him the following story:

"When the Baalshem had revealed himself and thus became known to the world, he used to sit in his apartment all the time, and multitudes of people from all over the world, Jews and Gentiles, would come to him to ask his advice and help and his intercession with God for them. He would usually receive one person at a time, for there came to the Baalshem people who had to tell him their innermost secrets. So all the week long the Baalshem sat secluded in his apartment. But the Sabbath he used to spend in the company of all the people, to eat together, be merry, tell stories, and teach. The third meal of the Sabbath the Baalshem would take with his disciples and numerous guests. The meal started in the twilight; then the whole company would recite the evening prayers, candles would be brought in, the meal would go on till very late at night. The Baalshem all the time behaved as one of the company, happy and merry; the disciples and guests sang songs and danced, all being one happy family.

"One Sabbath evening, after the candles had been lit, the Baalshem, who had sat all through the twilight deeply absorbed in thought, amid his company who were so silent that if a pin had fallen to the ground it would have been heard, called out to me and said: 'Jacob, go and tell Alexey'—that was the name of the Christian coachman who had served the Baalshem for many and many a year—'to harness the horses and make ready for a journey. And yourself take your Sabbath clothes, for you are to accompany me.' Alexey drove up to the house; the Baalshem and I took our seats in the carriage. When we came outside the town, the Baalshem commanded Alexey to seat himself with his back to the horses, and to drop the reins so that the horses might run wherever they ought to run, without impediment or hindrance. And so it was. The horses at once started with very great speed, and we only saw cities, towns, villages, forests, rivers rushing past us. So it went on all night long. And when it began to dawn we arrived at the very center of a large city and the horses stopped by themselves at a house. I got out of the carriage and began knocking at the gate. But for a time no one answered my knock. Then I began knocking with all my might, when a very old Jew ran out, opened the gate and told us to make haste and come in. When we entered the house there was not a living soul there. The Baalshem asked the old Jew where his family was. The old man whispered to him, saying: 'My family, just like all the rest of the Jews in the city, are in hiding today. The Pope hates Jews; he is a man of great learning, and people say that he knows the Talmud and Kabalah and all the commentaries even better than many a learned Rabbi. The Christians love their Pope dearly, for he does great good to them. But as the Pope hates Jews so bitterly, he published a proclamation to the effect that on this day any Christian meeting in the street a Jew, Jewess, or Jewish child has the right to kill them. This has been the custom here every year, on the first day of the Christian Easter, for many years. Christians from all over the world come to this city for Easter; they march with great parade to the Cathedral, and conduct the Pope there with great solemnity, all the bells in all the churches ringing; and all the Jews lie hidden in fear and trembling.'

"Whilst he was thus whispering, the bells in the churches began to ring. The old Jew became as pale as death, and said to us: 'For the love of God, go and hide yourselves; there is a corner behind the oven.' But the Baalshem walked to the window and opened it wide. When the old Jew saw this, he began to swear and to curse at the Baalshem. Then the Baalshem said to me: 'Jacob, go to the Cathedral and tell the Pope that I ask him to come here.' I went out of the house, walked to the Cathedral, and no one of the multitude of Christians ever touched me. I walked up to the Pope and told him that the Baalshem requested his immediate presence. The Pope said: 'Go and tell the Baalshem that I am coming presently.' So I went back with the Pope's message. But the Baalshem said to me: 'Go back quickly and tell the Pope that he must come at once.' And I went to the Pope again with that message. And the Pope said to me: 'I will be there in ten minutes,' when the ten minutes had passed and the Pope had not arrived, the Baalshem said to me: 'Run quickly to the Pope, seize him by his mantle and drag him here without fail.' So I returned to the Cathedral, walked up to the Pope, seized him by his mantle, and arrived at the house. When the Pope came in, the Baalshem retired with him into a private chamber and remained there for a long time. After that the Pope left, and the Baalshem told Alexey to get the horses ready so that we might return. What happened further I do not know. The only thing I know is that our return journey took us seventeen weeks."

Then the rich Jew said: "Now I will tell you the rest. The Pope was myself. I am a Jew of a good family of learned rabbis. When still quite young I possessed great learning, and walked in the paths of my fathers. But when at the age of sixteen I began to study the Kabalah, my mind went astray. I began to dislike my people and their way of life, and gradually got to dislike them so much that I could not endure them any longer. My father and mother began noticing the change in me; at first they talked to me lovingly; then they began being severe with me. It was all of no avail. I could not bear it any longer, and I told them that I was going away to the Christians. When I came to the Christian scholars and they saw how great my learning was, they received me with open arms, and soon I embraced the Christian faith. I was first made a priest and then in course of time was elected Pope. With my advancement in the Church grew my hatred of the Jews. I became their bitterest enemy, always devising how to wrong them more and more. Finally I published a proclamation allowing Christians to kill any Jew met in the street on Easter day. And the more wrong I did to the Jews, the more esteemed and loved I was by the Christians. In heaven, when it was seen what I had become and what I was going to become still further, my parents were spoken to and advised to take measures. Once my grandfather appeared to me in a dream saying to me: 'Why have you became so evil? We are all brought down lower and lower time after time. When we asked the reason for this, the heavenly powers said that our degradation on high was all through you; and I was told that there remained one remedy for it—that I should appear to you and tell you that you must return to the flock, become a Jew again and repent of your sins and perform various acts of charity; that although your sins are so very great, yet they may be forgiven. When I awoke I remembered the whole dream, and laughed at it. Since that night my father and mother had appeared in a dream to me every night, at first imploring me and crying bitterly, then saying that if I died a Christian, without having repented, my soul would wander about forever and ever, and that all my relations even to the tenth generation would be thrown down from their seats on high to the bottomless pit. In my sleep those dreams used to torment me; but when I awoke I thought it was all quite foolish to believe in them. Once I dreamt I was going to die in three days' time, and that dream impressed me very much. I also dreamed that my father and mother came to me and said: 'We died because of you, for we could not bear the disgrace.' Then in my dream, I said: 'But how can I get away from here, if I am being constantly watched by numbers and numbers of people; every step of mine is watched and known.'

"Then they said they would find a way and tell it me next night. Next night they appeared again and said: 'The Baalshem from Medzibozh will come to this city and send for you. You go to him at once and whatever he tells you to do, do it without fail,' I promised them to act as they requested. And when I woke up in the morning, crowds and crowds of people from all over the world were waiting for me to conduct me to the Cathedral. When you called for me then I wanted to go with you. But seeing the people and the great respect in which they held me, I wanted to prolong it for a while, and I sent word with you to the Baalshem that I would come soon. The same thing happened when you called for me the second time. But when you called the third time and seized me by my mantle, I followed you. And when the Baalshem saw me and retired with me into a private room, he told me then everything about myself, about my dreams, about my dead parents' great anxiety to rescue my soul. When he told me so clearly everything about myself, which I thought hidden and unknown to any living creature, I then realized who the Baalshem was, and falling on my knees I asked him what to do. He then told me how to get out of the city, and instructed me how to live and how to behave so that my sins might be forgiven. And he also appointed me a time when, if I led a good life, I should know that my sins were forgiven and my soul absolved, saying thus: 'When the men who called for you to bring you to me shall come to you at a future time and shall tell you the story of yourself, then you will know that from that moment you are absolved of your great sins.'

"So when you called on me last week and I saw you, I immediately recognized you; but I postponed asking you to tell me stories of the Baalshem, for I wanted meanwhile to perform some urgent acts of charity; and so I went on all these days repenting, praying, doing charity, and I thought that perhaps the moment of salvation was at hand. And all the days you were here and you could not remember any story of the Baalshem, I kept on doing penance, praying and fasting. On Tuesday morning I made a vow to divide all my possessions among the poor and to start on a pilgrimage, devoting the rest of my life to telling the people how the Baalshem saved a Jewish soul. When Tuesday morning came and you called to say goodbye, and then suddenly remembered the story you have just told me, I knew that the appointed time had come. Now take as much of my money as you want, and you need no longer wander about over the land, for the mission laid on you by the Baalshem has been accomplished."

SEVEN GOOD YEARS

by ISAAC LOEB PERETZ

ONCE UPON A TIME, IN THE POLISH TOWN OF TURBIN, THERE LIVED a very poor porter named Tovye. On a Thursday he was standing in the marketplace, his coattails rolled up around his hips and held by a cord. He was hoping for a bit of luck with which to eke out the Sabbath. But all the stalls were empty. Not one marketer who might need help in carrying bundles was in sight. Tovye looked toward the heavens and prayed that at least on the Sabbath his wife and children would not have to go hungry.

While he was praying, he felt someone pulling at his coat. Turning around, he saw a stranger dressed like a hunter, wearing a green suit and a bowman's hat with a feather.

"Listen, Tovye," the stranger said, "you are to be given seven years of plenty, seven years of wealth and happiness. Only decide *when* you want these years. If you desire, your good luck can begin today; even before the sun sets this evening, you can be rich enough to buy all that is in and near Turbin. But if you do this, after seven years you will again become as poor as you are now. On the other hand, if you choose to enjoy your good fortune at the end of your life, you will leave this world the wealthiest man in Turbin."

Tovye could not guess that he was listening to Elijah the Prophet disguised as a hunter. Believing that the stranger was a joker or magician, he answered: "My dear Sir, please leave me in peace. I am a simple, poor man—so poor that I haven't even a crust of white bread for the Sabbath. I cannot repay you for your advice or trouble."

But the stranger would not leave. He repeated his offer several times. Tovye finally gave in and said:

"If you are not talking for the fun of it, Sir, and really mean what you say, then I must tell you this: Whenever I'm troubled by something, I always ask my wife Sarah for her advice. So unless I talk with her, I cannot give you a definite answer."

"Very well," said the stranger, "it is a good idea to discuss this with your wife." He told Tovye to go along and that he would wait for the answer.

Looking around and seeing that there was nobody to give him work, Tovye decided he had nothing to lose. He adjusted his coattails and walked to his mud hut near the open fields on the outskirts of the town.

As soon as Sarah saw him, she ran out to meet him. She was very happy for she thought that his early return meant he had earned some money for the Sabbath. He quickly told her that God had not been so kind, but that he had met a stranger. Then Tovye told her the entire story. What did she think? Should he accept the offer? And if so, what should be their choice—seven good years now or later?

Immediately Sarah replied: "Go, my dear husband, tell the stranger that you want the seven good years to begin this very moment!"

Tovye was astonished. He said that after seven years they would be very poor again and that to descend from the ladder of wealth is worse than never to have climbed up. Why choose this moment?

"My dear husband and good friend, do not be concerned about what will happen in the future. Let us take now what is offered and thank God for our daily blessings. Right now we need money to keep the children in school. They were sent home for lack of tuition. Look at them over there playing in the sand."

A glance at the children and Tovye's mind was made up. He ran back to the marketplace, found the stranger and told him of the decision.

"Make sure that this is what you want," said the stranger, "now you are still a strong man and can eke out a living. But what will happen later when you are older and cannot work so hard?"

Tovye replied: "My wife Sarah wants the good years to begin now. She says that we should thank God for our daily blessings and not worry about the future. In addition, we cannot afford to send our children to school."

"Well, then," answered the stranger, "return home. Before you step into your house, you'll be a wealthy man."

Tovye wanted to ask him about what would happen after seven years, but the stranger had disappeared.

As he reached the end of the town, he saw his children playing in the sand at the back of the house. He watched them digging. Suddenly he saw that they were lifting up, not sand, but gold—gold of the finest grain!

So the seven years had begun, the seven lucky years.

Time flies. The seven years were over. The stranger came again to tell Tovye that all the gold would disappear from the ground, his home and wherever he had deposited it. He met Tovye standing in the marketplace just as he had been seven years earlier. He was dressed the same and still looking for marketers whom he could help.

"Listen, Tovye, the seven years are over."

"Please tell it to my wife Sarah," said he, "she has managed the wealth throughout the seven years."

They walked together and arrived at the same mud hut on the outskirts of the town. They met Sarah in front of the door. She was still poorly dressed, but her face was bright and happy.

When the stranger told her that the seven years were at an end, Sarah said that the good years had not even begun, for they had never considered the gold as their own. What is one's own, said Sarah, is what a person earns with his hands. Such wealth as one gets without effort and labor is only a pledge which God deposits with people for the use of the poor. "I have taken from the gold only enough to pay for the children's education, for the acquisition of God's wisdom may be paid for with God's gold. I have not touched the rest. If the good Lord has found a better keeper for His gold, let Him take it and turn it over to another."

Elijah the Prophet listened until she had finished speaking and then disappeared. He repeated Sarah's words to the Supreme Court in Heaven and the Court ruled that there was no better keeper of the gold anywhere on earth. The seven years did not come to an end so long as Tovye and his wife Sarah were alive.

BIOGRAPHICAL NOTES AND SOURCES

AHIMAAZ BEN PALTIEL lived in southern Italy at the end of the ninth and the beginning of the tenth centuries. He was the scion of a distinguished family of poet-scholars and statesmen whose traditions reached back a thousand years. He himself was a considerable poet, bequeathing us a family history written in Hebrew rhymed prose. *Emperor Basil and Rabbi Shephatiah* was excerpted from that chronicle, titled *Sefer Yuhasin,* and was freely translated by Leo W. Schwarz.

ANGOFF, CHARLES was born in Minsk in 1902. He was brought to the United States when he was six years old and educated at Harvard. After serving as editor of several leading weeklies and monthlies, he turned to writing fiction and has achieved distinction with his remarkable trilogy (which will be completed in three more volumes) *Journey to the Dawn, In the Morning Light* and *The Sun at Noon. Grandfather Tzalel* appeared in a volume of short stories titled *When I Was a Boy in Boston* (New York, 1947).

APOCRYPHA is derived from the Greek word meaning "hidden" and comprises a considerable literature written in Hebrew, Aramaic and Greek during the Graeco-Roman period. These books were not considered as sacred as those in the Bible and were consequently not included when the contents were fixed. *Bel and the Dragon* is one of the numerous apocryphal legends about the Biblical hero Daniel. It was adapted from the Greek by Leo W. Schwarz.

ASCH, SHOLEM was born in Poland in 1861 and subsequently lived in Paris, Warsaw, New York and London where he now makes his home. He is one of the foremost Yiddish writers, having won world renown as playwright, novelist and story-teller. Many of his novels like *Three Cities, Mottke the Thief* and *Salvation* have been popular in the United States. *The Duty to Live* appeared in *Stories of My People* (New York, 1950), translated by Meyer Levin.

AVNIERI, URI was born in Beckum, Germany, in 1923 and was brought to Palestine in the nineteen-thirties. He has been a youth leader and served in the War of Independence as a member of the Palmach. While working as an editor, he has written several books of stories. *The Prisoner* appeared in *Israel Youth Horizon*, Vol. I, No. 3, published by the Youth and Hechalutz Department of the Jewish Agency, Jerusalem.

BARASH, ASHER was born in Galicia, Poland, in 1889 and settled in Palestine in 1913. He is a Hebrew poet, novelist and author of numerous short stories. *Speed the Plough*, translated by I. M. Lask, was published in *Palestine Stories* (Jerusalem, 1942).

BERDITCHEVSKI, MICHAH JOSEPH was born in the famous Hasidic city of Medzibuz, Poland, in 1865 and died in Berlin in 1921. His collected writings comprise twenty volumes of essays, fiction and legendry. Combining scholarship with artistry, he composed a series of six volumes titled *Der Born Judas* (Insel-Verlag, 1916-1921) in which he adapted a vast amount of Jewish folklore and legend. *The Akiba Story, The Golem of Prague* and *Tales of Demons and Dervishes*, translated for this book by Libby Benedict, were chosen from these volumes.

BERG, LOUIS was born in Kovno, Lithuania in 1900. He was brought up in Portsmouth, Virginia, and now lives in New York City. He has distinguished himself as editor, storyteller and journalist, serving at present as a feature writer on the staff of *This Week* magazine. *The Snowball Man and Holy Writ* originally appeared under the title "Holy Writ" in Vol. XII, No. 4 (August-September, 1926) of *The Menorah Journal*.

BIALIK, HAYYIM NAHMAN was born in the Ukraine in 1873, settled in Tel Aviv in 1924 and died in 1934. He was the leading Hebrew poet and writer of his generation, and a number of his books and poems have been translated into English. An annual literary prize for exceptional achievement in Hebrew Literature as well as a publishing foundation have been established in his name in Israel. *The Legend of Three and Four*, translated by I. M. Lask, appeared in a volume of legends about David and Solomon, titled *Vayehi Hayom* (Tel Aviv, 1933).

BIBLE is the most commonly used title for the English translation of the Hebrew scriptures. It is the best known book of world literature and has been translated into more than six hundred tongues and dialects. *The Romance of Esther,* one of the so called "Five Scrolls," was abridged and translated from the Hebrew by Leo W. Schwarz.

BRINIG, MYRON was born in Minneapolis in 1900, spent his childhood in Butte, Montana, and was educated at New York University and the University of Pennsylvania. He has written a dozen popular novels several of which were made into films. Among his finest novels are those of Montana life, *This Man Is My Brother* and *Singermann* (New York, 1929) from which *Day of Atonement* was excerpted.

BROD, MAX was born in Prague, Czechoslovakia, in 1884. He was a government official, leading man of letters and advocate of Zionism there until he settled in Palestine in 1939. Two of his novels, *The Kingdom of Love* (London 1930) and *David Reubeni* (New York 1928) won popularity in English translation. *The Story of a Blanket,* translated by I. M. Lask, appeared in *Palestine Miscellany I* (Jerusalem, undated).

EDELMAN, MAREK was born in 1922 of a worker's family in Warsaw, Poland, and as a youth became a contributor to the Yiddish press and an active worker in the Jewish socialist Bund. He was a leader in the underground in the Warsaw Ghetto during the Nazi occupation, serving as chief of the Intelligence Corps of the Jewish Fighter Organization. He was one of the few survivors of the ghetto battle and now lives in Poland.

The Last Stand in the Warsaw Ghetto is part of his account of this epic experience, which first appeared in Polish in 1945 and in Yiddish in *In di Yorn fun Idischen Churbon* (New York, 1948).

FALSTEIN, LOUIS was born in the Ukraine and brought up in Chicago where he attended public schools and worked at a variety of jobs. His stories, book reviews and articles have appeared in national magazines. He has lectured and taught writing at New York University. During World War II he served as an aerial gunner with the U. S. 15th Airforce and he used his experience as a background for one of the finest war novels, *Face of a Hero* (New York, 1950) from which *Tail-Gunner Over Europe* was excerpted. An equally superb novel, *Sole Survivor* (New York, 1954) deals with the crisis of a survivor of a concentration camp, who attempts to reestablish his life in America.

FEIERBERG, MORDECAI ZEEB was born in Novgorod, Russia, in 1874 and died of tuberculosis twenty-five years later. His great talent became evident in several short stories and a novelette in Hebrew, which he wrote despite tragic poverty and illness. *The Calf* originally appeared in *Ha-Shiloah* under the *nom de plume* "Hofni the Dreamer." This story, translated by Moshe Kohn, presents Feierberg for the first time in English.

FERBER, EDNA was born in Kalamazoo, Michigan, began her career as a newspaper woman and gradually turned to fiction. She has written more than thirty volumes of autobiography, plays, stories and novels, which have won great popularity and several of which have been produced as leading films. Miss Ferber makes her home in New York City. *Molly Brandeis Takes Hold* is part of the novel *Fanny Herself* (New York, 1917).

FINEMAN, IRVING was born in New York City in 1893 and was educated at the Massachusetts Institute of Technology and Harvard. He has taught engineering and literature at various colleges and in recent years has worked on films in Hollywood. His fiction ranks with the best in the United States. *Elijah the Prophet* is taken from his famous chronicle of Jewish life, *Hear, Ye Sons* (New York, 1933).

FLEG, EDMOND was born in Geneva, Switzerland, in 1874 but has lived most of his life in Paris. Excelling as poet, critic, playwright, translator and philospher, he is a preeminent figure in French literature and a creator of a renascence of Jewish letters in French. Among his numerous books that have been translated into English the best known are *The Land of Promise, Why I Am a Jew* and biographies of Moses, Solomon and Jesus. *The Boy Prophet* is the epilogue to *La Terre Que Dieu Habite* (Paris, 1953).

GERCHUNOFF, ALBERTO was born in Russia in 1885 and was brought as a boy to one of the Baron de Hirsch agricultural colonies in Argentina. He became an outstanding newspaper man and distinguished himself as a writer of fiction in Spanish. His first book on the Jewish gauchos of the pampas, published in 1910, won fame in Latin America. *The Silver Candlestick,* one of the stories in that book, was revised from the translation of M. O. Carpenter, which first appeared in *The Talmud Magazine* (New York, 1922).

GOLDBERG, LEAH was born in Kovno, Lithuania, in 1911 and settled in Palestine in 1935. She is a highly talented Hebrew poet; her verse and stories have appeared in numerous books, periodicals and anthologies in Israel. *Growing Up,* translated by Pepita Haezrahi, first appeared in *The Living Rampart* (London, 1945) edited by Yehuda Haezrahi.

GRANACH, ALEXANDER was born in Werbewitz, Poland, in 1891 and died in New York in 1944. He began life as a baker and went to Berlin as a youth to embark on a career as an actor, and became one of the finest character actors on the German stage. He came to the United States as a refugee on the eve of World War II and won acclaim for his performances on Broadway and Hollywood. *Shylock, the Original Ancestor* is the epilogue to his delightful autobiography *There Goes an Actor* (New York, 1945).

HALPER, ALBERT was born in Chicago in 1904 and began his writing career there. He is the author of a dozen books of short stories and novels which have won him a solid reputation in the ranks of American writers. He now lives in Brooklyn, New York. *Warm Matzos* is one of the stories of Chicago life in his novel *The Golden Watch* (New York, 1953).

HASIDISM is a religious movement which was founded by Rabbi Israel ben Eliezer, the Baalshemtob (Master of the Good Name) in Eastern Europe during the 18th century. The masses of humble and poor folk flocked to the Baalshem and his disciples who preached a simple faith in God and communion with Him through prayer, good works and brotherhood. Hasidism, which still has active adherents in the United States and Israel, has given birth to a rich folklore and legendry of which *Salvation of a Soul* is an example.

HAZZAZ, HAYYIM was born in the Ukraine in 1898 and has been living in Israel since 1931. He is one of the most original of living Hebrew writers, portraying in his stories and novels life during the Russian Revolution and the character of Biblical as well as contemporary Israelian folk. *It's She!*, translated by Moshe Kohn, is an excerpt from a novel dealing with Yemenite life, titled *Yaish,* and has appeared in a Hebrew anthology.

HEINE, HEINRICH was born in Duesseldorf, Germany, in 1797, and died in Paris in 1856. A man of genius, he was plagued by illness, unhappiness and for a short while, as he put it, "was baptized but not converted." He excelled in almost every form of literature, and will be read as long as great writing is appreciated. *On a Seder Eve* is excerpted from an unfinished Passover novelette and was translated from the German by Leo W. Schwarz.

JOSEPH IBN ZABARA lived in Spain during the second half of the twelfth century. We know only that he was a physician and a Hebrew writer. *The Clever Girl* was freely translated by Leo W. Schwarz from his most important Hebrew work titled *The Book of Delight.*

KABALAH is a form of Jewish mysticism which has attracted circles of followers from late antiquity until our own time. The core of Kabalah, which comprises a large body of literature, is a cluster of ideas about man and God, which aim to bring them into communion and ultimately establish the realm of the Messiah on earth. In addition to the theological literature of Kabalah, there also grew up, especially in Palestine during the 16th and 17th centuries, a fascinating folklore which is illustrated in this book by the three tales under the general title *Tales of Demons and Dervishes.*

KAHANA, BATYA was born in Kamenitz, Podolia, in 1901 and settled in Palestine in 1921. She has published several books of stories and her work has been included in several Hebrew anthologies. *The Guitar,* translated by Moshe Kohn, is the first of her stories to appear in English.

KOBER, ARTHUR was born in New York City in 1900. His stories about the Gross family in the Bronx, which first appeared in the *New Yorker* have won a permanent niche as a folk saga. In the Thirties his play *Having a Wonderful Time* won acclaim on Broadway and later was made into a film. *Music in the Air* is taken from the collection of Gross stories titled *Thunder Over the Bronx* (New York, 1935).

KOTELIANSKY, SOLOMON SOLOMONOVITCH was born in Russia in 1880 and died in London in 1952. He was a writer, editor and a translator of the Russian masters into English. His mother Biela, a born storyteller, acquainted him with Jewish folklore, and it was her versions of *The Little Men in the Jar* and *Salvation of a Soul,* that he rendered into English. They first appeared in the *London Mercury.*

LEVIN, MEYER was born in Chicago in 1905 and began his writing career while studying at the University of Chicago. After working in a kibbutz for a year, he wrote *Yehuda,* the first novel dealing with kibbutz life. Subsequently he excelled as columnist, marionettist, war correspondent, translator, novelist and a producer of documentary films. Recently he published a unique autobiography, *In Search* (New York, 1951). *The Dance* is part of his acclaimed novel *The Old Bunch* (New York, 1937).

MENDELE MOCHER SEFORIM (real name Sholem Jacob Abramovitch) was born in Kopyl, Russia, in 1836 and died in 1917. One of the greats of modern Yiddish literature, his numerous works portray faithfully the Jewish village in 19th century Eastern Europe and are eloquent with a love of nature. Two of his novels, *The Travels of Benjamin III* and *The Nag* have been rendered into English. *A Nap, Prayers and Strawberries* was abridged and translated by Leo W. Schwarz from the early chapters of his yiddish novel *Fishke der Krumme* (*Lame Fishke*).

MIDRASH is a Hebrew word meaning "investigation" or "interpretation." It is used to describe a vast literature in Aramaic and Hebrew, which used verses of the Bible as a point of departure for religious and literary expression. The reader will find in Louis Ginzberg's *The Legends of the Jews,* published by the Jewish Publication Society (Philadelphia, Pa.) a splendid collection of Midrashic literature. The sample given here, *The Akiba Story* was translated by Libby Benedict from M. J. Berditchevski's adaptation of the original legends in his *Der Born Judas.*

NATHAN, ROBERT was born in New York City in 1894. He was educated at Harvard and now lives in Los Angeles. He is a direct descendant of Rabbi Gershon Seixas, a founder of Columbia College in the 18th century. Nathan has produced more than twenty volumes of verse and novels, several of which have been made into films. *A Parable of Peace and War,* excerpted from *Tapiola's Brave Regiment* (New York, 1941) is representative of his wise humor in the guise of light fantasy.

PALTIEL (see AHIMAAZ BEN PALTIEL)

PERETZ, ISAAC LOEB was born in Zamascz, Poland, in 1852 and died in Warsaw in 1915. He is preeminent both in modern Hebrew and Yiddish literature, and is considered one of the best storytellers of modern literature. A fascinating introduction to his life and writings is given in Maurice Samuel's *Prince of the Ghetto* (New York, 1948). *The Good Years* was translated from the Yiddish by Leo W. Schwarz.

ROTH, CECIL was born in London in 1899. He is a renowned historian, having served as Reader in Jewish Studies in the University of Oxford since 1939. His books have been translated into six languages, and he was included by the Nazis in a list of the first five hundred persons to be arrested when they landed in England. He has taught and lectured periodically in the United States, and his *A Short History of the Jewish People* (New York, 1954, revised) is widely known. *The Tree of Liberty*, originally titled *The Last Day of the Ghetto*, is one of his fictional historical tales. This story was included in Roth's collection of essays, titled *Personalities and Events in Jewish History* published by the Jewish Publication Society (Philadelphia, 1953).

SAMPTER, JESSIE E. was born in New York City in 1883, settled in Rehoboth, Palestine, in 1919 and died there in 1940. A gifted poet and talented writer, she devoted her literary efforts to interpreting Zionism for the American public. *Plow Deep* first appeared in the *Menorah Journal* (New York, 1922).

SCHNEOUR, ZALMAN, the scion of a notable Hasidic family, was born in Shklov, Russia, in 1887. He is a major figure in modern Yiddish and Hebrew Literature, his production ranging through verse, prose, drama and fiction. *The Slaying of the Wolf* comprises a chapter of his novel *Noah Pandre* (New York, 1936), translated by Joseph Leftwich.

SCHWARZ, LEO WALDER was born in New York City in 1906. Educated at Harvard, he has devoted himself to making available in English the best of the Jewish historical and literary tradition. His anthology series, published by Rinehart, includes such books as *The Jewish Caravan* and *A Golden Treasury of Jewish Literature,* and has become standard. His translations and adaptations in this volume are noted under the authors in the Biographical Notes.

SHENHAR, YITZHAK (born Shenberg) was born in the Ukraine in 1904 and settled in Palestine in 1924. He is one of the outstanding living Hebrew novelists and short story writers. A selection of his stories were recently made available in English under the title *Under a Fig Tree* (New York, 1953). *The Pit-falls of Love* appeared under the title "Israel-Zvi," translated by Israel Schen, in the *Palestine Miscellany I,* published by the Zionist Organization Youth Department (Tel Aviv, undated).

SHOLEM ALEICHEM (real name Sholem Rabinowitz) was born in Russia in 1859 and died in New York City in 1916. He is one of the masters of modern Yiddish literature, excelling as critic, humorist, storyteller and playwright. Many of his stories and novels have been translated into English, and in the nine-teen-forties and fifties his books won great popularity in the United States. *The Dead Citron* was abridged and translated from the Yiddish by Leo W. Schwarz.

SMILANSKI, MOSHE was born in the Ukraine in 1874, settled in Palestine as one of the earliest Zionist colonists in 1890, and died in Rehoboth in 1953. He was a prosperous farmer as well as a talented and prolific storyteller. More than any other author, Arab or Hebrew, he understood and portrayed the life of the Palestinian Arabs. *Abdul Hadi's Rifle* was translated from the Hebrew by Moshe Kohn.

TABAKAI, ARYEH (born Tabakman) was born in Russia and after spending some years in Argentina, settled in Palestine in 1935. He has worked as a stevedore in Haifa and a well-borer in the Negeb. He has published several books of stories. *Sergeant Shmueli Rides a Donkey,* translated by Moshe Kohn, is one of the tales in his latest book, *Life to the Full* (Tel Aviv, 1953).

WOUK, HERMAN was born in New York in 1915, educated at Columbia and served in the U. S. Navy in World War II. After serving as a script writer for the comedian Fred Allen, he turned to writing fiction. He has produced several best-selling novels of which *The Caine Mutiny* was filmed and produced on Broad-way and *Marjorie Morningstar* appears at this writing to be enjoying similar success. *Herbie Solves a Problem* is part of a novel about Bronx children, titled *The City Boy* (New York, 1948).

YAARI, YEHUDA was born in Poland in 1900, went to Palestine when he was twenty, studied in New York and Montreal for several years, and has lived and worked since in Jerusalem. He has distinguished himself as a Hebrew novelist, playwright and storyteller. One of his novels, *When the Candle was Burning,* was translated into English (London, 1947). *The Threefold Covenant,* translated by I. M. Lask, appeared in *Palestine Miscellany I,* published by the Youth Department of the Jewish Agency (Jerusalem, undated).

ZABARA (see Joseph ibn Zabara)

ZANGWILL, ISRAEL was born in London in 1864 and died at the age of sixty-two in Sussex. He established himself as a preeminent critic, novelist, essayist and playwright, and at the same time won distinction as an interpreter of Jewish life and culture. He also played a leading role as a champion of the downtrodden and persecuted. *The Prodigal Son* is one of the stories in his famous book *Children of the Ghetto* (Philadelphia, 1892).

ZEMACH, SHLOMO was born in 1886 in Poland and settled in Palestine in 1904. He worked as a farmer for many years and then turned to literature. He has written plays, stories and a novel *Between Sea and Desert,* and at present serves as the editor of a Hebrew literary quarterly, *Behinot. A Tale of Two Mules* is part of a long story, translated by I. M. Lask, which appeared in *Palestine Stories* (Jerusalem, 1942).